Oxford Textbook of Functional Anatomy

VOLUME 1

MUSCULO-SKELETAL SYSTEM

Oxford University Press makes no representation, express or implied, that the drug dosages in this book are correct. Readers must therefore always check the product information and clinical procedures with the most up to date published product information and data sheets provided by the manufacturers and the most recent codes of conduct and safety regulations. The authors and the publishers do not accept responsibility or legal liability for any errors in the text or for the misuse or misapplication of material in this work.

Oxford Textbook of Functional Anatomy

VOLUME 1

MUSCULO-SKELETAL SYSTEM
2ND EDITION

by Pamela C. B. MacKinnon and John F. Morris
Department of Human Anatomy and Genetics, University of Oxford

With drawings by Audrey Besterman

OXFORD
UNIVERSITY PRESS

OXFORD
UNIVERSITY PRESS

Great Clarendon Street, Oxford OX2 6DP

Oxford University Press is a department of the University of Oxford.
It furthers the University's objective of excellence in research, scholarship,
and education by publishing worldwide in

Oxford New York

Auckland Cape Town Dar es Salaam Hong Kong Karachi
Kuala Lumpur Madrid Melbourne Mexico City Nairobi
New Delhi Shanghai Taipei Toronto

With offices in

Argentina Austria Brazil Chile Czech Republic France Greece
Guatemala Hungary Italy Japan Poland Portugal Singapore
South Korea Switzerland Thailand Turkey Ukraine Vietnam

Oxford is a registered trade mark of Oxford University Press
in the UK and in certain other countries

Published in the United States
by Oxford University Press Inc., New York

First edition published 1986
Revised edition 1994
Second edition published 2005

A catalogue record for this title is available from the British Library

Typeset by Newgen Imaging Systems (P) Ltd., Chennai, India
Printed in Italy
on acid-free paper by
Grafiche Industriali

ISBN 0 19 262816 X (Volume 1: Musculo-skeletal system)
ISBN 0 19 262817 8 (Volume 2: Thorax and Abdomen)
ISBN 0 19 262818 6 (Volume 3: Head and Neck)
ISBN 0 19 262819 4 (Combined set)
10 9 8 7 6 5 4 3 2 1

Preface

Medicine is changing rapidly. Medical education must therefore change accordingly in order to prepare its students for their future professional lives. The trend to more scientific thinking that started in medical practice in the middle of the nineteenth century has increased, gradually gaining in momentum up to the present dramatic expansion of knowledge, both theoretical and practical, in all the sciences related to medicine. This trend, coupled with improvements in public health and nutrition, has been responsible for the marked increase in health and life expectancy which has occurred over the same period of time in many populations.

Among the many changes in Medicine, few have had more impact on diagnosis than the developments in imaging the interior of the living body. This started with the discovery of X-rays in the last century and developed via the use of radio-opaque substances to outline internal organs. The more recent and continuing explosion in computer technology has been harnessed to many aspects of Medicine, and its application to radiological, magnetic resonance imaging (MRI), and ultrasound investigations now permits the production of sectional images of the body in any plane which have increasingly fine spatial definition and which give ever increasing insight into the function of the tissues being imaged. Similarly, advances in optical technology in the form of flexible fibre-optic endoscopes now permit direct visualisation of the interior of hollow organs continuous with the outside world, such as the alimentary tract and airway. Similar instruments inserted through a small incision can be used to visualise the exterior of the gastrointestinal tract and of other structures in body cavities, such as the peritoneal cavity and synovial joints. Surgical procedures can also be performed by use of fine instruments passed along the endoscopes. All these new techniques have obviated the need for much of the surgery that was formerly necessary to determine a diagnosis. However, they demand, for their interpretation, a much better understanding of how the body is constructed and arranged. Sectional images cannot be interpreted unless the person trying to interpret the image has a really good grasp of the three-dimensional arrangement of all the tissues.

Time in educational programmes must therefore be found for new knowledge in traditional subjects, and for the emerging disciplines, in particular, molecular medicine which promises to change the face of Medicine in the future. It is not surprising that subjects such as topographical anatomy, with a heavy factual content, have had to be assimilated in much less time. Many programmes now rely on the use of prosected (pre-dissected) specimens rather than student dissection, on videos which can show both normal living function and dysfunctional states, and computer packages. It is clear, however, that, whatever changes are made to the curricula, a sound understanding of how the body is built and functions is fundamental to all aspects of Medicine, not least the interpretation of the products of the new imaging systems. Equally, most diagnoses have to be arrived at from an examination of the intact living body and so an understanding of the functional anatomy of the living body and how it should be examined, remains a critical skill for most practitioners.

In this 2nd edition of the *Oxford Textbook of Functional Anatomy*, we have been mindful of these continuing changes and have paid careful attention to whether or not some item of information is likely to be helpful either in aiding the understanding of the principles of body structure or in everyday clinical practice. As a result, all guidance on dissection has been removed from the text; the origins and insertions of individual muscles, on which students in the past have spent a disproportionate amount of time, have also been largely removed but are indicated instead in the relevant illustrations. Emphasis on the anatomy of the living subject has been increased; and to underline the increasing importance of non-invasive imaging, there are more computerised tomograms and magnetic resonance images, many of which have been merged with the text. Wherever appropriate, the clinical applications of the anatomical information have been highlighted by the use of 'clinical boxes'. Questions to stimulate thought and problem-solving remain as an important part of the text, the answers are now given at the end of each chapter/section. The broad margin on each sheet invites the addition of personal notes as an aid to future recall.

The three-volume format has been retained for ease of use, and is available as a set. Volume 1 covers the musculo-skeletal system; Volume 2, the thorax, abdomen and pelvis; Volume 3, the head and neck.

Acknowledgements

It is a pleasure to record our thanks to the many people with whom we discussed various topics and who encouraged us during the preparation of this second edition of the *Oxford Textbook of Functional Anatomy*. Our special thanks are due to:

• Mrs Audrey Besterman, for her anatomical drawings which are both informative and aesthetically pleasing.

• Dr Basil Shepstone and Dr Stephen Golding, who contributed Chapter 3, on medical imaging, and who, with Dr Niall Moore, Dr David Wilson, Mr Peter Burge, Miss Griselda George, Dr Daniel Nolan, and Dr Amit Atrey, provided most of the clinical images for this volume.

• Professor Claudio Stern and Professor Gillian Morriss-Kay, who have provided text and advice for the sections on the development of the limbs.

• Our academic and technical colleagues in the Department of Human Anatomy and Genetics, University of Oxford. In particular Professor Margaret Matthews, who provided helpful criticism of the text; Mr Roger White, who supervises our gross anatomy facility; Colin Beesley, for his expertise in scanning and photography; and Alicia Loreto-Gardner for cheerful support in the office.

• The many medical and surgical consultants and other colleagues at the Nuffield Orthopaedic Centre and other hospitals of the Oxford Radcliffe Hospitals NHS Trust who spent precious time reading the text, and making helpful criticisms and suggestions; in particular Mr Peter Burge (upper limb), Mr Chris Bulstrode and Mr Peter McLardy Smith (lower limb), and Mr James Wilson-Macdonald (spine).

• The medical production staff of the Oxford University Press, including Miss Catherine Barnes, our patient and understanding editor, and Mr Philip Longford, who skilfully transferred the many original drawings and other illustrations into electronic format.

• All those preclinical and clinical students who been both encouraging and thoughtfully enthusiastic, telling us candidly what they liked and disliked about various texts, including our own; in particular Deborah Home, James Gagg, and Matthew Tam, who went through the three volumes line by line and figure by figure.

• Last, but not certainly not least, we dedicate this book to all our students—past, present, and future. While searching for an appropriate form of words with which to express this, we happened on a dedicatory letter written to his students in the late eighteenth century by Sir Astley Cooper and which appears in *A Treatise on Dislocations and on Fractures of the Joints* (4th edn), Longman, London. The idiom differs from that of the twenty-first century, but the sentiment is identical. 'This work having been composed for your use, [our] principal object will be attained if you derive advantage from it.' We hope that this will be so, not only as you study the functioning anatomy of the body during your medical course, but throughout your subsequent careers.

Contents

Introduction to functional anatomy

Introduction to functional anatomy

Functional anatomy is the study of the structure and function of the body in its **living** state. It comprises a study of: the **skeletal system** which provides a structural framework to the body, protects vital organs, and gives attachment to muscles that move us; the **muscles** and **joints** which provide for movement between our various skeletal units; the **cardiovascular system** through which oxygen and nutrients are pumped to individual cells of the body and waste materials are collected for excretion; the **lymphatic system** which is closely associated with the blood vascular system for the collection of lymph but also has a protective and immune function; the **respiratory system** through which oxygen is acquired and carbon dioxide is excreted; the **alimentary system** through which nutrients are acquired and some wastes are excreted; the **urinary system** which controls the composition of body fluids in part through the excretion of wastes; the **reproductive system** which ensures continuity of the species; the **nervous system** which receives and integrates information from both the internal and external environments and which, through controlling our speech, movements, and behaviour, enables us to respond appropriately to stimuli and to express our individual character and personality; and the **endocrine system** which, through the secretion of hormones, forms the other major control system acting in conjunction with the nervous system.

The changing form of the body and its relations to function

Always remember that each body is unique and not an assembly-line product. Each of us inherited a slightly different set of genes from our parents when we were conceived. These govern the formation of every protein from which the body is made and therefore every biochemical reaction that occurs.

The body develops in the uterus and this development usually produces a 'normal' baby. It grows further during childhood and adolescence, in part in sexually dimorphic 'growth spurts', to produce the adult form. On occasion, any part of this development may be imperfect to a greater or lesser degree.

It will be obvious to you that variation among 'normal' individuals exists and can be quite striking. It is therefore very important that you develop a concept of the **range of normality** so that you can judge what is frankly abnormal and may require attention. For this purpose, many illustrations of abnormalities are included in this book.

External differences between males and females are mostly obvious. The mature female also undergoes a monthly reproductive cycle which causes marked changes in certain internal organs. In both sexes, other more subtle changes occur throughout the day which affect the function rather than the form of the body.

Throughout life, the structure of the body responds to functional demands (for example the muscle hypertrophy that results from exercise). It also responds to abuses and injuries by repair and healing. In later adult life, ageing changes lead to senescence. Never forget that most bodies donated for examination in dissecting rooms are those of very elderly people.

The 'body' which you must consider is therefore not the static, aged form which you see on a dissecting table or as a prosection, but rather a living, dynamic organism, constantly changing and responding to the functional challenges of its environment.

Terms used in anatomical description

For ease of communication and convenience of description, the body is always considered as standing erect, facing ahead, the arms by the sides and the palms of the hands facing forward with the fingers extended (**1.1**). Place yourself in this position and note that this 'anatomical position' differs in a number of ways from your normal standing posture (see 'position of function' of upper limb, p. 69).

The terms **anterior** (ventral) and **posterior** (dorsal) refer to structures facing the front and the back of the body, respectively (**1.2**). The situation is a little different in the head and brain.

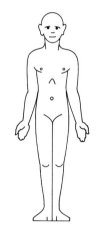

1.1 The 'anatomical position'.

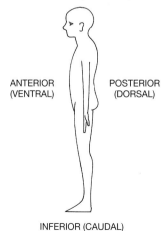

1.2 Anatomical terms denoting position.

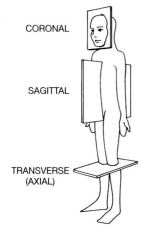

1.3 Anatomical planes.

Structures in the antero-posterior midline are said to be **median**; those close to the midline, **medial**; and those further away, **lateral**. Structures toward the head (above) are usually referred to as **superior** or **cephalic**, or, if they are in front and above, as **rostral**. Structures below are referred to as **inferior** or **caudal**.

Proximal means nearer to the origin of a structure; **distal** is the opposite. **Superficial** means nearer to the skin; **deep** is the opposite.

Anatomical planes (1.3)

- **Sagittal**—a vertical plane lying in the antero-posterior plane (longitudinal).
- **Coronal**—a vertical plane at right angles to the sagittal.
- **Transverse (axial)**—a horizontal plane at right angles to both coronal and sagittal.
- **Oblique**—any plane that is not sagittal, coronal, or transverse.

Movements (1.4)

- **Flexion**—a forward or anterior movement of the trunk or a limb.
- **Lateral flexion**—bending of the forward facing head and trunk to either side.
- **Extension**—a backward or posterior movement.
- **Abduction**—a movement away from the midline of the body.
- **Adduction**—a movement toward the midline of the body.
- **Circumduction**—a combination of flexion, abduction, extension, and adduction (without rotation).
- **Rotation** can occur at certain joints (such as the shoulder), and in certain parts of the spine. **Medial (internal) rotation** is rotation of the joint or part of the body toward the midline of the body; **lateral (external) rotation** is rotation away from the midline. Rotation of the head on the neck is referred to as a **pivot** movement.
- **Protraction**—a forward movement of the head, jaw, or shoulders.

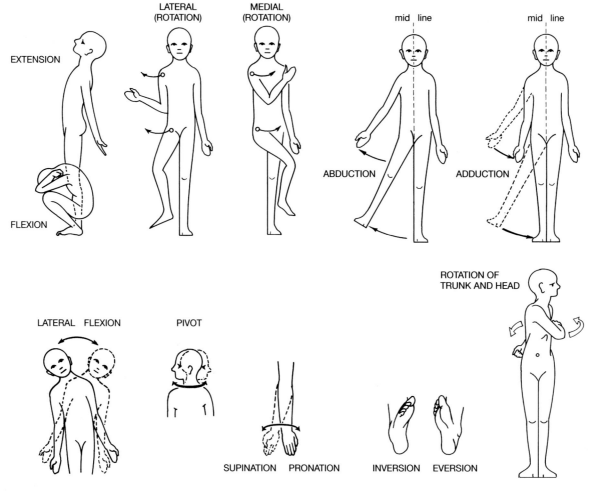

1.4 Movements of the body.

- **Retraction**—a backward movement of the head, jaw, or shoulders.
- **Pronation**—movement of the forearm so that the palm faces posteriorly.
- **Supination**—movement of the forearm so that the palm faces anteriorly. **Prone** and **supine** are also used to describe the position of the trunk, face down or face up.
- **Inversion**—movement of the foot which directs the sole of the foot medially.
- **Eversion**—movement of the foot which directs the sole of the foot laterally.
- **Opposition**—movement of the thumb (and to a certain extent the little finger) that is central to our ability to grip. The movement carries the thumb across the palm so that it can touch the tips of the other digits.

Body tissues and systems

CHAPTER 2

Body tissues and systems

The limbs and vertebral column, like any region of the body, are made up of numerous different tissues, and these tissues are organized into various body systems. The anatomical form that these tissues take in any region is the result of their evolution to fulfil a functional role. The structure of tissues can be considered at two levels. The microscopic structure is the object of study in histology. The macroscopic (naked eye) and radiological appearance of the structure is the subject of this book.

You will find it helpful to consider general aspects of each tissue and system in a logical manner before you proceed to the details of any particular part of the body. This chapter therefore outlines some of the important topics that should be considered for each tissue; it also considers the way in which the major systems of the body are organized, though not all will necessarily be relevant in the consideration of any individual part of the body. The outline concentrates on the gross aspects of the tissues and must be supplemented by a study of their microscopical anatomy if the functioning of the tissues is to be fully understood.

Skin

The skin consists of an epithelium of keratinized stratified squamous cells (**epidermis**) on a base of connective tissue (**dermis**).

Consider:

- **Skin colour**: black, brown, or yellow skin depends primarily on the amount of melanin pigment secreted by the melanocyte cells of the epidermis. Melanin helps protect the deeper layers of the epidermis from the harmful effects of ultraviolet light.
- **Degree of keratinization**: keratinization is protective (compare the sole of the foot and the eyelid) and is increased by mechanical stress on the skin (e.g. calluses caused by heavy manual work).
- **Dermal ridges** of the hands and feet: these improve the ability of the skin to grip and assist in texture recognition (movement of ridged skin over an object produces vibrations that are sensed by cutaneous nerve endings). The pattern of ridges forms the 'fingerprint' and 'palmprint', which are unique to an individual (except for identical twins).
- **Nails** (**2.1**) are horny plates of modified epidermis which cover the dorsum of the distal phalanges and provide a firm base for the pulp of the fingers or toes. The growing root of a nail extends as far as the white (lunule) of the nail and is overlapped by a fold of skin (eponychium); this fold extends along the lateral aspects of the nail (paranychium). The rest of the attached nail appears pink because of the underlying capillaries which supply the nail bed. Nails develop at the tips of digits but migrate on to the dorsum, taking their nerve supply with

them. Nails of the hand grow faster than those of the foot.

- **Degree of hairiness** and **type of hair**: the palms, soles, eyelids, and penis are hairless. The **density** and **coarseness** of the hair differs from region to region. The distribution of body hair is sexually dimorphic, the male pattern being dependent on circulating androgens. Abnormal hair distribution can therefore reflect endocrine imbalance.
- **Sweat glands**. There are two types:
  - **Eccrine** sweat glands (**2.2**) are present in almost the entire surface of the human body (but not the lips, eardrum, or parts of the genitalia). They are simple tubular glands, with a secretory coil in the dermis and a narrow duct which spirals up through the epidermis to open on to the skin surface. In response to increases in ambient or body core temperature they secrete a colourless, watery saline. Evaporation of this secretion causes loss of heat through the skin, thus helping to regulate body temperature. The secretion from sweat glands which open on to the surfaces of dermal ridges enhances touch sensation and, in moderate amount, may help grip. The number of active glands on the finger pads increases markedly in response to an alerting stimulus, but decreases with more prolonged stress. Eccrine sweat glands are innervated by sympathetic (postganglionic, cholinergic) nerves.
  - **Apocrine** sweat glands are larger. In humans they are found only in the axilla, ano-genital region and mammary areola. Their duct usually opens into a hair follicle Their saline secretion also

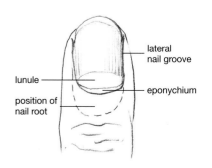

2.1 Nail and surrounding soft tissue.

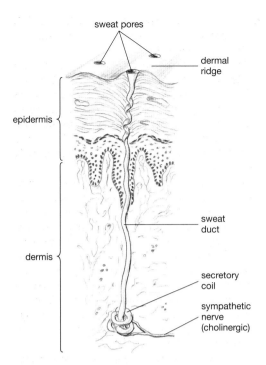

2.2 Eccrine sweat gland in the skin.

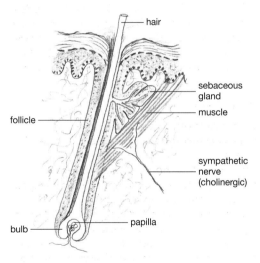

2.3 Hair follicle and sebaceous gland.

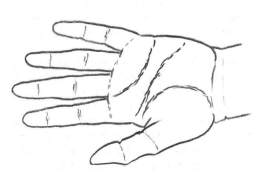

2.4 Skin creases in the hand and wrist.

contains organic material derived from the secretory cells and is thicker than that from eccrine glands. When extruded on to the skin the organic material is decomposed by bacteria, generating a characteristic musky odour thought to have sex attractant (pheromone) properties. Apocrine glands develop at puberty under the influence of sex hormones and are innervated by sympathetic (postganglionic but noradrenergic) nerves.

• **Sebaceous glands** also open on to hair follicles (**2.3**) and are found over most of the body surface (not palm or sole). Their oily secretion (sebum) is derived from the disintegration of whole cells in the secretory acini (holocrine secretion). It provides a protective covering for the skin and its hairs. Sebaceous glands are not innervated, but their secretion is stimulated by androgens in both males and females, and is therefore activated at puberty. If the ducts become blocked, the secretions stagnate and can become infected, causing acne.

   – The **areolar glands** of the nipple are specialized sebaceous glands.

• **Skin creases** (**2.4**): these are found especially around joints, where the skin is firmly attached to the underlying tissues. The pronounced creases should be distinguished from the fine crease-like lines that appear in the skin of old people and are caused by degeneration of collagen fibres and reduced attachment of the skin to underlying tissues.

• **Skin minimal tension lines** (**2.5**) develop, over time, as a result of skin movements caused by the

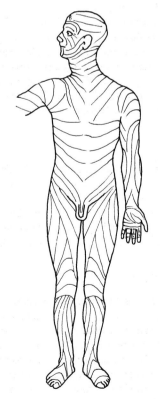

2.5 Skin minimum tension lines.

contraction of underlying muscles. In general, the lines are at right angles to the underlying muscle fibres and reflect the orientation of bundles of collagen in the dermis running parallel to the lines. In general, the lines approximate to skin wrinkles. Skin tension lines are of considerable importance in surgery because failure to follow their orientation when making a skin incision will predispose to large, unsightly scars. Incisions made along the lines heal with fine, inconspicuous scars.

- The **blood supply of the skin** is derived from local vessels. Capillary loops in the nail bed can be seen if the skin is cleared with a drop of oil and observed with a dissecting microscope. The thermal sensitivity of skin vasculature can be demonstrated readily by immersion in hot and iced water. In cold conditions much of the cutaneous blood supply is short-circuited from arterioles to venules by arteriovenous anastomoses.
- The **innervation of the skin**: stimuli to the skin vary in terms of their energy (mechanical or thermal), their spatial distribution, intensity, and rate of change. Many cutaneous sense organs are specialized to detect mechanical or thermal stimuli; yet others are less specific. Some respond rapidly and transiently, others in a more sustained manner.

Differences in packing density of the receptors produce large differences in the spatial discriminatory power of different regions. This is usually measured by the two-point discrimination threshold—the smallest distance between two simultaneously applied mechanical stimuli that can be perceived as two rather than one (see Appendix).

For any area of skin you will need to know: the **local nerve** that supplies the area (for diagnosis of peripheral nerve injuries and for administration of local anaesthesia) and the **spinal nerve root** that supplies the area (for diagnosis of spinal cord and spinal nerve damage). The area of skin supplied by a spinal nerve is called a **dermatome**.

Fascia

Fascia is the name given to the connective tissues that are interposed between, and surround, the other more discrete tissues of the body. All fascia consists of fibrous tissue, adipose (fatty) tissue, and fluid, in various proportions. For the purposes of description it is usually divided into superficial and deep fascia.

Superficial fascia

Superficial fascia is the subcutaneous connective tissue which merges with the dermis of the skin. It consists of an aqueous matrix in which are various types of cell, including fat cells, fibroblasts with their bundles of collagen fibres, plasma cells, mast cells, and macrophages. These vary considerably in amount from area to area. It therefore provides a compartment which either tethers the skin to the underlying tissues or allows it to move over them; it also provides a store of energy (fat), and cells which protect against invasive organisms.

You should consider:
- The **fibrous tissue** content: this determines the attachment of the skin to deeper structures. Compare the palm or sole (where the skin is tightly bound to facilitate grip) with the dorsum of the hand. Fibrous attachments are prominent at skin creases, and form the suspensory ligaments of the axilla, breast, and penis. In areas such as the anterior abdominal wall, distinct fibro-elastic sheets are present.
- The extent of **fat** deposition and its regional variation: compare the thigh and abdomen with the eyelids, dorsum of hand, and penis. Most subcutaneous fat is 'white' adipose tissue in which adipocytes store fat in single, large droplets. Its distribution becomes sexually dimorphic at puberty; its extent is dependent largely on the balance between food intake and energy expenditure. Some 'brown' adipose tissue is found in newborn humans. Its cells contain many small fat droplets and mitochondria. It is well supplied with capillaries and sympathetic nerves and provides a rapidly available source of energy.
- The presence of **fluid-filled** sacs: these subcutaneous **bursae** allow the skin to move freely over bony prominences.
- The **superficial vessels and nerves** which pass through the fascia to reach the skin. A superficial system of veins and lymphatics runs within the superficial fascia. The nerves control the blood vessels and sweat glands, and convey information from receptors in the skin to the central nervous system.

Deep fascia

Deep fascia is a dense fibrous connective tissue. It
- covers and ensheathes muscles and is attached to bones;
- provides extra sites for muscle attachment;
- forms partitions (intermuscular septa) between muscle groups with different actions.

In some parts the skin is strongly attached to it. In most regions it is mainly fibrous, but always contains some fat and fluid. Its thickness varies considerably. Over organs such as the pharynx, which have to expand, the deep fascia is very thin, but in areas such as the thigh it forms a non-expansile sleeve which is important in the mechanics of venous return. Many larger texts name the parts of the deep fascia according to the muscle that it covers, but only a few of these are important to remember.

The deep fascia that divides the limb muscles into functional groups creates, with the bones to which the fascia is attached, **compartments** with unyielding walls. If, for any reason, the contents expand, the pressure in the compartment can increase rapidly. This will compress the low-pressure capillaries and veins and prevent flow in them before it affects flow in the arteries. This not only deprives the muscle tissue of oxygen but also sets up a vicious cycle in which the pressure in the compartment increases still further ('compartment syndrome'). The relatively small compartments in the forearm and lower leg are most at risk, in particular the extensor and deep flexor compartments between the tibia and fibula. Therefore a fracture which causes bleeding into the compartment, or anything that causes the muscles to swell, can create an emergency that requires immediate surgical intervention to divide the enclosing fascia (p. 183). Should the muscle tissue die, it will be replaced by fibrous tissue which will undergo contraction, producing still more deformity.

The skeleton

Bone

Bone is a connective tissue which owes its great strength to a matrix containing collagen fibres on which crystals of calcium hydroxyapatite have been laid down. In most mature bone the collagen fibres are laid down by osteoblasts in osteons (Haversian systems) which consist of concentric lamellae of matrix and its cells (osteocytes), surrounding a central canal containing vessels, nerves and osteoclasts (cells which break down bone). In the earliest bone, and in bone formed immediately after fractures, the collagen fibres are randomly arranged, forming 'woven' bone.

Compact bone forms the cortex, and most of the shaft of long bones. The hollow interior of most bones is braced by **trabeculae**, bony struts arranged along lines of stress, to form trabecular or **cancellous** bone. Bone is slowly, but continuously, remodelled and can thus adapt to changing environmental stresses. Bone marrow occupies the spaces within bones. In the young, most of the marrow is haemopoietic (blood-forming) but as age progresses the marrow cavity is increasingly occupied by fat.

Development of bones (2.6)

Bones form from the mesoderm of the embryo. At first a model composed of mesenchyme (loose mesoderm) forms. In many sites, this mesenchyme chondrifies to form a cartilage model of the bone, which will later ossify (**ossification in cartilage**). In others, in particular the clavicle and the vault of the skull (not its base), the loose mesenchyme initially condenses to form a thin membrane-like sheet, which later ossifies (**ossification in membrane**).

The formation of bone tissue starts at a **centre of ossification** (**2.6a**), which frequently lies centrally in the model and then spreads centrifugally. At the same time cells of the perichondrium become osteoblasts and lay down a '**periosteal collar**' of bone around the developing shaft (c.f. ossification in membrane). Many bones, particularly smaller bones (such as those of the carpus, tarsus, and auditory ossicles), develop from a single **centre of ossification**. These appear over a wide period ranging from the sixth week of intrauterine life to the tenth postnatal year, appearing later in the smaller bones.

Other bones ossify in two stages. The **primary centre of ossification** appears near the middle of the bone (in long bones, the middle of the shaft) early in development, from the 6th (clavicle)–16th week *in utero*. From this primary centre, ossification proceeds towards the ends or periphery of the bone. **Secondary centres of ossification** then appear at the ends (periphery) of the bone. The first secondary centre appears just before birth (in the lower end of the femur); others continue to appear up to late teenage. The long bones of the limbs (including the metacarpals, metatarsals, and phalanges), the ribs, and the vertebrae form in this way.

While the bone develops, plates of specialized cartilage (**epiphyseal plates**) remain between the ossifying shaft (**diaphysis**) and ends of the bone (**epiphyses**). It is at these sites that linear growth of the bones continues. Linear growth is usually more marked at one end of a long bone (the '**growing end**') than at the other.

Growth gradually ceases towards the end of puberty and the epiphyseal plates become ossified, so that the shaft fuses with the epiphysis. This normally occurs earlier in girls than in boys. **Fusion** of the epiphyses to the shafts is usually complete by 18–21 years.

Increase in the girth of a developing bone is the result of **appositional growth** (**2.6b**) in which bone is deposited by osteoblasts beneath the periosteum. At the same time, the medullary cavity is increased in size by erosion of the endosteal surface of the bone by osteoclasts. This erosion leaves behind the trabeculae that make up the cancellous bone. Whereas fusion of the epiphyses halts the growth of a bone in length, appositional growth beneath the periosteum and on the surface of trabeculae can continue throughout life, strengthening the outer surface of the bone and the trabeculae to compensate for increased mechanical stress.

During the entire growth period, the developing bone is continually remodelled to 'keep pace with' the growth. Varying tensions on bone, such as are exerted by the insertions of muscles, tendons, or ligaments, alter the contour in that area, e.g. the deltoid tuberosity. Abnormal tension or pressure can lead to gross deformity.

Knowledge of the times of appearance, rates of growth, and times of fusion of the secondary centres of ossification is often needed in clinical practice, for instance in assessing the skeletal age of a child in comparison with its chronological age, also in forensic medicine. These can be looked up at the appropriate time. A radiologist will often examine images of both the normal and the abnormal limb on one film in order to assess the symmetry.

Individual bones

You should be able to identify any bone and hold it in the **position** that it occupies in the living body.

For any bone you should consider:
- The position of its **articular surfaces** and the bones with which they articulate.

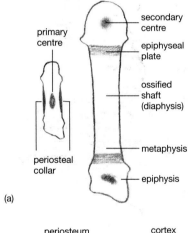

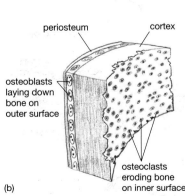

2.6 The development of bones.
(a) Ossification and growth in length via epiphyseal plates; (b) appositional growth.

- **Named parts** and **prominences**, especially those that are palpable in the living subject.
- The site of the major **muscle attachments**—these may or may not be associated roughened protrusions of the bone which give a larger surface area for attachment of the muscle.
- The site of major **ligament** and **membrane attachments**.
- The **blood supply** and position of nutrient arteries.
- The **marrow cavity** content of red or fatty marrow; its extent in children and adults.
- Any specializations of the **trabecular** pattern within the bone, or thickenings of the cortex, which reinforce particular lines of stress in the bone.
- The **ossification** of the bone; and whether ossification occurs in a **membrane** or **cartilage** model.

Cartilage

Cartilage is an avascular connective tissue which forms the articular surfaces of synovial joints, the cartilaginous models of developing bones and their epiphyseal growth plates, the pliable skeleton of the nose, pinna, and larynx, and the costal cartilages. Its cells (chondrocytes) lay down a resilient, very hydrated matrix, which contains, in varying proportions, collagen and aggregates of glycosaminoglycans (such as hyaluronic acid) with proteoglycans. Depending on the composition of the matrix, cartilage is classified as:

- **hyaline cartilage**: this has a 'glassy'-appearing matrix and forms most articular cartilage, and the costal cartilages; it resists compression stress very well;
- **fibrocartilage**, in which the amount of collagen in the matrix (and therefore its resistance to tensile stress) is much greater;
- **elastic cartilage**, which has many elastic fibres in the matrix and is therefore very flexible (e.g. in the pinna of the ear).

Joints and their movements (2.7)

Joints are the articulations between bones. They therefore consist of different types of tissue. Their form varies widely in relation to the functional requirements of the articulation.

The degree of **mobility** varies greatly. Some joints permit virtually no movement; at others, small gliding or angular movements occur; and at many, a large range of movement in different planes can occur.

You should consider the factors that will influence:
- the **type of movement** that can occur;
- the **range of that movement**;
- the **stability** of the joint.

In any joint, the movement that occurs will depend on two main factors: (1) the material between the two bones and the extent to which that can be deformed; and (2) the force that muscles can exert to produce that deformation.

All joints need to be relatively **stable**, but in joints that have evolved to be very mobile, stability is inevitably compromised. Therefore, in joints which have considerable mobility (e.g. the shoulder), you should consider specializations that give stability to the mobile structure. Similarly, in joints (e.g. the hip) where stability is very important, you should consider specializations that optimize the mobility of the joint.

Classification of joints

Joints can be classified in a number of ways. The most common classification depends on the material that separates the bones (fibrous tissue, cartilage, or a synovial cavity). Joints may be further classified according to the type or extent of movement that can occur and whether the joint is temporary or permanent.

Fibrous joints (2.7a)

The bones are united by fibrous tissue. The extent of possible movement depends on the length of the fibrous tissue between the two bony attachments in relation to its cross-sectional area. If it is long, as in the interosseous membrane between radius and ulna or the sutures of the skull of a child at birth, then considerable movement is possible. If, however, it is short, as in the sutures of the adult skull, the peg and socket joints between the teeth and jaws, or the interosseous ligament of the inferior tibio-fibular joint, then little movement can occur.

Cartilaginous joints

In '**primary**' cartilaginous joints (**2.7b**) the bones are united by hyaline cartilage. Such joints occur temporarily between the epiphyses and diaphyses of long bones and permanently in other places, such as between the first rib and the manubrium. A little flexing occurs between first rib and manubrium during respiration (Vol. 2), but no movement should occur at epiphyseal plates provided that the structure of the cartilage is sound (but see p. 34).

In '**secondary**' cartilaginous joints (**2.7c**) the articulating bony surfaces are covered with hyaline cartilage and united by fibrocartilage. Such joints all occur in the midline of the body: between the bodies of the pubic bones (pubic symphysis); between the bodies of the vertebrae (intervertebral discs); and between the manubrium and body of the sternum. A little movement occurs at all these joints, but endocrine-induced changes in the pubic symphysis allow greater movement during late pregnancy and parturition.

Synovial joints (2.7d)

In synovial joints the articular surfaces of the bones are covered with hyaline articular cartilage, and separated by a very thin layer of synovial fluid. These are the most common joints in the body. Many allow a considerable amount of movement between the bones, but at others virtually no movement occurs.

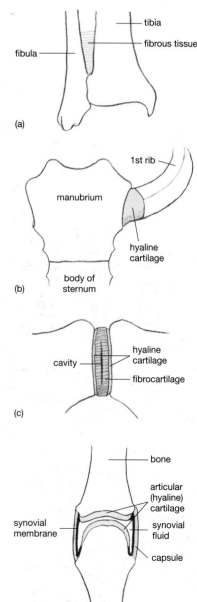

2.7 Different types of joint: (a) fibrous; (b) primary cartilaginous; (c) secondary cartilaginous (pubic symphysis); (d) synovial.

Mobility and stability

All joint movements can be categorized as either **sliding**, **rolling**, or **spinning** of one joint surface on the other. These fundamental motions are combined to produce the movements at a joint.

Classification of synovial joints is based on the movements that occur (determined by the shape of the articular surface):

- in **plane** joints, the articulating surfaces of the bones slide over one another in a single plane;
- **hinge** and **pivot** joints have one linear axis, respectively at right angles to and in line with the main axis of the stable bone;
- a **condylar** joint is a modified hinge joint in which the curvature, and therefore the axis of the (flexion/extension) movement, varies through the movement;
- **ellipsoid** and **saddle** joints both have two axes of movement and therefore permit flexion/extension and abduction/adduction, but not true rotation;
- **ball-and-socket** joints can move in any axis.

These descriptions are, of course, only approximations; all articular surfaces are ovoid to some degree. In one position the articular surfaces are most congruent (close-packed) and the joint is most stable.

For any joint you should consider:

- The **nature** and **range** of the **movements** possible. This depends on:
  - the shape of the articular surfaces;
  - the deformability of the tissues uniting the bones;
  - restrictions by ligaments;
  - restrictions by soft-tissue apposition (e.g. the arm against the trunk in adduction of the shoulder);
  - the mechanical advantage of muscles crossing the joint.

    Movements at a joint can be categorized as:
    Flexion–Extension
    Lateral flexion
    Abduction–Adduction
    Medial (internal)–(external) Lateral rotation
    of limbs
    Rotation (of head, trunk)
    Pronation–Supination (of the forearm)
    Inversion–Eversion (of the foot)
    Protraction–Retraction (of shoulder, head, jaw)
    Elevation–Depression (of the shoulder, jaw)
    Opposition of the thumb (and little finger)

- The **stability** of a joint. This depends on:
  - the shape of the articular surfaces;
  - the strength of the ligaments;
  - the activity of surrounding muscles.

Of these, only the muscles provide *active* support. If they are paralysed, the ligaments will soon lengthen and joint deformity will ensue.

The structure of any joint reflects an evolutionary compromise between mobility and stability in relation to the function of the joint.

- The **articulating surfaces**: the bones that take part in the joint, and the shape of their articular surfaces.

In some cases the area of contact in different movements is important.

- The **capsule** of the joint: its extent, attachments, strengths and deficiencies. The capsule is fibrous and usually attached to the *margins* of the articular surfaces. Note where it deviates from the articular margins.
- The ligaments:
  - **intrinsic ligaments** are thickenings of the capsule laid down along particular lines of stress;
  - **accessory ligaments** also limit movement of the joint but are separate from the capsule.
- The **synovial cavity** and **synovial membrane**: the synovial membrane usually lines all the non-articulating surfaces within a joint. The amount of fluid in any normal joint depends on the contours of the bones within the cavity, but some larger incongruities are taken up by mobile fat pads covered with synovial membrane so that the actual volume of fluid is usually very low, and is scarcely more than a molecular layer of fluid between the articulating surfaces. The fluid has thixotropic properties (i.e. when its molecules are under pressure cross-linkages break down and the fluid becomes less viscous). On radiographs, the 'space' between the articular surfaces of the bones is occupied almost entirely by the articular cartilage, which is radiolucent.
- **Bursae**: some bursae are extensions of the synovial membrane protruding out of the joint capsule. These fluid-lined sacs allow friction-free movement of, for example, tendons over bones. Other bursae related to the joint are not connected with the synovial cavity.
- **Intra-capsular structures**:
  - **fat pads** covered with synovial membrane help to spread synovial fluid;
  - intra-articular **discs of fibrocartilage** divide the cavity of certain joints in which movements occur in two distinct axes.
- The **blood supply** to a joint: there is usually a good anastomosis of the arteries around joints which have a large range of movement, and many of the local arteries give branches to the capsule. This arrangement provides for a continuous supply distal to the joint even if the position of the joint tends to reduce the flow in some of the larger arteries.
- The **nerve supply** to a joint: the capsule of a joint has an important **sensory** nerve supply. This conveys **mechanoceptive** information to the central nervous system concerning the direction, rate, and acceleration of any movement of the joint. It also signals excessive movement via **pain** fibres.

Any nerve which supplies a muscle acting over a joint also supplies sensory fibres to that joint. More specifically, a nerve supplies that part of the capsule which is made slack by the contraction of the muscles it supplies. An intact nerve supply is thus essential to protect a joint from damage due to excessive movement.

Vasomotor fibres of the sympathetic nervous system supply arterioles of the synovial membrane.

Muscle and its actions

Muscle tissue is formed from elongated cells which contain filaments of the proteins actin and myosin, which interact to move on one another and so generate tension when intracellular calcium is increased.

Types of muscle tissue

There are three main types:
- **Skeletal** or **striated** muscle contains myofilaments arranged in parallel longitudinal bundles (myofibrils). The regularly arranged units (sarcomeres) give the muscle its microscopic striation. Skeletal muscle contracts rapidly in response to nerve stimulation; 'white' fibres contract particularly rapidly, 'red' fibres contract more slowly but are less easily fatigued and are thus more common in muscles which have a primary postural function.
- **Cardiac** muscle shares many features of striated muscle, but its cells are branched and linked, both mechanically and electrically, so that the heart contracts as a co-ordinated whole.
- **Smooth** (non-striated) muscle occurs in the walls of blood vessels and of many viscera. Its single ovoid cells are very much shorter than the syncytial skeletal muscle fibres. Within the cells, the filaments of actin and myosin are not arranged in parallel sarcomeres. Rather, some of the actin is attached at various points to the plasma membrane of the cells. When intracellular calcium rises, movement of the myosin relative to the actin produces tension which can shorten the long axis of the cell. This histological difference reflects function. Smooth muscle contracts more slowly and in a more sustained manner than striated muscle.

The smooth muscle in the wall of arteries determines the resistance to flow, and in arterioles controls the blood flow into capillary beds. In the respiratory tract it regulates the diameter of the lumen and thus the resistance to air flow. Throughout the intestine it forms an inner circular and outer longitudinal muscle coat which mixes, segments, and propels the contents by peristalsis. In the urinary and gall bladders it can relax to allow urine or bile to accumulate, and contract to expel it.

Some types of smooth muscle depend less than others on their innervation; their cells form more of a functional syncytium. In the bowel wall individual muscle cells are not innervated (unitary) and have relatively few motor nerves. Much of their rhythmic contraction is myogenic and governed by pacemaker regions or by previous stretching of the muscle. Individual cells are linked by gap junctions through which a wave of electrical excitation can pass along the sheet of muscle. The innervation of such muscle enhances or depresses the rate and force of endogenous rhythmic contractions.

Circular muscle around certain parts of the alimentary and urinary tracts form **sphincters** which, controlled by autonomic nerves, can prevent the onward movement of contents. For example, the pyloric sphincter controls movement of contents from the stomach to the duodenum.

Contraction of the smooth muscle of the gall bladder and uterus is controlled much more by hormones than by nerves.

Muscles moving the skeleton

Many details of the topography and attachments (in particular the origins) of skeletal muscles are not of clinical importance, although there are obvious exceptions, such as the positions of the tendons of the wrist in trauma, and the arrangement of the muscle layers around the inguinal canal in understanding hernias. In general, it is much more important to understand the **muscle groups** that produce given movements at a joint and their innervation.

For any muscle, you should consider:
- The **action** of a muscle in a movement. This may be classified as:
  - **agonist** or **prime mover**: this action shortens the muscle to produce the required movement;
  - **synergist**: this prevents unwanted movements which would be produced if the prime movers acted alone;
  - **antagonist**: opposes the agonists in a particular movement; during movement the antagonists are usually relaxed in proportion to the power of the prime movement;
  - **essential fixator**: clamps more proximal joints in position so that distal parts can move; for example, to produce a simple flexion of the elbow, the humerus and shoulder must be fixed;
  - **postural fixator** (e.g. of the trunk): prevents the body being toppled by movements of heavy parts which shift the centre of gravity;
  - **'paradoxical'** actions counter the force of gravity; for example, when the elbow is extended while lowering a heavy weight held in the hand, biceps generates progressively less tension, to give a controlled extension of the joint.

A particular muscle may be a prime mover in one movement, an antagonist in another, a synergist or essential fixator in others. Depending on the relationship of the attachment of a muscle to the joint over which it acts, the major component of the tension generated by the muscle may act to produce the movement, or to maintain the articular surfaces in contact while the movement occurs (2.8). Muscles with a chief role as **prime movers** therefore tend to be attached so that they have a considerable degree of mechanical advantage (e.g. biceps); muscles with a primary postural function tend to be shorter and more closely

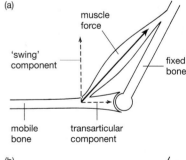

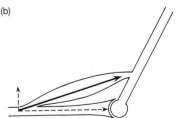

2.8 Components of muscle force at a joint in relation to their site of attachment: (a) muscle inserted close to joint; (b) muscle inserted distant from joint.

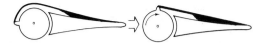

2.9 Attachment of muscles in relation to a mobile joint (shoulder). Muscles originate no nearer to a joint than would require a 25–30% shortening on maximum movement of the joint.

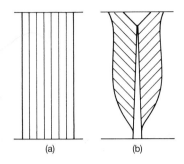

(a)   (b)

2.10 (a) Parallel and (b) pennate arrangement of muscle fasciculi.

applied to a joint. The extensor muscles of the spine illustrate this particularly well (p. 207).

- The **attachments** of the two ends of a skeletal muscle are to separate bones so that the muscle crosses at least one joint. Additional attachments to fibrous tissue are usually unimportant. Some muscles (especially in the face) are attached directly to the dermis of the skin.
  - The **origin** of a muscle is described as its more proximal attachment, or the attachment that usually remains fixed during the prime movement produced by the muscle.
  - The **insertion** is the more distal attachment and the part that usually moves.

These terms are really only used for convenience of description because muscles act differently in different movements.

An individual striated muscle fibre can contract by no more than one-third of its length. A muscle can therefore originate no closer to its insertion than the point at which the maximum movement of the joint would require around a 30% shortening of its fibres. Thus, muscles around very mobile joints must originate further away. Consider, for example, the origin of the short scapular muscles, which stabilize the very mobile shoulder joint. Their fibres originate only from the medial two-thirds of the scapular fossae and are separated from the lateral third by bursae. Fibres originating closer to the joint could not shorten sufficiently to allow the full range of medial and lateral rotation without buckling (**2.9**).

Some muscles appear to be attached directly to bone, but a small amount of fibrous tissue (microtendons) always intervenes. Others are attached via **tendons** (rounded bundles of fibrous tissue) or **aponeuroses** (flattened sheets of fibrous tissue). These allow: the bulk of a muscle to be separated from its point of action, the pull of a muscle to be concentrated into a small area, and the line of pull of a muscle to be altered. Where a tendon is subject to compression, i.e. at its attachment to an epiphysis, or where it winds around a bony pulley, fibrocartilage is present in a zone called an enthesis.

- The **shape** of a muscle and the **arrangement of its fibres**. Two basic principles govern the form of a muscle. Both determine the angle at which the muscle fibres are arranged:
  - the degree of shortening possible is proportional to the length of the muscle fibres;
  - the power of a muscle is proportional to the number of muscle fibres, because each fibre can only generate a certain force.

Muscles with parallel fibres (**2.10a**) can shorten most but, for a given volume of muscle tissue, contain the smallest number of fibres. The number of fibres can be increased if they are oriented obliquely (pennate) to the direction of pull (**2.10b**), although this reduces the length of the fibres and thus the degree of shortening possible.

Muscles can be categorized according to their form and orientation of their fibres, but memorizing this for individual muscles is rarely necessary, although a few examples of different types and their functions should be borne in mind. For example, deltoid—a powerful abductor of the shoulder—has its main fibres arranged in oblique sets ('multipennate'), whereas psoas major—which has to accommodate the flexion and extension of the hip—has its fibres arranged in parallel.

- The **nerve supply** to muscles. You will need to know
  - the **local nerve** supplying a muscle for the diagnose peripheral nerve injuries;
  - the **spinal segmental nerve** supplying the muscle for the diagnosis of spinal nerve and cord lesions.

Both of these are best learned for muscles grouped according to their main function (Tables 5.8.1, p. 121; 6.7.1, p. 187). All muscles producing a given movement of a joint have the same segmental spinal nerve supply. For example, elbow flexors are supplied from C5 and C6 segments of the cord, and the antagonists by adjacent spinal segments (elbow extensors are supplied from C7 and C8).

Posterior primary rami of spinal nerves supply only the extensor muscles of the spine. All other muscles are supplied by their **anterior primary rami**.

Flexor and extensor muscles (the two basic embryological groups) in any limb are supplied, respectively, by **anterior** and **posterior divisions** of the anterior primary rami of spinal nerves in the plexuses supplying the limbs.

The **size of the motor units** (the number of muscle fibres supplied by one motor axon) determines the precision of action possible. For example, muscles producing finger movement have small motor units while those in gluteus maximus are very large.

- The **blood supply** to muscles. Muscles need a good blood supply, but the arteries supplying them do not need to be learned. In general, adjacent arteries supply a muscle, and a main neurovascular bundle enters the muscle at a single point. The two ends of a muscle receive supply from local vessels.

The circulatory system

The circulatory system consists of a double pump—the heart—linked to a system of arteries which branch progressively to distribute blood to the capillary beds in the tissues, where exchange occurs. A system of veins returns blood from the capillaries to the heart; and a system of lymphatic vessels returns extracellular fluid, proteins, and particulate matter not collected by the veins to the circulation.

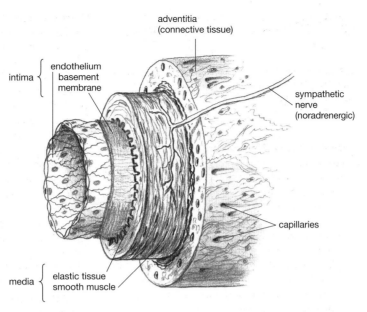

intima { endothelium basement membrane

adventitia (connective tissue)

sympathetic nerve (noradrenergic)

capillaries

media { elastic tissue smooth muscle

2.11 Layers of vessel walls, illustrated by an artery.

Two circulations are connected in series:
- a **systemic** circulation conveys oxygenated arterial blood from the left side of the heart to all the tissues of the body, except the lungs, and returns the deoxygenated blood to the right side of the heart;
- a **pulmonary** circulation conveys the deoxygenated blood from the right side of the heart to the lungs, and oxygenated blood back to the left side of the heart.

The vessels in which blood and lymph circulate consist of three layers (**2.11**):
- an **endothelium** (*tunica intima*), which provides a friction-minimizing lining to the vessel and, with its basement membrane, the exchange surface of capillaries;
- a **muscle coat** (*tunica media*), which consists of elastic, fibrous, and smooth muscle tissue in varying proportions; and
- an outer coat (*tunica adventitia*) of fibrous tissue, in which may run the vessels and nerves that supply the larger vessels.

Arterial supply

The **arteries** form a high-pressure distribution system. The largest arteries have a very elastic tunica media to absorb the pulsatile force of the heart contraction; smaller arteries have a more muscular coat. The **arterioles** that branch from them regulate blood flow to the tissues by contraction of the smooth muscle coat around their narrow lumen; their smooth muscle is controlled by sympathetic nerves.

For any artery, you should consider:
- Its **area of supply**.
- Its origin and parent vessel.
- Its **course**, in particular where its pulsations can be palpated, and where the vessel is exposed to injury. Arterial pulses are palpable only at certain points; usually where they cross bone. Such sites can also form useful 'pressure points' where pressure can arrest haemorrhage. The course of large vessels can readily be mapped in the living by use of an ultrasonic Doppler-based probe. Radiologically, vessels can be demonstrated by the injection of radiopaque material into the circulation at an appropriate point (angiography).
- Its **major branches** and **mode of termination**.
- The **extent of anastomosis** with other major vessels. Some vessels, such as the central artery of the retina, are **end arteries**; some are functionally end arteries because of very limited anastomoses; yet others have plentiful anastomoses with neighbouring vessels.

Vessels of the retina can be observed directly in the fundus of the eye by use of an ophthalmoscope.

Capillary beds

Capillaries form the essential exchange part of the circulatory system. The capillary bed, and arteriovenous anastomoses which provide controllable shunts between arterioles and venules, are too small to be visualized with the naked eye. However, capillary loops in the nail bed can be visualized with a low-power microscope if the skin is made translucent by application of oil.

The **degree of oxygenation** of the tissues and **haemoglobin content** of the blood can best be assessed where the covering epithelium is very thin, at places such as skin creases in the palm and the conjunctiva of the eyes and eyelids.

Venous drainage

The veins form a low-pressure capacitance system. In the limbs a system of **superficial veins** is separated from the **deep veins** by the deep fascia. Like arteries, veins are lined by endothelium. In smaller veins below the heart the endothelium forms **valves** which break up the hydrostatic column of blood. The tunica media is thinner and less muscular than that of arteries because pressure in the venous system is much less.

For any vein you should consider:

- Its **origin** and the **area drained** by the vein. Remember that the origin is distal.
- Its **course**, particularly where the vein can be punctured with a needle for intravenous administration of substances or withdrawal of blood for testing; also areas which are liable to trauma.
- Any **valves** within the veins. There is a marked regional variation in the incidence of valves. They are plentiful in the limbs, particularly in the leg. Most large veins of the thorax and abdomen lack valves; negative pressure in the thorax generated by respiration sucks venous blood back to the heart, and compression by abdominal muscles also aids venous return.
- The **major tributaries** and **termination** of the vein. All veins from the limbs, head and neck, and body wall drain directly into the right atrium via **systemic** veins. Veins from the abdominal alimentary tract drain first to the liver via the hepatic **portal vein** which forms sinusoids between sheets of hepatocytes in the liver. The hepatocytes control the amount of nutrient passing from the liver via the hepatic veins to join the systemic circulation at the inferior vena cava.
- The **extent of anastomosis** with other veins. In the limbs, **communicating** veins link the deep and superficial veins through the deep fascia and are important in the development of varicose veins. In the abdomen, there are small anastomoses between the portal and systemic circulations, which can become distended if pressure in the portal circulation is increased.

Lymphatic drainage

The lymphatic system is a very-low-pressure system that returns extracellular fluid, proteins, and cells to the blood system. It resembles the venous system, except that the endothelium of its blind-ending capillaries is discontinuous and therefore more permeable, and its vessels are much smaller and contain more valves.

The endothelium of lymphatics capillaries is connected to the surrounding connective tissue in such a way that the presence of excess extracellular fluid pulls on the connections and opens the vessels.

The blood vascular system is protected from invasion by microorganisms via the lymphatics by the presence of **lymph nodes** along their course. These are collections of cells of the immune system, which filter the lymph and respond to foreign proteins (antigens) with an immune response. Multiple afferent lymphatic vessels enter a node, a few efferents leave via its hilum.

Lymphatic vessels cannot be detected by routine examination of a living subject, unless they are inflamed or enlarged,, and only the largest can readily be dissected. They can be demonstrated radiologically after injection of radiopaque dyes. Despite the difficulty in visualizing lymphatics, it is crucial that you are familiar with the lymphatic drainage of an area, since both infection and malignant tumours can spread by this route.

For any area or organ you should consider:

- The **lymph vessels** that drain the area: *superficial* lymphatics tend to run with superficial veins, *deep* lymphatics tend to run with deep vessels, particularly the arteries (the distinction being the intervening layer of deep fascia between superficial and deep lymphatics).
- The **primary draining lymph nodes** and the extent to which these can be palpated.
- The **route** whereby lymph is returned to the bloodstream.
- The degree of **anastomosis** with other lymphatics. In general, there is very extensive anastomosis between the lymphatics serving adjacent areas, so that, when lymphatics are blocked by tumour, nodes not normally draining an area may become involved. However, in the leg, there is relatively little anastomosis between the superficial and deep lymphatics.

The nervous system

Cellular components

The nervous system acts as a unified whole, but is made up of many different specialized functional units. Each of these functional units is made up of one or more types of specialized cells. **Neurons** are the electrically excitable cells. All neurons are functionally connected with other neurons by synapses, at which the connection is achieved (usually) by the release and sensing of one or more neurotransmitter chemical signals. The neurons are supported by various **glial cells**. In the central nervous sytem myelin sheaths are produced by oligodendrocytes (oligodendroglia); astrocytes (astroglia) are in intimate contact with the neurons and control their environment and influence their activity in ways that are only recently becoming clear; microglia are phagocytic, becoming particularly active after injury. In the peripheral nervous system Schwann cells fulfil all these functions.

Some neurons—**sensory neurons**—are either themselves sensitive to non-neuronal stimuli arising either outside or within the body (e.g. touch, temperature, stomach distension), or are connected to organs which transduce such stimuli (**2.12**).

Other neurons—**motor neurons**—terminate on, and control, the activity of non-neuronal tissue such as muscles and glands.

Any neuron that is not sensory or motor is usually referred to as an **interneuron**. Interneurons are vastly more numerous than either sensory or motor neurons. Their activity provides all the subtle processing of sensory information and memories that leads to an output of behaviour controlled by the motor neurons.

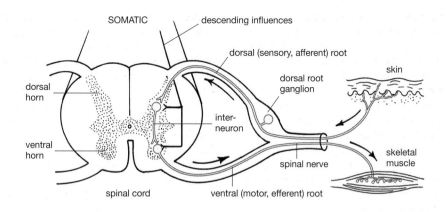

2.12 Organization of the somatic peripheral nervous system.

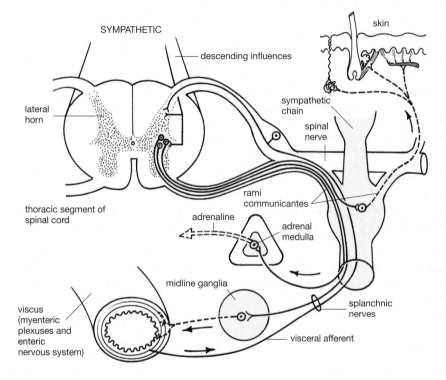

2.13 Sympathetic innervation.

Anatomical subdivisions of the nervous system

The nervous system, which is largely bilaterally symmetrical, is divided for convenience of description into a number of different parts, each of which has its particular anatomical location and/or function.
- The **central nervous system** comprises the **brain** and **spinal cord**; it is contained within the skull and spinal canal.
- The **peripheral nervous system**, which comprises all the connections between the central nervous system and the rest of the body.

The peripheral nervous system is further divided into:
- the **somatic** nervous system (**2.12**) which (broadly) receives information from the skin and musculoskeletal system and which controls the musculoskeletal system.

- the **autonomic** nervous system (**2.13–2.15**) which controls and responds to the viscera, glands, blood vessels, and the pupil.

The peripheral nervous system is also divided into:
- the **cranial nerves**, 12 pairs of which (usually designated by Roman numerals I–XII) emerge from the brain;
- the **spinal nerves**, which emerge from the spinal cord on either side and are named according to the part of the vertebral column from which they emerge. They comprise 8 **cervical**, 12 **thoracic**, 5 **lumbar,** and 5 **sacral** nerves. Note: the first seven cervical nerves (C1–C7) emerge *above* the corresponding vertebra; C8 emerges *below* the seventh cervical vertebra, and all the remaining spinal nerves emerge *below* the corresponding vertebra.

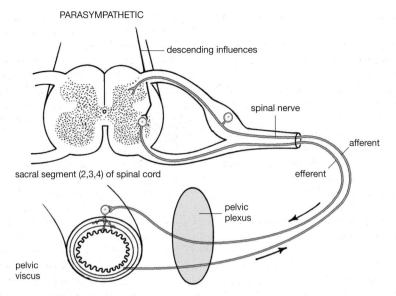

2.14 Parasympathetic innervation.

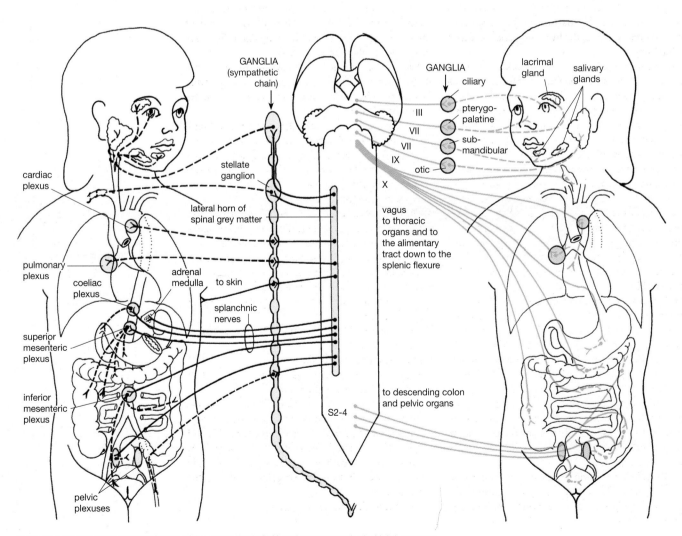

2.15 The organization and distribution of the sympathetic (left) and parasympathetic (right) systems.

The autonomic nervous system is further subdivided into:

- the **sympathetic** nervous system (**2.13**, **2.15**), which controls many of the body's reactions to acute stress ('fight or flight');
- the **parasympathetic** nervous system (**2.14**, **2.15**), which is active when body resources are being restored ('rest and recovery');
- an **enteric** nervous system of neurons intrinsic to the gastrointestinal tract.

All the nerves that make up the peripheral nervous system can be classified as either

- **sensory,** or **afferent**, nerves, which convey information *toward* the central nervous system;
- **motor,** or **efferent**, nerves, which convey information *from* the central nervous system to the peripheral targets.

Twelve pairs of **cranial nerves** emerge from the brainstem within the cranial cavity. The first two—the olfactory (I) and optic (II) nerves—are actually extensions of the brain rather than nerves. The cranial nerves mostly supply parts of the head and neck, but the vagus nerve (X) also supplies the thoracic viscera (heart and lungs), a large part of the gastrointestinal tract, and organs such as the liver and pancreas which develop from it.

Motor fibres in cranial nerves originate from cell bodies in the brainstem; their sensory fibres have cell bodies in ganglia associated with the nerves. Four cranial nerves [the oculomotor (III), facial (VII), glossopharyngeal (IX), and vagus (X)] also contain parasympathetic fibres, which control the pupil and lens of the eye and glands in the head.

The **spinal nerves** are each formed from a **sensory** (dorsal) and a **motor** (ventral) **root**. Every spinal nerve contains both sensory and motor somatic fibres (which supply the skin and musculoskeletal system). In addition, the ventral roots of all the thoracic and the upper two lumbar nerves (i.e. T1–L2) contain sympathetic preganglionic fibres, and the last three sacral nerves (S3–S5) contain parasympathetic preganglionic fibres.

All sensory (afferent) neurons have cell bodies either in the **dorsal root ganglia** of the spinal nerves or in the sensory ganglia of the various cranial nerves. This is true for somatic sensory fibres from the skin and musculoskeletal system, and also for the sensory fibres from the viscera, which reach the central nervous system via peripheral autonomic nerves.

Somatic **motor** (efferent) neurons originate in the ventral horn of the spinal cord and pass uninterruptedly to their target muscle fibres. Each somatic motor neuron branches to supply a number of fibres within a muscle (motor unit).

Motor (efferent) components of the autonomic nervous system always comprise a two-neuron chain linked by a synapse in an **autonomic ganglion** (see

2.13, 2.14, 2.15). Thus, there are **preganglionic** sympathetic and parasympathetic neurons, which originate from cells bodies in the central nervous system, and ganglionic neurons which give rise to **postganglionic** sympathetic and parasympathetic axons. It is the postganglionic axons which supply the target smooth muscle and secretory systems of the viscera. In the gastrointestinal tract the postganglionic fibres influence the activity of the intrinsic enteric neurons.

The motor components of the sympathetic and parasympathetic nervous system differ in the ways in which the preganglionic and postganglionic parts are arranged and, to a certain extent in the transmitters used. In the parasympathetic system, the preganglionic fibres synapse in ganglia situated either near to (cranial ganglia) or in the walls of the viscera they supply. In the sympathetic system the synapses occur either in the **paravertebral chain of sympathetic ganglia** or in **midline ganglia** associated with the viscera and the large arteries that supply them.

Despite the restricted origin of preganglionic sympathetic neurons from T1–L2 segments of the spinal cord, the paravertebral chain of sympathetic ganglia extends from the base of the skull to the end of the sacrum, and postganglionic sympathetic fibres are distributed to all parts of the body.

Every mixed spinal nerve therefore contains nerve fibres of various types, together with their supporting **Schwann cells,** and delicate surrounding vascular connective tissue.

Each spinal nerve, on leaving the vertebral column, divides into an **anterior** and a **posterior primary ramus**. The posterior primary rami supply the extensor muscles of the spine and the skin over them; the anterior primary rami supply all the remainder, including the limbs.

For any nerve you should consider:

- The **types of fibre** that it contains. In the limbs most nerves contain sympathetic fibres and their somatic component may be motor, sensory, or mixed.
- The **origin** of the various fibres: for somatic nerves, the spinal root and peripheral nerve of origin; for autonomic nerves, the ganglion or cranial nerve of origin. Many sympathetic fibres travel as a plexus around major vessels.
- The **course** of the nerve, particularly where it is palpable or liable to trauma.
- The **major branches** of the nerve.
- Any **muscles** supplied by the nerve and the effect on function of damage to the nerve.
- Any **skin** supplied by the nerve and the area of anaesthesia that will be produced by damage to the nerve.
- Any **organ(s)** supplied by autonomic nerves, and their effects on the function of the organ(s). In the limbs, sympathetic fibres supply not only blood vessels, but also sweat glands and arrector pili muscles.
- The effects of **damage** to the nerve.

The endocrine system
(see Ch 8, Vols 2, 3)

In addition to control by the nervous system, all tissues receive chemical signals—hormones—produced by endocrine cells. Many of these are produced by endocrine cells grouped together to form **endocrine glands** (there are no endocrine glands in the limbs); other endocrine cells are scattered in organs such as the gastrointestinal tract and form **diffuse endocrine systems**. Still other hormones are produced by tissues such as adipose tissue (leptin). Many hormones circulate widely through the body via the blood system and can affect many different tissues; others act on local cells (paracrine action).

For any endocrine tissue you should consider:
- Whether the cells are grouped as a gland or are scattered.
- The **hormones** that are produced and their effects.
- The stimuli (hormonal, nervous, chemical, e.g. blood glucose) that **control** secretion of the hormones.
- The effects of too much or too little secretion.

Internal organs

The internal organs of the body form the component parts of the various functional systems.

For any internal organ you should consider:
- Its principal function(s).
- Its connections with other parts of the system.
- Its position in the body and principal relations.
- Its blood supply and nerve supply.
- The effects of failure of the organ's function.

CHAPTER 3

Medical imaging

CHAPTER 3

Medical imaging

One of the most important adjuncts to physical examination of the anatomy of living subjects is medical imaging. Since the turn of the century, images (radiographs) obtained with X-rays have been the standard method of visualizing many of the internal areas of the body. Images have also been obtained by use of sound waves (ultrasound imaging), or by using radiation emitted from substances which have been administered to the patient (nuclear imaging). Powerful computers are now harnessed to imaging methods to produce virtual 'slices' (often cross-sections) of the body. The first of these, computed tomography, uses conventional X-rays as the energy source. The same principles have been extended to nuclear medicine to produce emission computer-assisted tomography, and to the nuclear magnetic resonance effect to produce an image based on magnetic fields, known as magnetic resonance imaging. These techniques have proved enormously powerful in diagnosis and, in many cases, obviated the need for investigative operations. Development in computer processing now allow the slices to be recombined to produce virtual three-dimensional images of the tissues.

Radiology

Conventional radiology

X-rays are part of the electromagnetic radiation spectrum and can be produced by bombarding a tungsten anode with electrons, using high voltages. When the electrons strike the anode, their kinetic energy is converted to heat and radiation, including X-rays. In medical radiography the tungsten anode is suspended over the patient so that the beam of X-rays passes through the body; the emerging radiation is then picked up by a detector which is usually photographic film (**3.1**). Since photographic film is sensitive to X-rays, the film will be exposed to a degree that depends on how much of the beam has passed through the patient and how much has been absorbed by the different tissues of the body. Air is radiolucent, bone and metal, radiopaque. In the chest, good contrast is provided by the bone, soft tissues, and air-containing lungs, and a clear image of most major structures such as heart, liver, and pulmonary vessels (**3.2**, H, L, and arrows, respectively) can be obtained. In the abdomen, however, most of the organs are of similar density with respect to X-rays and, although gas in the bowel (**3.3**, broad arrow) and bone can be distinguished, there is very little extra information to be obtained from soft-tissue structures, although the outlines of the kidneys are just visible (**3.3**, arrowheads).

Fluoroscopy ('screening')

If a fluorescent screen is substituted for photographic film, a direct image is produced. This enables movements of organs to be studied. It is customary nowadays to view the image on a television screen; an amplifier system or 'image intensifier' is usually employed which ensures a good picture with a reduction in the dose of radiation. The fluoroscopic image can then be recorded by photography or video, or by a digital computer which stores the information received (digital radiography).

Small-angle tomography

This is an old technique which has nothing to do with computed tomography, except that a 'slice' is produced. It is used to overcome the superimposition effects present in the conventional radiographic image. The X-ray tube and the film move around the patient in a constant

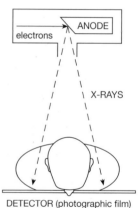

3.1 Conventional radiography.

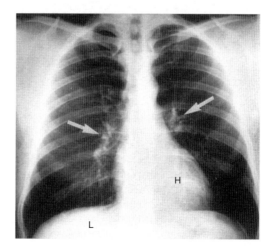

3.2 Radiograph of the chest.

25

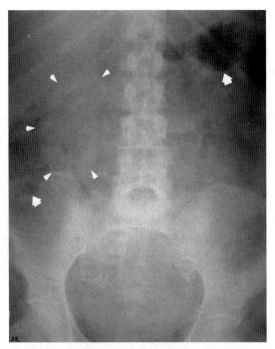

3.3 Radiograph of the abdomen.

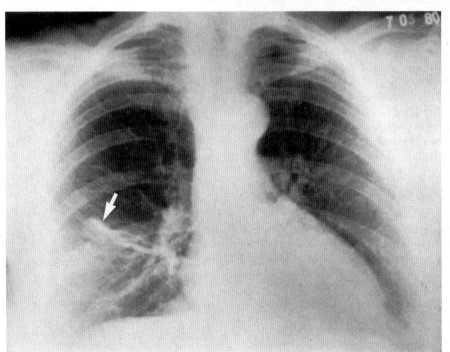

3.4 Radiograph of chest; opacity in right lung (white arrow).

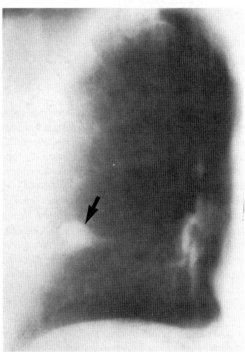

3.5 Tomogram of opacity seen in **3.4**.

relationship to the plane of interest, which therefore appears as a sharp image; the overlying and underlying areas move relative to the tube and film so that their image is blurred. The effect of tomography is therefore to produce a clear image of one plane only. It is widely used in the investigation of the chest, kidneys, and skeleton. Examine the conventional radiograph (**3.4**) which shows an opacity in the right lung (arrow). Note that in the tomogram (**3.5**) the plane of focus is such that only the nodular opacity is seen clearly.

Contrast media

It is often not possible to distinguish many organs by conventional radiography, especially in the abdomen. This problem can be overcome by the use of contrast media, which are usually either pastes of inorganic barium salts for rectal or oral ingestion, or organic substances containing iodine for intravenous administration. To demonstrate the oesophagus and stomach, a suspension of barium sulphate is given to a patient by

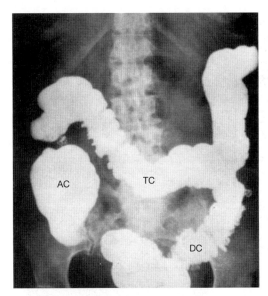

3.6 'Single contrast' radiograph of abdomen after barium enema.

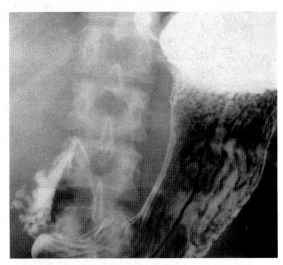

3.7 'Double contrast' radiograph of stomach. The patient has been tipped cranially, causing the barium to collect in the upper part (fundus) of the stomach.

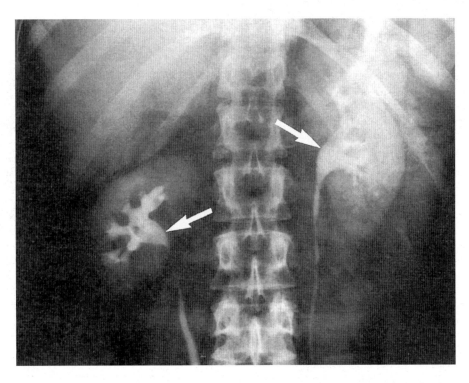

3.8 Intravenous urogram.

mouth. The colon can be similarly studied if barium is introduced through the rectum, note that in **3.6** it has filled the descending colon (DC) transverse colon (TC) and ascending colon (AC). More information is provided about the lining of the intestine if a small quantity of suspension is used and the gut is then distended with air, giving a 'double contrast' image. In **3.7** barium fills the upper part of the stomach of the recumbent patient, while the mixture of gas and barium allows detail of the lining mucosa to be seen.

Iodine contrast media have many applications; they can be injected intravenously to be excreted by the kidneys (**intravenous urogram**) (**3.8**). The contrast medium is concentrated by the renal parenchyma, making the kidney more obvious than in **3.3** and is excreted into the renal collecting system, renal pelvis, and ureter (arrows). Injections of contrast medium can also be made into a joint (**arthrogram**; see **6.3.12**). In the past the method was also used to outline the bronchial tree (bronchogram) or spinal cord (myelogram) but this has now been superceded by magnetic resonance imaging (MRI).

Contrast media are still used to study blood vessels (**angiography**). A fine tube (catheter) is inserted into

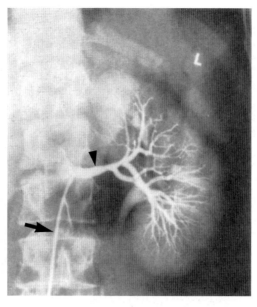

3.9 Arteriogram of left kidney.

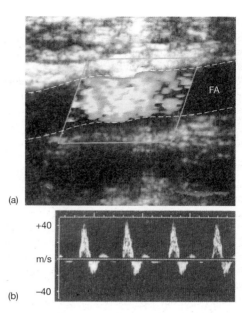

3.12 (a) Doppler colour flow image of normal femoral artery (FA); (b) Doppler frequency signals.

an accessible vessel, for example the femoral artery, and its tip manoeuvred under radiographic control into the desired vessel, where contrast media can be injected. In **3.9** the catheter (arrow) has entered the left renal artery (arrowhead) and contrast medium has outlined small vessels within the kidney. This procedure can be applied to vessels of the gut or head and neck, and even the chambers of the heart.

Digital radiography

In digital radiography, each image is divided into a matrix of picture elements (pixels) and the density of each pixel is converted to a digit. The digitized image is stored on a computer and can be retrieved to a viewing screen, transmitted via telephone, and processed to improve its information content. One method of processing is **digital subtraction angiography (3.10)** in which images of the background are subtracted from images of the same area after injection of contrast material. It provides more information than is possible with film, and enables images of the arterial system to be produced after intravenous injection of contrast material, which was not possible with conventional techniques. It also avoids the hazards of intra-arterial injection of contrast medium, and the expense of silver-coated film.

Ultrasound imaging

Sound waves travelling in a medium are partly reflected when they hit another medium of different consistency. This produces an echo, and the time taken for the echo to reach the source of the sound indicates the distance from the reflecting surface (distance = time × velocity).

Ultrasound consists of high-frequency sound waves that cannot be detected by the human ear. When ultrasound travels in human tissue it undergoes partial reflection at tissue boundaries; thus a proportion of

the sound waves return as an echo, while the rest continue (**3.11**). Bone absorbs the sound almost totally and therefore no signal can be obtained from bone or the structures beyond. Neither can a signal be obtained from gas-containing viscera. These two facts are responsible for significant limitations to the use of this technique. However, it has the great advantage that there are no damaging effects at the sound energies used, and it can therefore be used to monitor the developing fetus. The images are sectional in that they represent a 'slice' of the body in the plane of the ultrasound beam. In addition to its use in obstetrics, ultrasound is used in the investigation of the urogenital system, liver and biliary system, and in all joints (for ultrasound images of the shoulder see **5.3.9**). All current machines have a rapidly repeated scanning action, which enables movement of various organs to be studied in 'real-time'. In cardiology, for example, the movement of heart valves and chambers of the heart can be visualized (see Vol. 2, **5.4.19**).

Doppler colour-flow imaging

When a wave motion is radiated from a moving source, there is a change in frequency of the wave—the Doppler effect. This principle can be used to study moving structures, such as blood flowing through peripheral vessels. Probes emit ultrasonic waves of a given frequency. The signal received back from the body by the transducer contains the emitted frequency (due to waves reflected from stationary sources) and Doppler-shifted frequencies reflected from moving structures. The Doppler-shifted frequencies (**3.12b**) can then be filtered out, sorted for the extent of the shift, and recorded. The information can then be presented on a colour monitor with the vessels represented in different colours. An initial colour-flow image

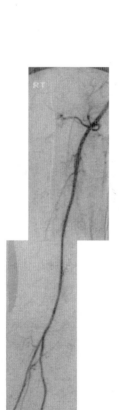

3.10 Digital subtraction angiogram of the main arteries of the arm and forearm.

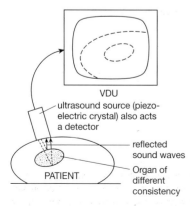

3.11 Ultrasound imaging.

(**3.12a**) is used to locate the vessel being studied (in this case, the femoral artery) and, from the colour, to determine the direction of flow. Graphic presentation shows the speed of forward flow during systole (contraction of the heart) and the small backward flow during diastole (heart relaxation). This technique is often used to evaluate conditions in which flow is restricted (stenoses) or increased (tumour vessels).

Nuclear imaging

Nuclear medicine may be defined broadly as the use of radioactive isotopes ('radionuclides') in the diagnosis and treatment of disease. Of particular relevance is that branch of nuclear medicine called nuclear imaging or 'scintigraphy', whereby a 'map' of the uptake of radionuclide in a given organ system or pathological lesion can be produced by means of an instrument called a gamma camera. Analysis of such an image (which depends not only on morphology, but also on function) is then of use to the diagnostician in elucidating the nature of the patient's problem.

The basis of the gamma camera is a large, flat crystal of sodium iodide, which converts into light rays the gamma rays emitted from radionuclides which have been injected into the patient. These light rays strike a photosensitive surface and cause the emission of electrons. The latter are amplified by a photomultiplier and eventually electrical pulses are formed. These electrical pulses can be used to produce an image on a television screen, or be used as input to a computer system (**3.13**).

A number of radionuclides are used in a form described as 'radiopharmaceuticals'. The principal radionuclide used is technetium-99m (which is very safe for the patient in terms of absorbed radiation dose, and has a convenient half-life of 6 hours), but others are also available, e.g. iodine-123, thallium-201, gallium-67, indium-111. These radionuclides are coupled to various compounds designed to deposit them in the organ of interest. For example, technetium-99m coupled to sulphur colloid will be phagocytosed by macrophages and so be deposited in the reticulo-endothelial system. Technetium-99m phosphates will deposit in bones. In **3.14**, note the focal areas of increased isotope uptake in the spine and pelvis, which are due to tumour deposits from breast cancer. Iodine-123 as sodium iodide will be taken up by the thyroid. The normal uptake of such a radiopharmaceutical in an organ must be familiar to the radiologist, so that any deviation from the normal pattern is detected rapidly.

Sectional images (emission computed tomography, ECAT) can also be produced using methods very similar to those for emission computed tomography (see below). There are two varieties of this technique: single photon emission tomography (SPET), in which solitary gamma rays (say, from technetium-99m) are used, and positron emission tomography (PET), in which positrons (positive electrons) are produced (for example, from a cyclotron-produced radionuclide such as fluorine-18-deoxyglucose). Both methods produce functional cross-sectional images and are widely used to investigate the brain and the heart.

Computed sectional imaging

Computed tomography

Computed tomography (CT) is similar to conventional radiography in that a beam of X-rays is passed through the body and is measured after it emerges. The differences between CT and conventional X-ray

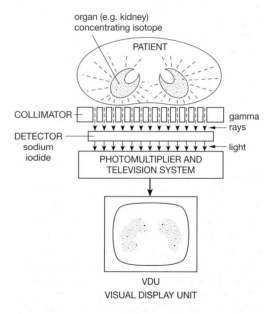

3.13 Nuclear imaging.

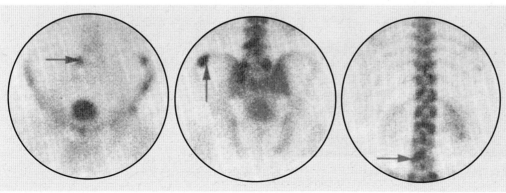

3.14 Nuclear images of the pelvis and spine, showing patches of increased uptake of isotope consistent with secondary tumour deposits (arrows).

methods is that a very narrow beam is used and an array of highly sensitive photoelectric cells is substituted for photographic film. The beam is rotated around the patient and density measurements are made from many different angles. The data are analysed by a computer and the whole image is displayed on a TV monitor (**3.15**), dense structures such as bone conventionally being shown at the white end of the spectrum.

CT images are usually true axial sections, although coronal sections can be taken of the head by positioning the patient appropriately. However, computer programs are available whereby a sagittal or coronal image can be built up from data derived from successive axial images. CT produces extremely clear and finely detailed cross-sectional radiographs without any superimposition of surrounding structures.

Instead of producing discrete cross-sections, a spiral motion of the gantry is now used. This produces continuous cross-sections (**spiral CT**) and also operates much faster. Thus it is possible to see organs or small differences in density caused by disease which are almost impossible to demonstrate by conventional radiography. **3.16** is a transverse section CT of the abdomen in which the kidneys (K) liver (L), pancreas (P), and small bowel (B) are all clearly seen because they are outlined by body fat.

It is a convention that all such transverse sectional images are presented as if the section is viewed from the feet of the patient. Thus, structures on the right of the image are on the left-hand side of the patient and vice versa.

The development of computer techniques and spiral CT now allows the sectional images to be combined to reconstruct the **three-dimensional shape** of the tissues being imaged and to display these on a screen. This has proved very useful, for example, in reconstructive surgery (**3.17**).

Emission computer-assisted tomography (ECAT)

This is based on the same principle as transmission computed tomography described above, except that it depends on gamma rays emitted from a radionuclide concentrated in an organ rather than on a transmitted X-ray beam (**3.18**). In **3.19** technetium-labelled methylene diphosphonate has been taken up

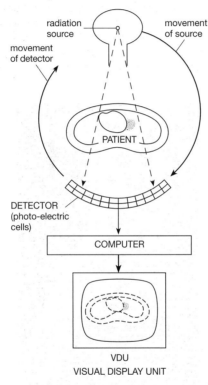

3.15 Computed tomography.

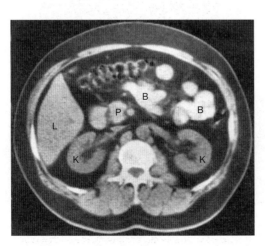

3.16 Transverse CT of abdomen.

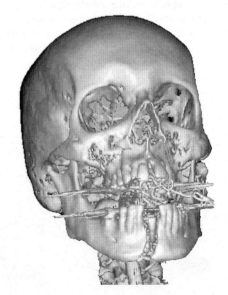

3.17 Three-dimensional reconstruction of the facial skeleton after a major accident. The mandible has been fractured and a tooth displaced down into the fracture. Within the mouth are surgical rods and wires.

in the skeleton of the chest in the same way as in the examination in **3.14**. This however is a cross-sectional image, so that you see the nuclide activity in the vertebral body posteriorly (V) and the sternum anteriorly (S). The uptake within the left side of the thorax (arrow) is in an area of muscle infarction in the heart. This would not have been seen on a conventional scintigram as it would have been obscured by activity in the overlying ribs.

Magnetic resonance imaging (MRI)

MRI is the most recent of the diagnostic techniques and is based on radio signals emitted from resonating atoms within the body.

The nuclear magnetic resonance effect depends upon the fact that atoms carry a charge and can therefore be regarded as small magnets. When a large magnetic field is applied across a body there is a tendency for the nuclei to line up with this field. Nuclei spin and, rather like spinning tops, can be displaced from their axis by a field applied at an angle to the main one. If the second field is of an appropriate frequency, the atoms can be made to resonate. Since the atomic nuclei carry a charge, any movement sets up radio signals which can be detected outside the body. The interest of magnetic resonance centres on the fact that the behaviour of the resonating nuclei depends upon the atoms surrounding them, in other words their chemical environment. Thus the radio signals measured outside the patient can reflect the biochemistry of the area under examination.

The magnetic resonance scanner looks rather like a CT machine, in that the patient lies on a couch and enters a gantry which, in this case, is a very large electromagnet. Sections are taken through the area being examined and the resulting MR images are superficially similar to CT. However, CT is based on the **density of tissues** to X-rays whereas MR images reflect some aspects of the **biochemical composition of the tissues**. The sequence of magnetic pulses can be altered (T_1- and T_2-weighting) to vary the signal from different tissues but, in both, fat (including fatty bone marrow) produces a high signal intensity (white), muscle produces an intermediate signal, and cortical bone and fibrous tissue produce low-intensity signals (black). T_2-weighting produces a high-intensity signal from fluid, which gives a low-intensity signal with T_1-weighting. **3.20** shows an MR image of the spinal column and spinal cord.

Functional magnetic resonance imaging

This is a variation on the magnetic resonance principle, whereby increased brain blood flow in response to a motor or sensory stimulus can be detected and superimposed on a routine MRI of the brain (**3.21**). Even the desire to move a finger can now be mapped on the brain, as well as the origin of the motor action!

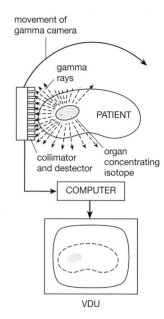

3.18 Emission computer-assisted tomography.

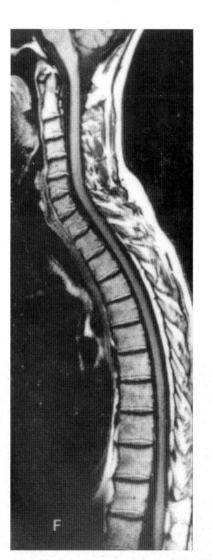

3.20 Midline sagittal MRI, showing the spinal column and spinal cord in the subarachnoid space. The bright line at the lower end of each vertebral body is an artefact.

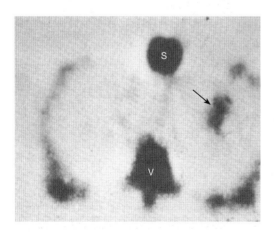

3.19 ECAT image (transverse section) of chest, showing increased uptake of isotope in heart muscle consistent with tissue damage.

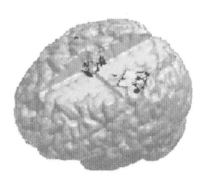

3.21 Functional MRI image, showing parts of the left hemisphere of the brain (red, yellow) which increase in activity when moving fingers of the right hand.

Embryonic development of the musculoskeletal system

Embryonic development of the musculoskeletal system

Why study the embryonic development of the body? There are several reasons: embryology enables us to understand how, during development, the adult arrangements of tissues and cells are generated; it can help explain the aetiology (cause) of congenital anomalies; and it can reveal basic principles about cell behaviour that govern processes, both normal and pathological, such as cancer.

In recent years, the revolution in molecular genetics has enabled the discovery of many of the mutations that underlie human congenital abnormalities. Developmental studies, mainly using mouse embryos, are now helping us understand how a mutation in a known gene leads to an abnormality of a specific developmental pathway. Such studies also reveal the role of the gene in normal embryogenesis.

Some basic embryological concepts

Our bodies can be regarded as a **clone** of cells, all of which are derived from a single cell—the fertilized egg. All our cells contain identical genetic material (DNA), but there is great diversity in the characteristics of cells in different parts of the body; this is generated during embryonic development.

The musculoskeletal system consists of a subset of the many diverse cell types that make up the human body. These are the cells that form the muscle, bone, cartilage, skin, loose connective tissues, blood and lymph vessels, and nerves. The generation of all tissue-specific differences during embryogenesis is the result of differential expression of tissue-specific genes.

One of the great organizational feats of the embryo is to generate the right cell types in the right quantities in the right places. This leads to the formation of an organized **pattern** within the embryo. The limbs provide a good example of this. The upper and lower limbs contain the same cell types in similar proportions. In all four limbs the skeleton comprises a single proximal bone (humerus or femur) with, more distally, a pair of bones (radius and ulna or tibia and fibula), then a group of small bones (carpals or tarsals), and finally a five-digit hand or foot skeleton. Yet, within this overall pattern, considerable function-related differences have evolved.

Thus, embryonic development consists of three major processes: **cell proliferation**, which is tightly controlled to ensure that each developing structure reaches the required size before growth ceases; **cell differentiation**, in which cell populations undergo a restriction of potential leading to the formation of specialized tissues; and **morphogenesis**, in which movements of cell populations and regional shape changes generate embryonic form (e.g. rotation of the limb buds). Programmed **cell death** (apoptosis) also plays a role, for instance in the separation of the digits through the death of some of the mesenchymal cells between the digits.

Origin of the tissues that form the musculoskeletal system

All embryonic tissues are derived from three basic layers of cells that appear during the first 2 weeks of development. They are called **ectoderm** (a surface layer that gives rise to the epidermis of the skin and to the entire nervous system), **mesoderm** (which gives rise to most of the internal organs, such as muscles, dermis, circulatory system, etc.), and **endoderm** (which generates the epithelium of the gut and most of its associated organs).

Paired mesodermal structures, called **somites**, flank the embryonic axis (**4.1**, **4.2**). Each somite starts as a rosette which then loses its rosette structure and subdivides into two parts:
- the ventromedial **sclerotome**, the cells of which come to surround the future spinal cord and give rise to the axial skeleton (vertebral column and ribs) (for the development of the spine see p. 197);
- dorsolaterally, the somite remains an epithelium for longer, and this region is called the **dermamyotome**. From its most lateral part some cells become very active and invade the limb buds to generate skeletal muscles and probably also the dermis, whilst the medial part of the dermamyotome forms the myotome, which will give rise to the segmental axial musculature.

Formation of the limb buds

The limbs are first visible in the human embryo as two pairs of **limb buds**, at about 4 weeks of gestation.

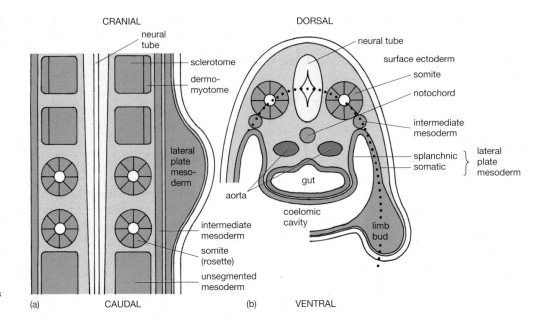

CRANIAL

neural tube

sclerotome

dermo-myotome

lateral plate meso-derm

intermediate mesoderm

somite (rosette)

unsegmented mesoderm

(a)   CAUDAL

DORSAL

neural tube

surface ectoderm

somite

notochord

intermediate mesoderm

splanchnic } lateral plate mesoderm
somatic }

aorta

gut

coelomic cavity

limb bud

(b)   VENTRAL

4.1 Diagrammatic (a) longitudinal section (along the dotted line in (b)) and (b) transverse section of an early embryo, to show somites and other principal mesodermal structures. The left limb bud is not included.

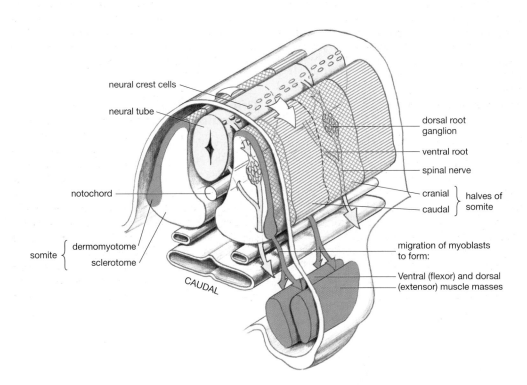

neural crest cells

neural tube

notochord

somite { dermomyotome
sclerotome

CAUDAL

dorsal root ganglion

ventral root

spinal nerve

cranial } halves of somite
caudal }

migration of myoblasts to form:

Ventral (flexor) and dorsal (extensor) muscle masses

4.2 Diagram of early embryo. The myoblasts migrate from the dermomyotome into the limb, where they form ventral (flexor) and dorsal (extensor) muscle masses. Motor innervation from the ventral root region of the neural tube migrates through the cranial half of each sclerotome, where it joins sensory (dorsal root ganglion) nerve cells and their processes and Schwann cells, both derived from neural crest cells. Other neural crest cells forming melanocytes migrate dorsal to the somites. Surface ectoderm forms skin, hair, nails, and sweat and sebaceous glands.

By this time, the embryo measures about 4 mm in crown–rump length and already contains a variety of structures (**4.1**). The limb buds arise as paired outgrowths of ectoderm and lateral plate mesoderm. The ectoderm covering the limb bud forms the epidermis of the skin; the lateral plate mesoderm forms the skeleton, connective tissues, and blood vessels of the limbs. The limb muscles form from the lateral part of the dermamyotome (see above). They are innervated, like the lateral and ventral trunk muscles, by the anterior primary rami of the adjacent spinal nerves, which follow the migrating pre-muscle cells into the limb buds.

Spinal nerves supplying the limbs contain motor, sensory, and autonomic (sympathetic) nerve fibres. Cells in the ventrolateral part of the **neural tube** (developing spinal cord) innervate the muscles (motor nerves). The sensory and sympathetic fibres, by contrast, are derived from a group of cells called the **neural crest** (**4.2**). Neural crest cells originate within the neural plate, but migrate away from it at the time of neural tube closure (earlier in the head, see Vol. 3). They give rise to all the neurons (nerve cells) whose cell bodies lie outside the central nervous system. For the limb this means the sensory neurons, cell bodies of which lie in the dorsal root ganglia, and the postganglionic sympathetic neurons, cell bodies of which form the ganglia of the sympathetic chain (**2.13**). Neural crest cells also form the pigment cell (melanocytes) of the skin, the Schwann cells that surround and insulate nerve fibres, the hormone-secreting cells of the adrenal medulla, and much of the skull (see Vol. 3).

The development of pattern

It is important to realize that the pattern of the various elements in the limb (such as the shape of individual muscles, the shape and number of bony elements, etc.) is not a function of the type or origin of the cells in any particular part of the limb bud, but rather depends on the position at which cells find themselves with respect to other structures around them. Thus, if any two somites are exchanged by transplantation, either somite can give rise to the appropriate muscles and a normal limb develops. Experiments involving surgical removal or transplantation of specific regions can therefore be designed to find which, if any, portions of the limb bud are essential for establishing the pattern of these elements.

Each developing limb has three axes, which apparently depend on different mechanisms to generate its polarity. These axes are: the **proximo-distal axis** (shoulder to finger tips/hip to toe tips); the **pre-/post-axial axis** (radius–ulna and tibia–fibula); and the **dorso-ventral axis** (extensor–flexor).

Proximo-distal polarity

The specification of proximo-distal polarity depends on two special regions at the tip of the developing limb bud. At the tip of the bud there is a ridge, or ectodermal thickening, which follows the distal outline of the limb bud. This is called the **apical ectodermal ridge** (**4.3**, **4.4**) and it is necessary for the continued outgrowth of the limb. If it is removed, the limb that develops is truncated at a level related to the time of operation: the later the operation, the more distal are the last structures that form.

Immediately underlying the apical ectodermal ridge is a rapidly dividing population of mesenchymal cells, the **progress zone** (**4.3**). Its proliferation is responsible for the proximo-distal growth of the limb bud. The apical ectodermal ridge secretes growth factors that are required for the maintenance of the progress zone. The progress zone cells furthest from the source of this growth factor signal stop proliferating and form pre-cartilage condensations. These differentiate to form cartilage models of the limb bones, which then undergo endochondral ossification to form the limb bones, which continue growing at the epiphyseal growth centres (Chapter 2). The shape of each skeletal element that forms from a condensation is related to the length of time the progress zone cells remain in the proliferating state before undergoing skeletal differentiation. The mechanism involves two sets of genes (*HOXA* and *HOXD*) which are expressed sequentially, defining the form of the skeletal elements in a proximal to distal sequence. Mutations involving the gene *HOXD13*, which controls the form of the hand bones, result in shortened metacarpals/metatarsals and fused or branched digits. In phocomelia (a condition that has been be caused by exposure of expectant mothers to the drug thalidomide), digits develop prematurely and proximal elements are deleted.

Pre-/post-axial polarity

This is controlled by a signalling centre, the **zone of polarizing activity**, located within a discrete group of posterior (ulnar side) mesenchyme cells. Expression of a gene called *Sonic hedgehog* in these cells initiates a sequence of molecular events that stimulate cell proliferation in the posterior (skeletogenic) limb-bud mesenchyme. A gradient of a factor secreted by the zone of polarizing activity has been postulated to explain how the pattern of five different digits is determined, but no candidate molecule has yet been discovered. The polarizing function of the posterior wing-bud mesenchyme was revealed by experimental work in chick embryos, in which grafts of posterior

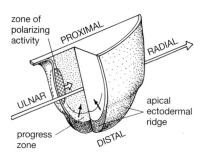

4.3 The limb grows from proximal to distal. The apical ectodermal ridge maintains the underlying progress zone. As cells leave the progress zone, the proximo-distal axis is determined. The zone of polarizing activity in the ulnar margin of the developing limb signals the radio-ulnar polarity.

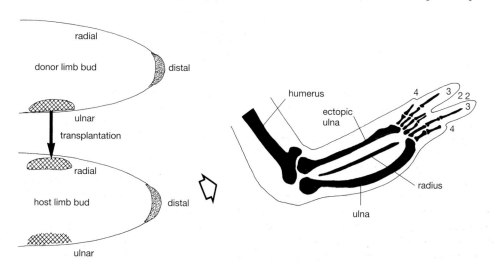

4.4 Experimental transplantation of a second zone of polarizing activity in the radial border of a developing chick limb results in the development of symmetrically duplicated distal limb skeletal elements.

wing-bud mesenchyme were placed in an anterior position in the wing bud of another embryo, which was then allowed to continue development. The resulting skeletal patterns were mirror images, consisting of the normal three-digit pattern of the host and another three digits stimulated by (but not formed from) the graft (**4.4**). Some forms of **polydactyly** in mutant mice are known to result from an extra zone of polarizing activity on the anterior side of the limb bud; a similar mechanism may underlie some forms of human polydactyly.

Dorso-ventral polarity

The dorsal aspect of the limb is defined by extensor muscles, hairy skin, and nails; the ventral aspect by flexor muscles and the hairless palms and soles. The dorso-ventral axis is controlled by the limb-bud ectoderm, in which a secreted signal from the dorsal ectoderm interacts with the underlying dorsal mesenchyme. In chick embryos, if the ectoderm is removed, rotated and replaced, the polarity is reversed. In a mutant mouse in which the dorsal signal is absent, ventral structures develop on both sides.

Refining the pattern

Formation of neural connections

The **motor innervation** of the limbs is derived from axons which grow out from the ventral root region of the neural tube (**4.2**). As they emerge, the axons become segmented into individual nerve roots because they are only able to grow through the cranial halves of the adjacent somites (**4.2**). As soon as the nerve roots emerge from the somite, their component axons diverge and regroup to form the limb plexuses. The nerves then grow toward the appropriate muscles, which they appear to recognize according to their position in the limb. In general, muscles developing in the ventral, flexor aspect of the upper limb bud, such as biceps, are innervated by more cranially located motor nerves than those developing more dorsally (e.g. triceps). Also, in both limbs, muscles are innervated in roughly a proximal-to-distal sequence. Thus, proximal muscles (shoulder, arm; C5–7) are innervated earlier and by more cranial motor roots than

distal muscles (small muscles of the hand; C8–T1) (p. 113, Table 5.8.1). Subsequent rotation of the limb buds (see below) partly obscures this arrangement.

Despite this apparently simple topographical correspondence, individual motor nerve roots are able to seek their appropriate muscles. If a small portion of developing neural tube is rotated about its craniocaudal axis, axons emerging from the caudal (originally cranial) part of the rotated piece still innervate muscles located cranially in the limb (e.g. radial side) and those emerging cranially (original caudal) seek more caudally located targets (ulnar side). This experiment shows that individual motor nerve roots have defined identities which enable them to seek their appropriate target. The mechanisms underlying such remarkable behaviour are not understood.

The **sensory innervation** of the limb seems to obey similar principles. The dorsal root ganglia, which are derived from the neural crest, also develop in the cranial half of each somite. From there, they send sensory axons towards the limb to supply the nearest region of skin at the time of axon outgrowth. This is most easily visualized in the upper limb, where the sensory dermatomes (**4.5** and see **5.8.3**) follow the limb outline in order: cranial (pre-axial), distal axial, caudal (post-axial). In the lower limb, the same process occurs but the final arrangement is complicated by the rotation of the limb bud, which generates a spiral arrangement of the sensory dermatomes (see **6.7.1**).

Formation of digits: the role of cell death

As the limb bud grows, the distal part forms a flat, broad structure, the hand/foot plate or autopod. The apical ectodermal ridge remains active over each of the extending digits, but loses its activities in the interdigital areas. At the same time, some of the mesenchymal cells between the presumptive digits undergo genetically 'programmed' cell death (apoptosis). Thus, the formation of five separate digits is the result of their intrinsic growth, combined with the cessation of growth and death of cells in the interdigital region. Failure of cell death results in interdigital webbing, which is normal in webbed species such as ducks, and occurs to a lesser extent in some human mutations. At the start of digital development, interdigital mesenchyme

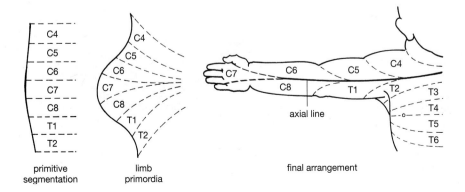

4.5 Development of segmental sensory innervation (dermatomes) of skin of upper limb.

primitive segmentation   limb primordia   final arrangement

axial line

is required for the maintenance of separate digits, and failure of cell proliferation of interdigital mesenchyme causes fusion of digits (**bony syndactyly**).

Development of limb vasculature

In each limb a primary axial artery develops in the mesenchyme and supplies a primitive capillary plexus. This main trunk in the upper limb forms from the fourth aortic arch and the sixth intersegmental artery; it will form the definitive subclavian, axillary, and brachial arteries and, more distally, the anterior interosseous artery and deep palmar arch. In the lower limb the primary axial artery arises from the umbilical artery and follows the developing sciatic nerve. The external iliac artery and its continuation, the femoral artery, develop separately from the common iliac artery and provide a new channel to the lower limb, which anastomoses with, and eventually takes over, the supply of the great majority of the lower limb.

Veins and lymphatics develop in the limb to form a deep system which lies alongside the major arteries and a more superficial system which lies in the subcutaneous tissue and which eventually drains into the deep vessels.

Rotation of the limbs

Later in development, the limb buds undergo complex rotations and, in the case of the lower limbs, a descent down the body axis. The upper limbs rotate only slightly, and therefore the (sensory) dermatomes still reflect the original organization of the sensory innervation. Nevertheless, the rotation is evident in the arrangement of the radius and ulna and the hand, which are rotated laterally by about 60° with respect to the humerus. In the lower limbs the rotation and descent are more marked, and the dermatomes therefore assume a spiral pattern. The original sensory innervation of the lower limb buds with respect to the pre- and post-axial elements is retained, but the anterior surface of the thigh (extensor compartment) comes to face dorsally in the embryo.

Rotation of the lower limbs is a relatively recent event during evolution. To visualize this process, think of how you would have to rotate your lower limbs to generate the position of the limbs in a lizard. The flexed knee would have its convexity facing dorsally and laterally. The reverse rotation, back to the human position, mimics the rotation that occurs during human limb development.

Note: The term 'dermatome' has two quite different meanings. In anatomy, it refers to a region of skin innervated by a single sensory nerve root (sensory dermatome). In embryology, it refers to dermatome derived from a single somite. Although the dermatomes of the skin may correspond directly to the somite-derived dermatomes of the embryo, this has not been demonstrated experimentally.

The upper limb: introduction

About 75 million years ago, when primates appeared in the fossil record, one of the major adaptations to evolve was the increasing dominance of the forelimb for purposes of climbing, grasping, and feeding. Joints of the forelimb became more mobile, distal forelimb bones began to rotate about each other, and the thumb was set apart from the remaining digits to improve the grasp. With the emergence of hominids some 72 million years later bipedalism became increasingly successful and, with it, the 'emancipation of the forelimb'. Subsequent selection pressures led to the evolution of *Homo sapiens*, with an upper limb set well away from the trunk by a long collar bone, and with the ability both to rotate the hand on the arm through 180° and also to oppose the thumb and forefinger.

These evolutionary adaptations have resulted in an upper limb which is the principle means whereby humans interact mechanically with their environment. The upper limb is primarily the means whereby we position our hand to perform some function. The hand itself is specialized for grasping items and for moving them with various degrees of power and precision. The ridges which make up the fingerprint, and the firm anchorage of palmar skin both aid the mechanical interaction of grip. The hand can also be used to push or strike objects, as can the forearm, arm, and shoulder.

The more proximal parts of the limb, which contain relatively coarse muscle groups in comparison to the small muscles responsible for exquisitely precise finger movements, therefore function largely to steer and position the hand. You will find that, when performing many manual tasks, the forelimb is placed in the '**position of function**' in which the elbow is semi-flexed and the forearm is in the mid-prone position.

The shoulder joint is a multiaxial ball-and-socket joint and the shoulder girdle itself is mobile, being attached to the trunk largely by muscle. As a result, the humerus, and thus the hand, can be moved widely in any direction with respect to the trunk. The elbow is a hinge joint but its movement, combined with the pronation and supination movements of the forearm, and the movements of the wrist, enable the hand to be moved widely with respect to the humerus.

In the hand, all the digits, but particularly the thumb, can be moved independently; movements of the more proximal bones enable the palm to take up particular configurations during grasping movements. These developments in mechanical function could not have taken place in isolation and without parallel changes in the central and peripheral nervous systems which control the various groups of muscles involved in any movement.

The hand is also one of the principal means by which humans actively explore their environment. The skin of the fingers is therefore particularly richly supplied with sensory receptors which convey mechanical, thermal, and painful stimuli to the central nervous system for analysis and evaluation. Movement of the fingers and hand around an object enables us to identify complex shapes and the materials of which they are made without looking at them; the sensory system also provides essential feedback in the control of fine movements.

It is important, therefore, that while studying the upper limb, its role in communication via sensory information and gesturing, in balance, in carrying, in making a variety of different grips, and in performing delicate manipulations, should all be considered carefully.

Before starting to study the internal anatomy of the upper limb, examine its external appearance, starting with the **skin** (see Chapter 2). The skin is the interface between body tissues and the outside world. It acts to protect the body from injury and invasion from without and from loss of fluid from within; loss of 60% of body skin (e.g. by burning) is usually fatal. Skin is also the mechanical interface through which forces generated by our muscles can act on objects around us, and a sensory interface through which we analyse our contact with our surroundings.

The skin covering your upper limb varies in appearance in different areas. The extensor surface is more **hairy** than the flexor surface and the palm is hairless. Except in the palm, the **texture** of the skin is coarser over the extensor aspect (especially at the elbow) than over the flexor aspect. Look at the skin around joints at which flexion and extension occur (e.g. elbow, wrist, fingers) and locate the distinct **skin creases** which mark firm attachment of the skin to the underlying deep tissues. Examine the skin creases on your hand as you move your thumb and index finger, and the middle, ring, and little fingers; the creases reflect the independent movement of the thumb and index finger. In Down syndrome, there is usually a single 'simian' transverse crease across the palm at the base of the fingers. Examine the fine **dermal ridges** on the skin that form the 'fingerprint' and 'palmprint' and compare them with those of your partner.

By use of a hand lens, locate the openings of eccrine **sweat glands** on the forearm and on the dermal ridges (p.223). These glands are derived from the epidermis of the skin and secrete a watery saline which, in evaporating, draws heat from the skin and thereby assists in thermoregulation. Blood flow through the skin is also important in thermoregulation; to assess this, look at skin colour, especially the nails and finger pads. Watch one finger pad carefully and prick an adjacent finger pad with a pin. The sweat glands of the fingers, unlike those of the rest of the body, respond to alerting or emotional rather than to thermal stimuli.

Pain and temperature are only two of the cutaneous sensations; our fingers, in particular, are immensely sensitive to touch and vibration.

Examine the **axilla** (armpit) and note the coarse texture of its hair, which starts to grow at puberty under the influence of androgen hormones. Many axillary sweat glands are apocrine in type, which explains the odour that can arise from the armpit (p. 10).

Bones of the shoulder girdle and upper limb

Bones of the shoulder girdle and upper limb

The bones of the upper limb and shoulder girdle form its skeletal framework. They give shape to the limb, and form a series of levers moved by the muscles and articulating at the joints. Each bone has its own surface contours and internal architecture. These reflect the forces and articulations to which the bones are subject and the attachment of muscles to the bones. Although bones change only slowly, bone is a dynamic living tissue capable of adapting to the forces placed on it and, if necessary, repairing when fractured. Growth of limb bones is an essential part of body growth; if the 'long' bones do not lengthen, neither do the muscles. As bones lengthen they must also increase in girth, in order to retain the appropriate strength. The human upper limb is specialized for mobility and manipulation. It does not have to bear weight and therefore its bones are less massive than those of the lower limb. The specialization of the upper limb for mobility has influenced primarily the articular ends of the bones.

Living anatomy

The living anatomy of the upper limb skeleton is best studied in your own limb, or that of a colleague. For this, it is most convenient to wear clothes that will permit such an examination (e.g. a sports vest). It is also good practice to note your findings alongside the text and figures in this book. This will aid rapid recall at a later date. Before you start the work of this topic, review the section on bones in Chapter 2 (p. 12).

Identify on yourself or a colleague, and on an articulated skeleton, the bony features of the shoulder girdle and upper limb illustrated in **5.1.1–5.1.3**. Only the most clinically important features are labelled, although many others have names.

Bones of the shoulder girdle

Clavicle

The clavicle acts as a strut holding the upper limb, to which it is attached via the scapula, away from the trunk. The clavicle also transmits forces from the upper limb to the axial skeleton and is therefore not infrequently fractured. The clavicle is unusual in that it is the only 'long' bone to lack a medullary (marrow) cavity. It is also the only bone in the limbs to ossify in membrane (p. 12). Identify the:
- sternal end
- acromial end
- the sigmoid shape of the bone
- roughened areas on the inferior surface

On an isolated clavicle, note the roughened areas on its undersurface, close to either end and in the middle.

Qu. 1A *What forces might have been responsible for these bony roughenings during the course of development?*

Qu. 1B *Orientate the isolated clavicle and place it as close as possible in its correct position on a colleague. How can you tell which is a right or left clavicle?*

Scapula

The scapula articulates with both the humerus and the clavicle. It also provides large, flat surfaces and roughened processes for the attachment of muscles acting on the joints. Identify the:
- coracoid process
- acromial process
- spine of the scapula
- supraspinous fossa
- infraspinous fossa
- subscapular fossa
- lateral and vertebral borders
- inferior angle
- glenoid (articular) fossa
- supraglenoid tubercle
- infraglenoid tubercle

By feeling (palpating) its various landmarks, place a scapula as close as possible to its correct position against your colleague. Now repeat this with his/her arm raised above the head and note the change in the position of the scapula. It should have rotated by about 40° so that the glenoid fossa points more vertically upward. This movement also shows that the medial border of the scapula is attached to the spine only through muscles. Note also the associated movement of the clavicle as the arm is raised.

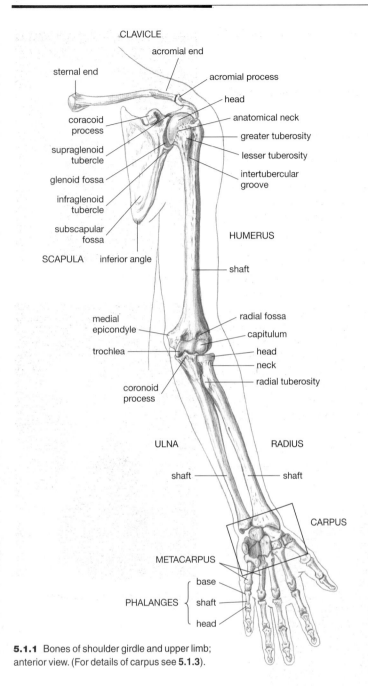

5.1.1 Bones of shoulder girdle and upper limb; anterior view. (For details of carpus see **5.1.3**).

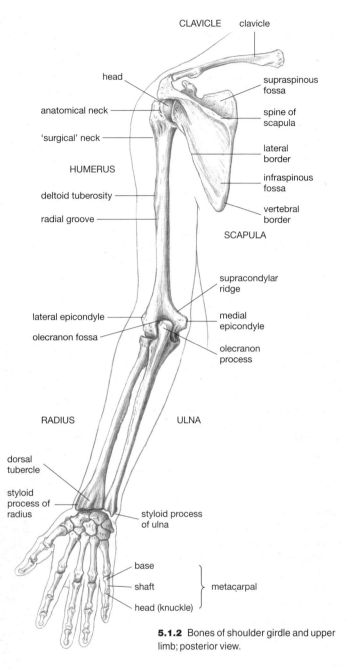

5.1.2 Bones of shoulder girdle and upper limb; posterior view.

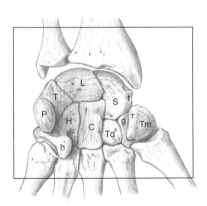

5.1.3 Carpal bones; anterior view.

Bones of the upper limb

Humerus

The humerus acts as a very mobile lever which directs the forearm and hand in almost any direction. The articulations at its proximal and distal ends are very different and reflect this. Identify the:

- head, anatomical neck, and shaft
- surgical neck (a common site of fracture)
- greater tuberosity
- lesser tuberosity
- intertubercular (bicipital) groove
- deltoid tuberosity
- lateral epicondyle
- medial epicondyle
- trochlea
- capitulum
- olecranon fossa
- radial fossa
- coronoid fossa
- radial (spiral) groove

The forearm has two bones (radius and ulna) rather than the single bone (humerus) in the arm. Movements of the radius relative to the ulna enable the palm of the hand to face in opposite directions.

Ulna

Identify the:

- shaft
- coronoid process

- olecranon process
- trochlear notch (not labelled)
- radial notch for articulation with head of radius (not labelled)
- distal end (head) of ulna with its styloid process

Radius

Identify the:
- head (proximal end), neck, and shaft
- radial tuberosity (bicipital tuberosity)
- dorsal tubercle on the distal end of the radius (Lister's tubercle)
- expanded distal end of radius with its styloid process and facet for the ulna (ulnar notch)

With the upper limb held straight by the side and the palm facing forwards you will note that the forearm is angled laterally with respect to the arm; this is known as the 'carrying angle'. It is more pronounced in women than in men.

Carpus

The carpus provides a slightly flexible region of the skeleton just distal to the wrist joint. It comprises a series of small bones which are organized as two rows. The carpus is arched transversely due to the shape and articulation of the individual bones. This provides a hollow in front of the wrist in which are located many tendons, nerves, and vessels passing into the palm of the hand.

Its component bones form a proximal row comprising the:
- scaphoid (S), with its tubercle (t), waist, and proximal pole
- lunate (L)
- triquetral (T)
- pisiform (a sesamoid bone) (P)

and a distal row comprising the:
- trapezium (Tm), with its groove (g) and ridge (r)
- trapezoid (Td)
- capitate (C)
- hamate (H), and its hook (h)

Qu. 1C *Which carpal bone would transmit the greatest force if a person fell on to the outstretched hand?*

Metacarpus

The metacarpals give length and flexibility to the palm. Try moving the distal end of each metacarpal with your other hand. The third and second are relatively immobile, while the fourth and fifth, and especially the metacarpal of the thumb, are more mobile. Each of the five metacarpal bones has a
- base
- shaft
- head (which forms the knuckle)

Phalanges: proximal, middle, and distal

The proximal, middle, and distal phalanges form the bony skeleton of the fingers (the thumb has only a proximal and a distal phalanx). Move your fingers about to demonstrate that each finger moves as a whole unit, rather than as a series of isolated bones. Each phalanx has a
- base
- shaft
- head (note the expansions which support the pads of the fingers)

Imaging the upper limb bones

Radiology can be used to image the bones because the calcium that they contain in high concentration is radiopaque. When radiographs of bones are examined, the following points should be checked routinely:
- The *outline* of the bone, including the various prominences listed above. This is important because the ability to diagnose an abnormal appearance depends on a clear knowledge of what is normal.

Qu. 1D *Compare the radiographs (5.1.4, 5.1.5) and comment on their appearance; which is abnormal and why?*

- The *consistency* of the bone. Note the appearance of the hard outer cortical bone and the less opaque inner trabecular (cancellous) bone. The relative thickness of these two components differs in different bones and in different parts of the same bone. In some bones, the pattern of fine bony struts (trabeculae) in the cancellous bone has a particularly important functional arrangement (p. 133; **femur, calcaneus; 6.1.6, 6.1.7**).

Qu. 1E *What abnormality can be seen in 5.1.6?*

- The relationship between the ends of bones; where they meet to form joints (see p. 13).

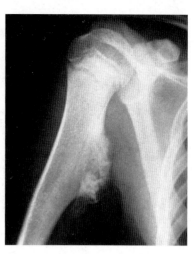

5.1.4 See Qu. 1D.

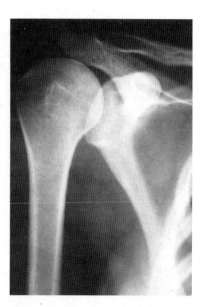

5.1.5 Radiograph of shoulder region.

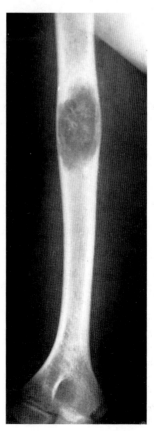

5.1.6 Shaft of humerus; Qu. 1E.

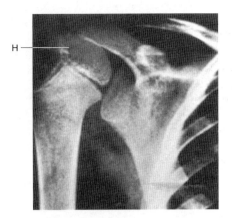

5.1.7 Shoulder (AP; 15 years). Epiphysis of upper end of humerus (H).

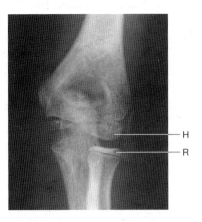

5.1.8 Elbow (AP; 15 years). Epiphyses of lower end of humerus (H) and proximal end of radius (R).

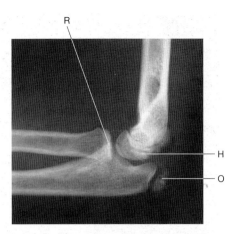

5.1.9 Elbow (lateral; 15 years). Epiphyses of lower end of humerus (H), head of radius (R), and olecranon process of ulna (O).

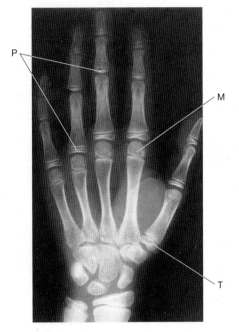

5.1.10 Hand (AP; 15 years). Epiphyses at base of phalanges (P), head of second metacarpal (M), and base of metacarpal of thumb (T).

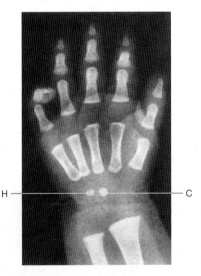

5.1.11 Hand (AP; 2 years). Note ossification beginning in the capitate (C) and hamate (H).

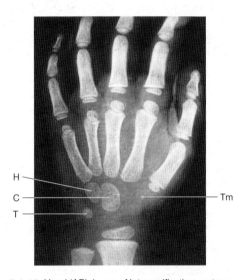

5.1.12 Hand (AP) 4 years. Note ossification centres in the capitate (C), hamate (H), triquetral (T), and trapezium (Tm) and in the epiphyses of metacarpals, phalanges and radius.

Examine radiographs **5.1.4**, **5.1.7–5.1.9**, **5.1.13** and see **5.4.9**, **5.4.10** and identify all the features that you have identified on the isolated bones.

Development of upper limb bones

General aspects of the ossification of bones are covered in Chapter 2 (p. 12).

All the upper limb bones except the clavicle develop by ossification in cartilaginous models formed by chondrification of the mesenchyme.

The clavicle is the first bone in the body to ossify. This starts at about the sixth week of intra-uterine life at primary centres which ossify a membranous model of the shaft of the bone. Late in puberty, secondary centres appear in a small area of cartilage at the sternal, and sometimes the acromial, end of the developing bone.

All the other 'long' bones of the upper limb, including the metacarpals and phalanges, are formed by ossification of a cartilaginous model. Primary ossification centres appear in their shafts at about 8 weeks of intra-uterine life. Secondary centres at the ends of the bones appear after birth and fuse with the shafts as linear growth ceases at the end of puberty. The proximal end of the humerus and the distal ends of the radius and ulna are the 'growing ends'; their ossification centres appear earlier and fuse with the shaft later.

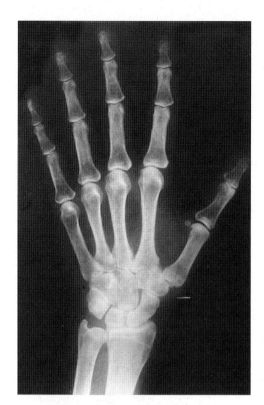

5.1.13 Hand (adult).

The carpal bones ossify from single centres which form during childhood.

Identify the bones and epiphyses in radiographs **5.1.7–5.1.13**. Note especially the secondary centres of ossification in the elbow region. In children, fractures of the elbow are relatively common and, unless one is aware of the pattern of ossification, it is possible to mistake an epiphyseal plate for a fracture.

In the wrist, note especially the scaphoid and the lunate (**5.1.13**) and the overlapping articulation of the distal row of carpal bones with the bases of the metacarpals. These overlapping surfaces can also simulate fractures unless they are delineated carefully.

Qu. 1F *Note the secondary centres of ossification in the fingers. The first metacarpal (of the thumb) might be referred to as a phalanx; why?*

Questions and answers

Qu. 1A *What forces might have been responsible for these bony roughenings during the course of development?*

Answer The principal form of the bone is determined genetically but the extent of ligament and muscle markings is determined by the tensile forces exerted by these tissues on the bone.

Qu. 1B *Orientate the isolated clavicle and place it as close as possible in its correct position on a colleague. How can you tell which is a right or left clavicle?*

Answer A clavicle can be 'sided' by recognizing the superior and inferior surfaces, the larger medial end, and the convexity of the anterior border in its medial third (check your own right and left clavicles by feeling the superior and anterior borders).

Qu. 1C *Which carpal bone would transmit the greatest force if a person fell on to the outstretched hand?*

Answer The scaphoid, because it has the greatest contact with the radius.

Qu. 1D *Compare the radiographs (5.1.4, 5.1.5) and comment on their appearance; which is abnormal and why?*

Answer 5.1.4 is abnormal. A large radiopaque excrescence (bone) is seen on the profile of the medial border of the humerus, which is consequently not well defined. The outer cortex is absent in the area of irregularity. This is caused by a tumour of bone-producing cells.

Qu. 1E *What abnormality can be seen in 5.1.6?*

Answer The medulla or cavity of the bone is wider and the cortex is thinner in the abnormal part of the shaft. This is due to a cyst within the humerus.

Qu. 1F *Note the secondary centres of ossification in the fingers. The first metacarpal (of the thumb) might be referred to as a phalanx; why?*

Answer The first metacarpal has a secondary centre of ossification at its proximal end, as have the phalanges.

The shoulder girdle and its movements

The shoulder girdle and its movements

The human upper limb and shoulder girdle have evolved with the upright stance to provide the mobility by which the hand can be used in almost any position relative to the trunk. The limb is attached to the axial skeleton indirectly: first, by a long bony strut (the clavicle) which articulates with the sternum (sternoclavicular joint) and holds the scapula, and thus the limb, away from the torso; secondly, by strong muscles which attach the humerus to the scapula and strong ligaments which attach the scapula to the clavicle. The scapula is connected to the spine by muscles alone. Most movements of the upper limb involve either associated movements of the shoulder girdle, or contraction of the shoulder girdle muscles to provide a stable base on which the distal part of the limb is moved.

Living anatomy

Feel the outline of your **clavicle**, noting that its anterior aspect is convex medially and concave laterally, and that its medial end is bulbous whereas its lateral end is flattened. The clavicle acts as a bony strut, holding the shoulder joint away from the chest wall. In a rare congenital condition in which the clavicles fail to develop, the shoulders are situated on the anterior aspect of the chest wall.

Palpate the **sternoclavicular joint** at the medial end of the clavicle, moving your shoulder in different positions as you do so. Now locate the **acromioclavicular joint** at the lateral end of the clavicle; this is easier if you elevate and depress your entire shoulder and then move it forward (protraction) and backward (retraction).

Next, examine the movements of the scapula while palpating its inferior angle and spine. The scapula is retracted as the shoulder is braced back and is protracted around the chest wall as the arm and shoulder are pulled forward. As the shoulder is elevated and depressed the entire scapula moves up and down. Finally examine the rotation of the scapula on a colleague as the arm is raised above the head. Try to repeat this movement while preventing the scapula from moving by grasping its inferior angle; the extent of arm abduction will be less than 90°.

Attachment of the scapula to the axial skeleton

The **sternoclavicular joint** (5.2.1) is a plane synovial joint between the prominent medial end of the clavicle and the articular notch on the upper lateral aspect of the manubrium. Within the joint is a fibrocartilaginous disc, attached around its margins to the fibrous

capsule. The capsule is lined by synovial membrane and is reinforced by a **sternoclavicular ligament**, which strengthens the capsule superiorly and extends across the midline to the joint of the other side. However, the principal stability of the sternoclavicular joint comes from the short, tough **costoclavicular ligament**, which attaches the medial end of the clavicle to the first costal cartilage.

The **acromioclavicular joint** is also a plane synovial joint, between the small articular surfaces on the lateral end of the clavicle and the medial aspect of the acromion. This joint owes its stability almost entirely to the **coracoclavicular ligament** which attaches the undersurface of the clavicle to the coracoid process of the scapula.

A small muscle (subclavius) runs from the medial end of the first rib laterally to the inferior surface of the

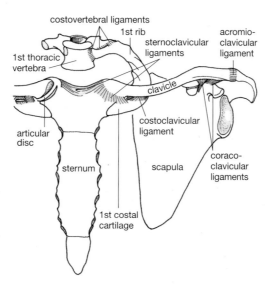

5.2.1 Bones and ligaments of the shoulder girdle.

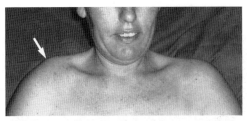

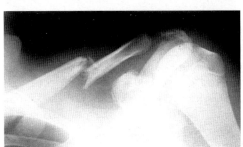

5.2.2 Dislocated right acromioclavicular joint (arrow); compare with the patient's left side.

5.2.3 Fracture of the clavicle. See Qu. 2A.

Fractured clavicle (5.2.3)

When people fall, they often put out their hand to 'cushion' the blow. Because the clavicle is the only bony strut that links the upper limb directly to the axial skeleton, it takes the main force of the impact. It is therefore not uncommonly fractured during a fall, e.g. from a horse.

Qu. 2A *Why does the fracture usually occur in the central third of the clavicle? And why does the fractured end of the outer half come to lie beneath that of the inner piece?*

clavicle, further stabilizing the clavicle in the sternoclavicular joint.

Therefore, whether the upper limb is pulling or pushing, the force from the arm is transmitted largely from the coracoid process of the scapula via the mid part of the clavicle to the first costal cartilage. The sternoclavicular and acromioclavicular joints transmit rather little of the force and are only infrequently dislocated.

Dislocation of the acromioclavicular joint (**5.2.2**) can, however, occur if there is a direct downward blow on the acromion, but only if this is of sufficient force to rupture the coracoclavicular ligament. The joint can also undergo arthritic changes which make movements of the shoulder painful.

Movements of the shoulder girdle

The entire shoulder can be raised (elevated, 'shrugged'), lowered (depressed), pushed forward (protracted), or braced back (retracted). These movements involve the two synovial joints of the shoulder girdle, with varying degrees of rotation of the scapula around the chest wall.

Elevation

Elevation is produced by muscles passing down from the skull or cervical vertebrae to the shoulder girdle. Most important are the upper fibres of **trapezius** (**5.2.4**; spinal accessory nerve) which pass downward from the superior nuchal line and external occipital protuberance of the skull and the spines of the cervical vertebrae to insert into the outer third of the clavicle, the inner aspect of the acromion, and the spine of the scapula.

Qu. 2B *How could you test this action simply?*

Depression

Depression of the shoulder is produced by muscles arising from the rib cage and passing upward to insert

into the shoulder girdle. The lower fibres of **trapezius**, which arise from the spines of the lower thoracic vertebrae and pass up to insert into the lower part of the spine of the scapula, will have this effect, together with pectoralis minor on the anterior aspect of the chest.

Protraction

Protraction of the shoulder is produced by muscles attached to the anterior and lateral chest wall and which insert into the scapula. The main muscle involved is **serratus anterior** (**5.2.5**; long thoracic nerve) which arises from the upper eight ribs and is inserted into the vertebral border of the scapula. This is assisted by **pectoralis minor** (**5.2.5**; medial pectoral nerve) which inserts into the coracoid process. The two muscles together pull the scapula forward around the lateral chest wall.

Qu. 2C *How would you test the action of protractor muscles? What would happen to the scapula if serratus anterior was paralysed?*

Retraction

Retraction of the shoulder is produced by muscles attached to the spines of cervical and thoracic vertebrae and attached to the skeleton of the shoulder girdle.

Qu. 2D *Which large muscle acts to brace back (retract) the shoulders?*

The rhomboid muscles (**5.2.4**; nerve to rhomboids, C5) assist in this action and also, with levator scapulae, raise its vertebral border.

Rotation of the scapula

Rotation of the scapula is an essential component of the movement of raising the arm above the head (p. 61). Trapezius is the principal muscle involved. Its lower fibres stabilize the tuberosity of the spine of the scapula while its upper fibres elevate the acromion.

The axilla

Between the upper end of the arm and chest wall is a region called the **axilla**. This is continuous above with the space between the upper ribs and the shoulder girdle; its inferior limit is the armpit.

The axilla is shaped like a three-sided pyramid (**5.2.6**). Its anterior wall is formed by the pectoralis major and minor muscles and the clavicle, its medial wall by the upper ribs, covered by serratus anterior, and its posterior wall by the scapula with the muscles that cover its anterior surface (see 5.2.6).

All the nerves and vessels which supply the upper limb must pass through the axilla. The nerves are derived from the lower cervical (C5–C8) and first thoracic (T1) spinal nerves, which form the brachial

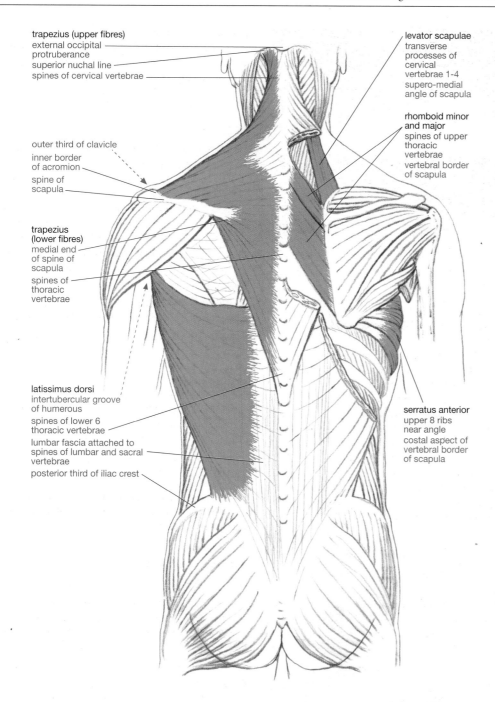

trapezius (upper fibres)
external occipital
protruberance
superior nuchal line
spines of cervical vertebrae

levator scapulae
transverse
processes of
cervical
vertebrae 1-4
supero-medial
angle of scapula

rhomboid minor
and major
spines of upper
thoracic
vertebrae
vertebral border
of scapula

outer third of clavicle
inner border
of acromion
spine of
scapula

trapezius
(lower fibres)
medial end
of spine of
scapula
spines of
thoracic
vertebrae

latissimus dorsi
intertubercular groove
of humerous
spines of lower 6
thoracic vertebrae
lumbar fascia attached to
spines of lumbar and sacral
vertebrae
posterior third of iliac crest

serratus anterior
upper 8 ribs
near angle
costal aspect of
vertebral border
of scapula

5.2.4 Superficial muscles of the
shoulder girdle and back.

plexus; the vessels from the subclavian artery and vein which emerge from/pass back to the thorax. To reach the axilla, the cervical spinal nerves pass downward toward the triangular aperture between the clavicle, the scapula, and the upper ribs. As they cross the first rib the cervical nerves are joined by the T1 spinal nerve root and by the subclavian vessels to form a neurovascular bundle ensheathed by fascia continuous with that of the neck.

The neurovascular bundle crosses the first rib to enter the apex of the axilla (the artery and vein are then known as the axillary artery and vein). Within the axilla the vessels and nerves give branches to the walls of the axilla (p. 103). The vessels and nerves are surrounded and protected by fat and by groups of lymph vessels and nodes which drain lymph from the upper limb and limb girdle, the superficial tissues of the anterior and posterior chest wall, and the breast (p. 105).

Grip, in turn, the lower border of the anterior and posterior walls of your own axilla; the anterior wall is entirely soft tissue, the posterior wall contains the scapula. The floor of the axilla (armpit) is dome-shaped because suspensory bundles of fascia continuous with that covering pectoralis minor are attached to the skin and superficial fascia of the armpit.

Table 5.2.1 Shoulder girdle: movements, principal muscles, and their innervation.

Movement	Principal muscles	Peripheral nerve	Spinal root origin
Elevation	Trapezius (upper fibres)	Spinal accessory nerve (XI)	C 3, 4
	Levator scapulae	Cervical roots	C 3, 4, 5
Depression	Trapezius (lower fibres)	Spinal accessory nerve (XI)	C 3, 4
Protraction	Serratus anterior	Long thoracic nerve	C 5, 6, 7
	Pectoralis minor	Medial pectoral nerve	C 5, 6, 7, 8, T1
Retraction	Trapezius	Spinal accessory nerve (XI)	C 3, 4
	Rhomboid major and minor	Nerve to rhomboids from brachial plexus	C 4, 5
Scapula rotation	Trapezius upper and lower fibres	Spinal accessory nerve (XI)	C 3, 4

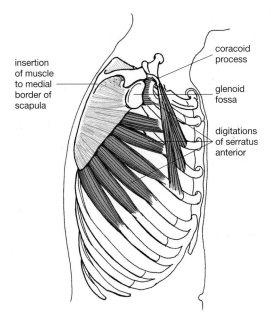

5.2.5 Chest wall and scapula to show serratus anterior and pectoralis minor.

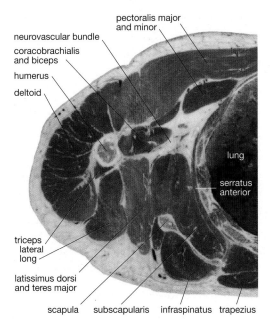

5.2.6 Axilla in horizontal section. Image derived from 'Visible Human' data set to show boundaries of axilla.

Questions and answers

Qu. 2A *Why does the fracture usually occur in the central third of the clavicle? And why does the fractured end of the outer half come to lie beneath that of the inner piece?*

Answer The clavicle is S-shaped, its anterior border being convex medially and concave laterally, and weakest at the junction of the curves. Furthermore, its medial and lateral ends are firmly attached by strong ligaments to the first rib and the coracoid process of the scapula, which relieve the force from the sterno- and acromioclavicular joints. Therefore, when a sufficient force is applied the clavicle tends to fracture in its middle third; its medial end will then be pulled up by contraction of the clavicular fibres of sternomastoid, while the lateral end is pulled down by the weight of the arm and contraction of deltoid.

Qu. 2B *How could you test this action simply?*

Answers Contraction of the upper fibres of trapezius can be detected easily by placing both hands on the shoulders of a subject, who is then asked to shrug them.

Qu. 2C *How would you test the action of protractor muscles? What would happen to the scapula if serratus anterior was paralysed?*

Answer Pushing forward against a wall with both hands will involve contraction of serratus anterior, which pulls on the vertebral border of the scapula from an origin on the sides of the upper eight ribs, to protract the scapula and shoulder. Paralysis of the muscle leads to 'winging' of the scapula. Its medial border becomes prominent because the oblique pull of pectoralis minor, which also protracts the scapula, is now unopposed.

Qu. 2D *Which large muscle acts to brace back (retract) the shoulders?*

Answer Contraction of the middle fibres of trapezius, which pulls on the medial end of the spine of the scapula from the spines of the upper thoracic vertebrae, will help to 'brace' back (retract) the shoulders.

The shoulder joint and its movements

The shoulder joint and its movements

The shoulder joint has developed with the shoulder girdle to enable the upper limb, and particularly the hand, to be moved to the widest possible range of positions with respect to the trunk. Movements of the arm on the trunk involve both the highly mobile shoulder joint (the articulation between the head of the humerus and the glenoid fossa of the scapula—technically the glenohumeral joint) and associated movements of the shoulder girdle. The great mobility of the shoulder joint inevitably compromises the stability of the articulation; therefore, active stabilization of the joint by muscles is particularly important.

Living anatomy

The contour of the normal shoulder, when looked at from the front, is formed, from above downward, by trapezius, the acromion, acromioclavicular joint, and proximal end of the humerus, which is covered with the deltoid muscle. This gives the normal shoulder a rounded contour. Medial to this, below the clavicle, is a depression, the infraclavicular fossa, in which the coracoid process of the scapula can be felt.

The shoulder joint is the articulation between the head of the humerus and the glenoid fossa of the scapula. The scapula, which glides around the chest wall, is orientated at about 45° forward from the transverse axis of the body (see **5.2.6**).

Explore the range of movements that can occur at the shoulder joint on yourself and a colleague. The humerus can be moved to a greater or lesser extent in almost any direction, but the movements are subdivided into: flexion and extension; abduction and adduction; medial and lateral rotation; and circumduction—a combination of all these movements (p. 4).

Bony landmarks of the shoulder region

Locate the outer end of your clavicle and its articulation with the acromion of the scapula. Run your fingers backward along the spine of the scapula to its root close to the medial border.

Beneath the clavicle, you should be able to feel the tip of the coracoid process of the scapula in the infraclavicular fossa.

Place the palm of your hand flat against the fossa so that your fingers are lying across the head and greater tubercle of the humerus. Now rotate your shoulder joint laterally and you should be able to feel the lesser tubercle. If you alternately medially and laterally rotate your shoulder joint, you will feel the intertubercular sulcus (bicipital groove) in which lies the tendon of the long head of biceps. It will feel like a cord being rolled under your fingers.

Place your right upper limb in the (very unnatural) 'anatomical position' (p. 3) and abduct your shoulder as far as possible without rotating the humerus; the movement will be limited to about 90°. Now raise your arm above your head naturally and note the lateral rotation of the humerus and movement of the scapula that occurs. Repeat the movements on an articulated skeleton and note how the rotation of the humerus makes more articular surface available for the abduction movement.

Qu. 3A *What implications does this mechanism have for the capsule of the shoulder joint?*

When you have studied the muscles involved in these movements, repeat each movement against resistance and confirm the activity of the prime mover muscles (**5.3.1**).

Qu. 3B *When movements are occurring at the shoulder joint, are movements also occurring at other joints?*

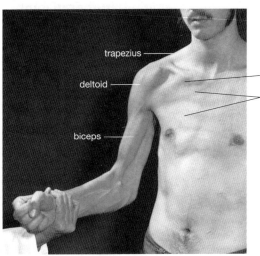

5.3.1 Anterior muscles of arm and shoulder girdle demonstrated by adduction and medial rotation of the arm against resistance.

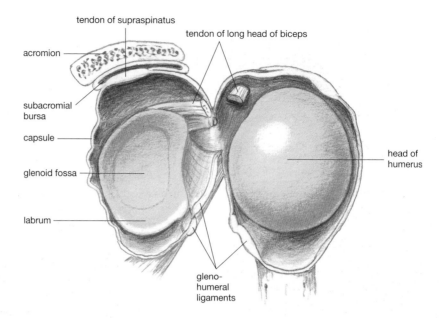

5.3.2 Interior of shoulder joint.

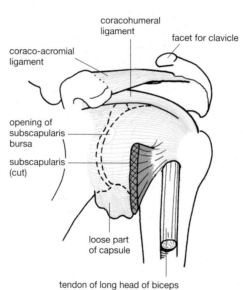

5.3.3 Shoulder joint; attachments of the capsule and extrinsic ligaments.

The shoulder (glenohumeral) joint

The shoulder joint is a freely mobile, ball-and-socket synovial joint (**5.3.2**). The articular surface on the glenoid fossa of the scapula is shallow, but is deepened by a rim of articular fibrocartilage (glenoid labrum). The articular surface on the head of the humerus forms about a third of a near sphere. Thus, the humerus can move in any plane with respect to the scapula.

The capsule of the joint (**5.3.3**) is attached round the glenoid labrum and to the anatomical neck of the humerus, except inferiorly where the attachment passes downward on to the medial aspect of the shaft. The capsule is loose inferiorly and this, with the shallow articular surfaces, permits a wide range of movements.

The capsule itself is quite thin, to allow for the wide range of movement. It is thickened anteriorly by three insubstantial intrinsic (glenohumeral) ligaments, which add passive stability. Superiorly a coracohumeral ligament extends from the base of the coracoid process of the scapula to the tubercles of the humerus.

The capsule is lined, as is the tendon of the long head of biceps within it (see below), with synovial membrane which secretes synovial fluid (p. 14). The very thin layer of synovial fluid between the congruent articular surfaces exerts a cohesive effect.

Qu. 3C *What are the other functions of synovial fluid? What is meant by its thixotropic properties?*

Movements of the shoulder joint: muscles and their innervation

Strictly, movements of the shoulder joint are defined in relation to the plane of the scapula (i.e. flexion is a forward and medial movement). Practically, however, the plane of the scapula is neglected; flexion and extension are considered as simple forward and backward movements of the arm with respect to the trunk; abduction and adduction as movements away from and toward the trunk. In real life what concerns us is the extent to which we can move our upper limb; whether we can raise our arm to reach an object on a high shelf, or comb our hair!

Flexion

Flexion is produced by muscles which pass down across the anterior aspect of the joint. The prime movers are:

- the clavicular head of **pectoralis major** (**5.3.4**; pectoral nerves);
- anterior fibres of **deltoid** (**5.3.5**).

The short head of biceps (see **5.4.12**) and coracobrachialis (see **5.4.13**) can help but their main action is to help stabilize the joint.

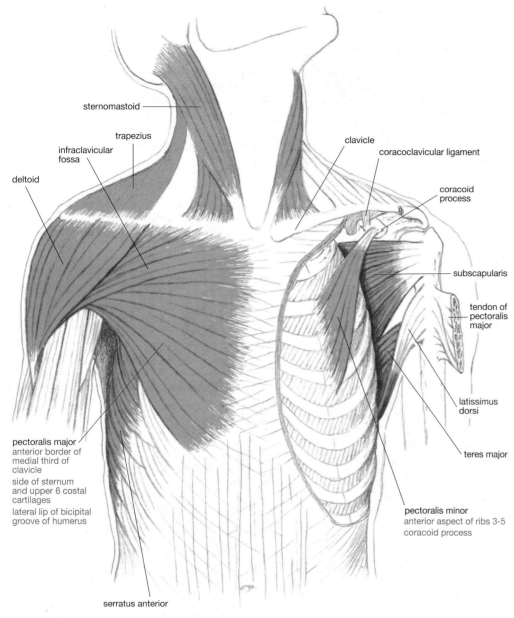

5.3.4 Muscles of the axilla and shoulder (anterior view).

Extension

Extension is produced by muscles which originate from the dorsal aspect of the trunk and pass up behind the joint to insert into the upper end of the humerus. The principal prime mover is:
- **latissimus dorsi** (**5.2.4**, **5.3.4**), which inserts into the floor of the bicipital groove.

Abduction

Abduction is produced by muscles which pass above the joint before inserting into the humerus. The prime movers are:
- **supraspinatus** (**5.3.6**; suprascapular nerve); this is essential for the first 10° of abduction because

deltoid has almost no moment when the arm is by the side.
- **deltoid** (**5.3.5**; axillary nerve); This muscle produces the power for abduction, but only once the movement has been initiated by supraspinatus. If supraspinatus is paralysed, the patient can produce the first 10° of abduction by leaning to one side and letting the joint abduct passively. This is often enough to allow deltoid to act as an abductor.

Raising the arm above the head, however, requires more than simple abduction of the shoulder joint. The movement is combined with **lateral rotation of the humerus**, which makes more of its head available for articulation, and **rotation of the scapula**, largely by trapezius, which elevates the glenoid fossa.

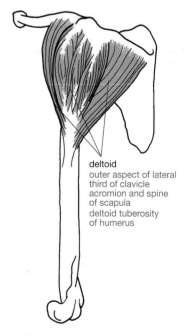

deltoid
outer aspect of lateral
third of clavicle
acromion and spine
of scapula
deltoid tuberosity
of humerus

5.3.5 Deltoid.

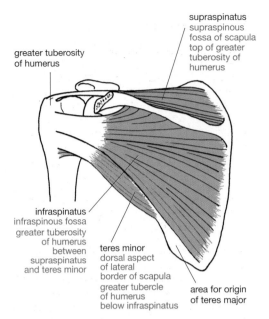

5.3.6 Supraspinatus, infraspinatus, teres minor; acromion removed.

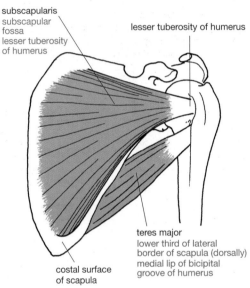

5.3.7 Subscapularis and teres major.

Adduction

Adduction is produced by muscles arising from either the front or back of the trunk and passing to insertions on the upper end of the humerus. It is the power movement used in climbing when the arm has been raised above the head to secure a hand-hold, and then the trunk is pulled upward by adduction of the shoulder joint. The prime movers are:

- **pectoralis major**, from the anterior chest wall and clavicle (**5.3.4**; pectoral nerves);
- **latissimus dorsi**, from the posterior trunk wall (**5.2.4**).

Note how the fibres of both these muscles spiral to their insertion on the humerus. When the arm is raised above the head, the spirals unwind, reflecting their main function as powerful adductors of the arm raised above the head, as in climbing.

Qu. 3D *Which other muscles assist in adduction?*

Medial rotation

Medial rotation of the shoulder joint is produced by muscles which exert their pull anterior to the joint. The principal medial rotators are:

- **pectoralis major** (**5.3.4**);
- **latissimus dorsi** (**5.2.4**);
- **subscapularis** and **teres major** (**5.3.7**; subscapular nerves from posterior cord of brachial plexus);
- the clavicular head of **deltoid** (**5.3.5**).

Lateral rotation

Lateral rotation of the shoulder joint is produced by muscles acting posterior to the joint. They insert into the upper end of the humerus. The principal muscles involved are:

- **infraspinatus** (**5.3.6**; suprascapular nerve);
- posterior fibres of **deltoid**.

Circumduction

Circumduction of the shoulder joint is the combination of all these movements.

Although the principal muscles with a prime mover action in any movement have been listed above, it is important to remember that single muscles, and even groups of muscles, do not act alone. Almost all movements recruit not only prime movers but also antagonists, synergists, and fixators (see p. 15).

Stability of the shoulder joint

Stability of any joint depends on both active and passive mechanisms.

Active stabilization of the shoulder joint in any position is provided largely by the '**rotator cuff**' muscles (subscapularis anteriorly; supraspinatus, infraspinatus, and teres minor posteriorly; see below). These muscles arise from the anterior and posterior surfaces of the blade of the scapula and insert into the lesser and greater tuberosities of the humerus. They surround the capsule of the joint on all but its inferior aspect, and their connective tissues blend with the capsule. During movements of the shoulder joint, the rotator cuff muscles pull the head of the humerus firmly inward on to the shallow glenoid fossa, so stabilizing the joint.

Large forces applied to the upper limb cause a reflex contraction of all the muscles around the joint (even if the joint is not moving). However, when you stand with your arms hanging quietly by your side, there is no recordable electromyographic activity in the muscles around the shoulder, and stability then depends on passive mechanisms.

Arching over the joint, the extrinsic **coracoacromial ligament** is triangular in shape, spanning between the coracoid process and the acromion. It prevents upward dislocation of the humerus. Beneath the ligament is a large subacromial bursa which does not open into the shoulder joint.

The **tendon of the long head of biceps (5.3.3)** is attached to the supraglenoid tubercle within the shoulder joint. It passes over the head of the humerus then downward through the intertubercular (bicipital) groove to reach the flexor compartment of the arm. Here it joins the short head of biceps, which originates from the coracoid process of the scapula. It also provides active support to the head of the humerus during movement.

Qu. 3E *In which direction does a dislocation of the head of the humerus usually occur, and why?*

Qu. 3F *Which nerve is most likely to be damaged by a dislocation of the shoulder joint? (answer when you have studied p. 120)*

Blood and nerve supply to the shoulder joint

The joint is supplied by arteries lying close to the joint and is innervated by all the nerves supplying the muscles that act on the joint. These provide proprioceptive and pain-sensing fibres to the joint, in addition to sympathetic fibres to the blood vessels of the synovial membrane.

Imaging the shoulder joint

Examine radiographs of the shoulder in the position of rest (**5.3.10**) and in full abduction (**5.3.11**). Note that the articular surfaces of the humeral head and the glenoid fossa lie parallel to one another (see **5.1.5**). Use the positions of the greater and lesser tubercles of the humerus to confirm the rotation of

the humerus that occurs when the shoulder joint is fully abducted.

MRI and ultrasound investigations (**5.3.8, 5.3.9**) of the shoulder can show both bone and soft tissues and are therefore very useful in determining the cause of painful shoulders.

The painful shoulder

Shoulder pain is a common complaint and often associated with strenuous sports. Apart from fractures and joint disorders, such as arthritis, the cause is often soft-tissue damage. This includes disorders ranging from tears of the rotator cuff muscles, degeneration and rupture of the supraspinatus tendon, to trapping of tissue between the head of the humerus and the coraco-acromial ligament.

Qu. 3G *What sort of tissues lie between the head of the humerus and the coraco-acromial ligament?*

One such disorder—'frozen shoulder'—often follows mild trauma to the glenohumeral joint in a middle-aged man, who then complains of pain and stiffness of the joint with an inability to perform a full range of shoulder movements. There may be thickening of the capsule or degeneration of the rotator cuff.

These conditions cannot be visualized by conventional radiology, but magnetic resonance imaging (MRI) (**5.3.8**) and ultrasound imaging (**5.3.9**) are particularly useful methods in the diagnosis of these and other soft-tissue damage.

Single ultrasound images are more difficult to interpret than MRI images. On the other hand, ultrasound allows the joint to be examined rapidly in any position.

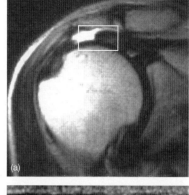
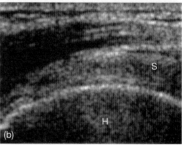
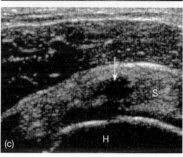

5.3.9 T$_2$-weighted MRI and ultrasound scans of shoulder. (a) MRI to show area illustrated in (b) and (c); compact bone appears dark; fluid white. (b) Normal supraspinatus tendon (S) fused with capsule passing over head of humerus (H); (c) tear in supraspinatus tendon (arrow).

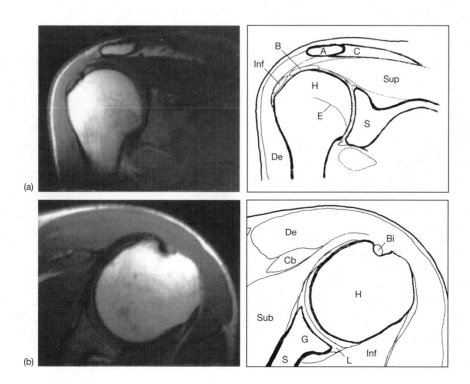

5.3.8 MRI of shoulder joint: (a) sagittal plane, (b) horizontal plane. Head of humerus (H), epiphyseal line (E), glenoid labrum (L), glenoid fossa (G) and acromion (A) of scapula (S), clavicle (C), deltoid (De), infraspinatus (Inf), supraspinatus (Sup), subscapularis (Sub), tendon of biceps (Bi), coracobrachialis (Cb).

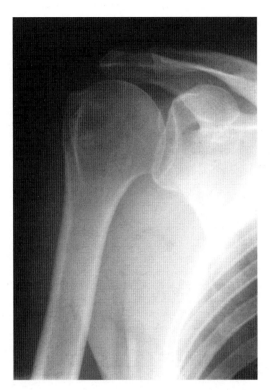

5.3.10 Shoulder at rest.

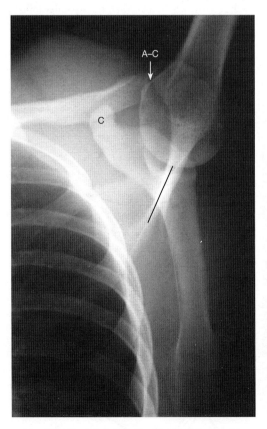

5.3.11 Shoulder in full abduction. The black line marks the spine of the scapula; A-C, acromioclavicular joint; C, coracoid process.

Dislocation of the shoulder

Dislocation of the head of the humerus most commonly occurs in a downward and anterior direction, as a result of a downward blow on the abducted humerus. The head of the humerus stretches the weakest (inferior) part of the capsule and comes to lie below the coronoid process. Less frequently it dislocates posteriorly to lie beneath the spine of the scapula.

5.3.12 and **5.3.13** are a photograph and radiograph of a young man who was injured playing rugby football. His left shoulder is very painful and he cannot move it. Instead of the normal smooth curve from acromion to deltoid there is a rather sharp angle. The deltoid lacks its normal bulged appearance and appears 'empty' with one or two shallow dimples. Also, there is a bulge below the coracoid process where the normal shoulder shows a depression (infraclavicular fossa). Instead of the coracoid process, a large, hard lump produced by the head of the humerus is palpable at this site.

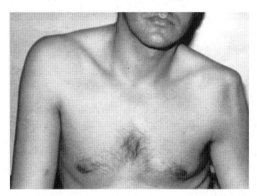

5.3.12 Dislocated left shoulder.

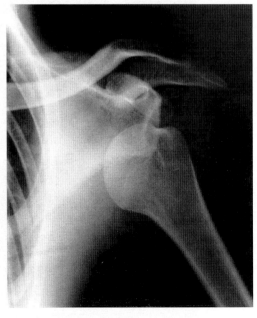

5.3.13 Radiograph of dislocated shoulder.

Table 5.3.1 Shoulder (glenohumeral) joint: movements, principal muscles, and their innervation.

Movement	Principal muscles	Peripheral nerve	Spinal root origin
Flexion	Pectoralis major (clavicular part)	Pectoral nerves (medial and lateral)	C 5, 6
	Deltoid (clavicular part)	Axillary nerve	C 5, 6
Extension	Latissimus dorsi	Nerve to latissimus dorsi (thoracodorsal nerve)	C 6, 7, 8
Abduction	Supraspinatus (initial 20°)	Suprascapular nerve	C 5, 6
	Deltoid	Axillary nerve	C 5, 6
Adduction	Pectoralis major	Pectoral nerves (medial and lateral)	C 5, 6
	Latissimus dorsi	Nerve to latissimus dorsi	C 6, 7, 8
Medial (internal) rotation	Pectoralis major	Pectoral nerves (medial and lateral)	C 5, 6
	Latissimus dorsi	Nerve to latissimus dorsi	C 6, 7, 8
	Subscapularis	Subscapular nerves (upper and lower)	C 5, 6
	Teres major	Lower subscapular nerve	C 5, 6
Lateral (external) rotation	Infraspinatus	Suprascapular nerve	C 5, 6
	Teres minor	Axillary nerve	C 5, 6
	Deltoid (posterior fibres)	Axillary nerve	C 5, 6
Circumduction	Combinations of the above		

Questions and answers

Qu. 3A *What implications does this mechanism have for the capsule of the shoulder joint?*

Answer Because the shoulder joint has evolved to permit a very wide range of movement of the head of the humerus, the capsule of the joint must necessarily be lax. The capsule gains its strength, and the shoulder its stability, largely from the insertion of the rotator cuff muscles.

Qu. 3B *When movements are occurring at the shoulder joint, are movements also occurring at other joints?*

Answer Yes. Probably many other joints, especially the sternoclavicular. Any movement of the shoulder will require postural adaptation of other parts of the body to maintain balance.

Qu. 3C *What are the other functions of synovial fluid? What is meant by its thixotropic properties?*

Answer Synovial fluid lubricates the joint, distributes pressure within it, and helps to nourish the hyaline articular cartilage. When pressure on synovial fluid is increased, cross-linkages within its glycoprotein molecules decrease and the fluid becomes less viscous, and vice versa (the principle of 'non-drip' paint).

Qu. 3D *Which other muscles assist in adduction?*

Answer Muscles attached to the scapula and the upper end of the humerus, in particular subscapularis, will help adduct the arm.

Qu. 3E *In what direction does a dislocation of the head of the humerus usually occur, and why?*

Answer Shoulder dislocation initially occurs antero-inferiorly into the dependent, least well-supported part of the capsule. Thereafter the head comes to lie either inferior to the coracoid process anteriorly or beneath the spine of the scapula, posteriorly. Very occasionally it might dislocate upwards with the arm in a vertical position.

Qu. 3F *Which nerve is most likely to be damaged by a dislocation of the shoulder joint? (answer when you have studied p. 120).*

Answer The axillary nerve, because it lies just beneath the dependent part of the capsule.

Qu. 3G *What sort of tissues lie between the head of the humerus and the coraco-acromial ligament?*

Answer The supraspinatus tendon passes beneath the coraco-acromial ligament to reach the greater tuberosity of the humerus and the capsule. A fluid-lubricated sac, the subacromial bursa, separates the tendon from the acromion and coraco-acromial ligament. The predominant tissue is white fibrous tissue.

The elbow joint and its movements

The elbow joint and its movements

The elbow joint is a synovial hinge joint allowing flexion and extension of the radius and ulna on the humerus. It acts as a link in the lever arm system which positions the hand in space, enabling it to operate at different distances away from the trunk. It also acts as a fulcrum for the forearm lever, transmitting the power to perform lifting movements. In addition, a part of the elbow joint is also a part of the proximal of the two radio-ulnar joints that allow the forearm and hand to be pronated and supinated on the arm, again extending the versatility of placement of the hand.

Living anatomy

Place your arm naturally as if you were about to write or perform some natural task; your elbow is probably semiflexed, with the forearm in approximately the mid-prone position (p. 77). As this position is commonly adopted it has been called the 'position of function', although, of course, the upper limb is used with its joints in the widest possible range of positions.

The movements of the elbow joint are limited to flexion and extension. Flexion stops when the soft tissues of the arm and forearm contact one another; extension is limited to 180°.

Muscles which flex the elbow joint cross anterior to it and occupy the anterior (flexor) compartment of the arm; those in the posterior compartment extend the joint. Explore the actions of muscles in the anterior and posterior compartments of the forearm by getting a colleague to flex and extend the elbow against resistance (see **5.3.1, 5.4.1**).

Abduct your arm as far as possible with your elbow extended, and lower it slowly, noting the distance away from the trunk that the arc of your hand describes. Repeat this with your elbow flexed 30°: the arc is now much smaller and closer to the trunk. Therefore, varying the degree of flexion of the elbow enables the hand to operate at different distances from the trunk.

Examine the bony landmarks of the elbow. The medial and lateral epicondyles of the humerus and the olecranon process of the ulna can be felt just beneath the skin, but the head of the radius is covered with muscle. With the elbow flexed, the epicondyles and the olecranon should form a roughly equilateral triangle (**5.4.2**). If they do not, the elbow may be dislocated.

Reflexes to elicit at the elbow

Sit down and ask a colleague to rest a semiflexed right forearm on your knee. Hold the dorsal aspect of your colleague's right elbow in the palm of your left hand (if you are right-handed), press with your left thumb firmly over the tendon of biceps as it runs downward across the front of the elbow joint, and then tap your thumb with a 'patellar hammer'. This will stretch biceps and should cause its reflex contraction—a '**biceps jerk**'.

The strength of this reflex depends on the excitation of spinal cord motor neurons and the integrity of the nerve which supplies biceps, on the neuromuscular junction, and on the muscle itself.

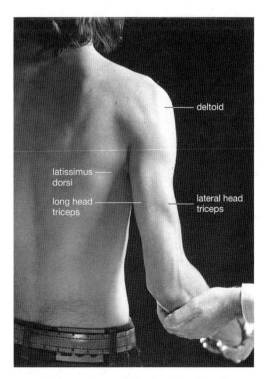

5.4.1 Triceps; demonstrated by extension of the elbow against resistance.

5.4.2 Triangle formed by medial and lateral epicondyles and olecranon at the elbow.

Try also to elicit a 'triceps jerk'. Hold your colleague's arm so that the elbow is in the semiflexed position, then tap the triceps tendon just above the elbow. This should elicit a reflex extension of the elbow. Compare the responses of both these reflexes on the two sides of the body.

The elbow joint

The elbow joint is a synovial hinge joint. The articular surfaces (**5.4.3**, **5.4.5**, **5.4.7**) are the **trochlea** of the humerus which articulates with the **trochlear notch** of

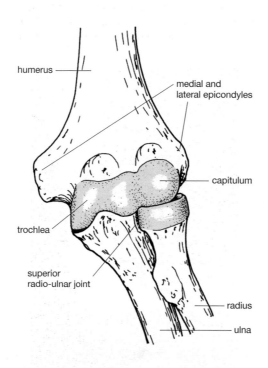

5.4.3 Articular surfaces of elbow joint (anterior aspect).

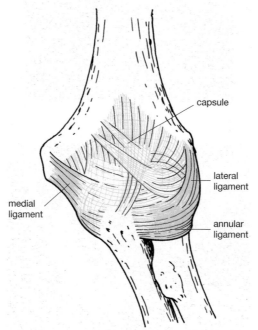

5.4.4 Capsule and ligaments of elbow joint (anterior aspect).

the ulna, and the rounded **capitulum** of the humerus which articulates with the rounded concave upper end of the **head of the radius.** The head of the radius also articulates on its medial aspect with the **radial notch** on the upper lateral aspect of the ulna to form the **superior radio-ulnar joint**.

The head of the radius is held against the ulna by a sling-like **annular ligament** (**5.4.8**) attached to either side of the radial notch. This ligament allows the head of the radius to rotate against the ulna (and also against the capitulum of the humerus) when its lower end is rotating around the lower end of the ulna in pronation and supination of the forearm.

Examine the radiographs of the elbow joint. Note the position of the bones in the extended (**5.4.9**) and semi-flexed (**5.4.10**) positions of the joint. Revise the secondary centres of ossification of the bones (p. 12).

In **5.4.10**, draw a line along the middle of the shaft of the radius through the centre of the head of the bone. Note that it passes through the centre of a circle which is outlined in part by the capitulum. In certain injuries, for instance a fracture of the shaft of the ulna, the head of the radius may be displaced from its position against the capitulum (**5.4.11**).

Draw a second line down the anterior border of the shaft of the humerus (**5.4.10**). This too should pass through the centre of the circle referred to above.

On the lateral radiograph (**5.4.10**) note that the lower end of the humerus is normally angled 45° forward with respect to the shaft of the bone. If the lower end is displaced, it is probably due to a supracondylar fracture of the shaft of the humerus.

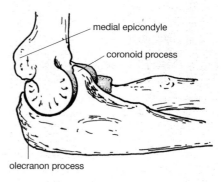

5.4.5 Articular surfaces of elbow joint (medial aspect).

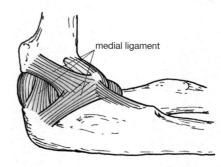

5.4.6 Capsule and ligaments of elbow joint (medial aspect).

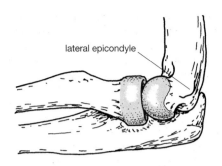

5.4.7 Articular surfaces of elbow joint (lateral aspect).

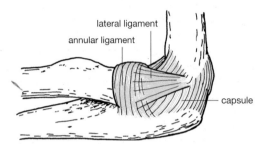

5.4.8 Capsule and ligaments of elbow joint (lateral aspect).

The **capsule** (5.4.4, 5.4.6, 5.4.8) is common to both the elbow joint and the superior radio-ulnar joint. It is attached to the humerus immediately above the coronoid and radial fossae and to the inferior aspects of the medial and lateral epicondyles (thus avoiding the common origins of the superficial long flexor and extensor muscles of the forearm). Posteriorly it is attached to the *upper* margin of the olecranon fossa so that, when the elbow is fully extended, the olecranon process of the ulna fits snugly into its fossa. Inferiorly, the capsule is attached to the annular ligament, to the margins of the trochlear notch, and to the olecranon process.

The **synovial membrane** lines the capsule and all those parts of the joint which are not covered with hyaline articular cartilage; it also extends beneath the

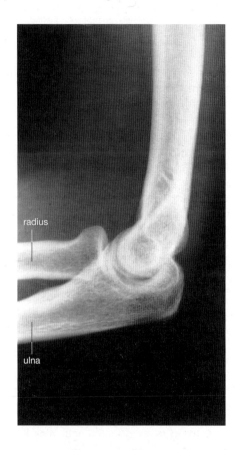

5.4.10 Left elbow joint, semi-flexed (lateral).

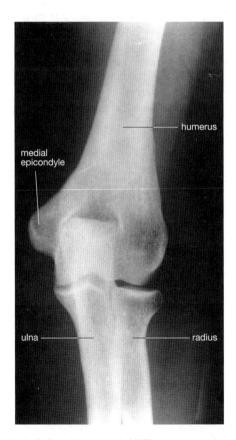

5.4.9 Left elbow joint, extended (AP).

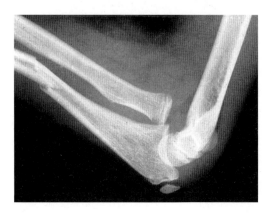

5.4.11 Fracture of shaft of ulna with displacement of head of radius in a child aged 14 years; note the secondary centre of ossification in the olecranon process.

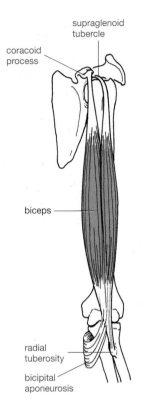

5.4.12 Biceps.

annular ligament of the head to surround the neck of the bone.

As you would expect for a hinge joint, the capsule is reinforced medially and laterally by intrinsic **collateral ligaments**. The **lateral ligament** is fan-shaped and runs from the lateral epicondyle to the annular ligament. The **medial ligament** is triangular in shape with thickenings that pass from the medial epicondyle to the coronoid process and the olecranon of the ulna.

Olecranon bursitis

Between the olecranon process and the skin is a bursa, which does not communicate with the elbow joint, which can become enlarged, inflamed, and painful. It is caused by localized pressure, friction, or infection.

Movements of the elbow joint: muscles and their innervation

Flexion

Any muscle that is attached to bones of the shoulder girdle or humerus and which crosses anterior to the elbow joint to insert into bones of the forearm has a flexor action on the joint. The prime movers are:

- biceps (**5.4.12**; musculocutaneous nerve);
- brachialis (**5.4.13**; musculocutaneous nerve).

Biceps arises from the scapula by two heads, a **short head** from the tip of the coracoid process, and a **long head** from the supraglenoid tubercle. The tendon of origin of the long head passes over the head of the humerus within the shoulder joint to emerge beneath the capsule in the intertubercular groove. The two heads then join to form a large superficial muscle belly which is inserted, by a flattened tendon passing in front of the elbow joint, into the tuberosity of the radius. An expansion of this tendon, the **bicipital aponeurosis**, crosses medially over the superficial flexor muscles of the forearm to attach to the posterior border of the ulna via the deep fascia. In this way biceps exerts its flexor action on both bones of the forearm.

In the position of function (elbow semiflexed; p. 69), biceps is also a strong supinator. It is active when a screw is being driven home or when a cork is removed from a bottle.

Because the short head passes anterior to the shoulder joint, it also has a flexor action at this joint, while the tendon of the long head helps stabilize the head of the humerus during movements of the shoulder joint.

Qu. 4A *Are there any other muscles that could flex the elbow joint?*

Ruptured biceps tendon

Within the shoulder joint the tendon of the long head of biceps is enclosed within a synovial sheath which can become inflamed and painful. The tendon is also prone to spontaneous rupture (**5.4.14**) due to degeneration of collagen in the tendon. During an activity that puts a strain on biceps, which is not necessarily severe, the patient feels a sudden pain in the front of the upper arm. The contour of biceps is altered but there is surprisingly little dysfunction: there may be some weakness of supination, but flexion is preserved because both the short head, which is quite strong, and brachialis can act.

Brachioradialis (**5.4.15**; radial nerve), which arises from the lateral supracondylar ridge and inserts into the distal end of the radius, is a flexor of the elbow despite being supplied by the radial (extensor) nerve. It is active primarily in rapid flexion and extension movements, to counteract the centrifugal force that these movements exert on the forearm bones.

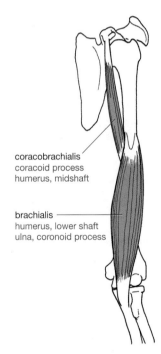

5.4.13 Coracobrachialis; brachialis.

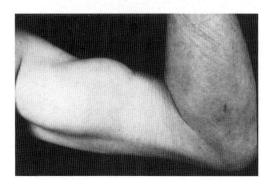

5.4.14 Ruptured long head of biceps.

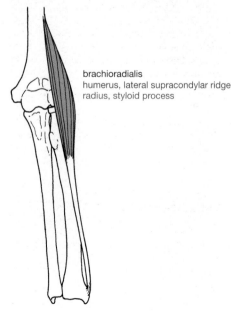

5.4.15 Brachioradialis.

Table 5.4.1 Elbow joint: movements, principal muscles, and their innervation.

Movement	Principal muscles	Peripheral nerve	Spinal root origin
Flexion	Biceps	Musculocutaneous nerve	C 5, 6
	Brachialis	Musculocutaneous nerve	C 5, 6
Extension	Triceps	Radial nerve	C 7, 8

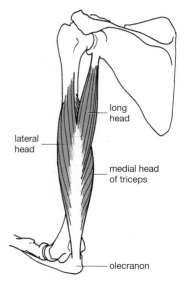

5.4.16 Triceps.

Extension

Only the large **triceps** muscle (**5.4.16**: radial nerve) passes posterior to the elbow joint and therefore extends it. Its fibres originate from the infraglenoid tubercle (**long head**), and the posterior aspect of the shaft of the humerus above (**lateral head**) and below (**medial head**) the radial groove. The three heads join to form a tendon which inserts into the olecranon process of the ulna.

Intermuscular septa in the arm

In the upper limb, the flexor and extensor groups of muscle are separated by sheets of fascia—intermuscular septa—which pass from the deep fascia to the underlying bone and to which the muscles are also partly attached. This arrangement creates an anterior (flexor) compartment and a posterior (extensor) compartment. It reflects the basic embryological division of limb musculature into flexor and extensor groups.

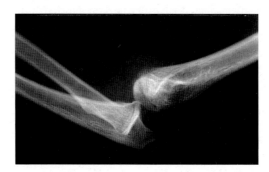

5.4.17 See Qu. 4B.

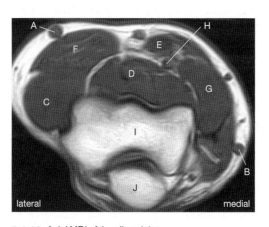

5.4.18 Axial MRI of the elbow joint. See Qu. 4C.

Supracondylar fracture of the humerus

A supracondylar fracture of the humerus is one of the most common of all fractures in children and is usually caused by a fall on the outstretched hand. The shaft of the humerus is broken just above the condyles and the lower fragment is pushed and tilted backward (**5.4.17**). A severe, though uncommon, complication is ischaemia (reduction of the blood supply) of the forearm muscles (see p. 104).

Qu. 4B *How do you explain this complication? (answer when you have completed Section 5.7). How could you distinguish very simply (i.e. without radiography) between this injury and a dislocation of the elbow joint?*

Imaging the elbow

MRI of the elbow is used primarily to visualize changes in soft tissues. **5.4.18** is an axial MRI of the elbow.

Qu. 4C *In 5.4.18, what are the soft-tissue structures labelled A–H, and the parts of the bones labelled I and J?*

Questions and answers

Qu. 4A *Are there any other muscles that could flex the elbow joint?*

Answer Muscles attached to the common flexor origin on the anterior aspect of the medial epicondyle cross the anterior aspect of the elbow joint to reach their insertions in the forearm and hand and therefore will also flex the elbow joint. Brachioradialis, which runs from the lateral supracondylar ridge of the humerus to the distal end of the radius will also help flex the elbow, particularly when it is already partially flexed.

Qu. 4B *How do you explain this complication? (answer when you have completed Section 5.7). How could you distinguish very simply (i.e. without radiography) between this injury and a dislocation of the elbow joint?*

Answer The brachial artery lies ventrally, separated from the shaft of the humerus only by fibres of the brachialis muscle. The displacement of the distal fragment can compress the brachial artery and occlude blood flow to the forearm and hand, leading to ischaemia and death of the forearm muscles. In the normal flexed elbow, the medial and lateral epicondyles of the humerus and the tip of the olecranon form a roughly equilateral triangle (**5.4.2**). This arrangement is preserved after a supracondylar fracture, but not if the elbow joint is dislocated.

Qu. 4C *In 5.4.18, what are the soft-tissue structures labelled A–H, and the parts of the bones labelled I and J?*

Answer A, cephalic vein; B, basilic vein; C, muscles arising from lateral epicondyle (common extensor origin); D, brachialis; E, biceps; F, brachioradialis; G, muscles arising from medial epicondyle (common flexor origin); H, brachial artery; I, lower end of humerus; J, olecranon process of ulna.

Joints and movements of the forearm and wrist

Joints and movements of the forearm and wrist

To enable the hand to grip an object in almost any orientation, the bones of the forearm are articulated in such a way that the radius, which carries the hand, can be rotated around the ulna. Movement of the forearm so that the palm is facing downward (posteriorly in the 'anatomical position') is called pronation; the reverse movement, to face the palm upward, is called supination. Movements of the wrist—flexion and extension, with more limited abduction and adduction—add to our ability to place the hand in almost any position to perform a manual task.

PRONATION AND SUPINATION OF THE FOREARM

Living anatomy

With your elbows by your sides, place your upper limb in the position you would use to start writing. The elbow will be semi-flexed, and the forearm and hand in the 'mid-prone' position ('position of function'). Rotate your forearm so that the palm faces the ceiling—it is now supinated; again rotate your forearm so that the palm faces the floor—it is now pronated. The range of movement is about 150°.

Qu. 5A *Against resistance, is pronation or supination the stronger? Why do screws have right-hand threads?*

Extend your arm and touch a wall in front of you with one extended finger; now pronate and supinate your forearm and do the same with each finger in turn. You will see that the forearm can rotate about an axis that can pass through any finger. Now pronate and supinate the forearm freely without contact with the wall.

Qu. 5B *Through which finger does the axis of movement pass in this free movement?*

Hold a colleague's hand as in a hand-shake. Supinate your forearm against your colleague's resistance and feel the contraction of your biceps. Repeat this action while palpating over the upper end of the radius; you should be able to feel the contraction of the supinator muscle (see **5.5.6**). Now pronate your forearm against resistance and feel the contraction of a muscle (pronator teres) which arises from the medial epicondyle of the humerus.

Rest your right forearm on a flat surface and supinate it. Mark the position of the styloid process on the distal end of the ulna with your left index finger and then pronate your forearm.

Two things occur: the radius and hand rotate around the lower end of the ulna, but also the ulna is abducted slightly during pronation so that the axis of pronation/supination is through the centre of the wrist and palm.

When the forearm has to be immobilized, as after a fracture, the limb is usually fixed in the 'position of function' with the elbow semi-flexed and the forearm mid-prone.

Joints between the radius and ulna

The position of the radius and ulna in supination and pronation are shown in radiographs **5.5.1** (supinated) and **5.5.2** (pronated). Pronation and supination are the result of rotatory and pivoting movements at both the **proximal** and **distal radio-ulnar joints** (**5.5.3**).

Both the proximal and distal radio-ulnar joints are synovial pivot joints. The articular surfaces of the proximal radio-ulnar joint are the sides of the head of the radius which articulate with the radial notch on the proximal end of the ulna; in addition, the concavity of the head of the radius pivots on the capitulum of the humerus. The joint cavity and capsule are continuous with that of the elbow joint.

The head of the radius rotates within, and is retained by, an **annular ligament** attached to the two edges of the radial notch.

Dislocation of the head of the radius

If a child's forearm is suddenly tugged (e.g. if it falls while holding its mother's hand) the head of the radius may dislocate distally through the annular ligament. There is transient pain but if the arm is supported in a sling the injury usually resolves spontaneously within a few days.

The shafts of the radius and ulna are joined by a flexible sheet of fibrous tissue—the **interosseous**

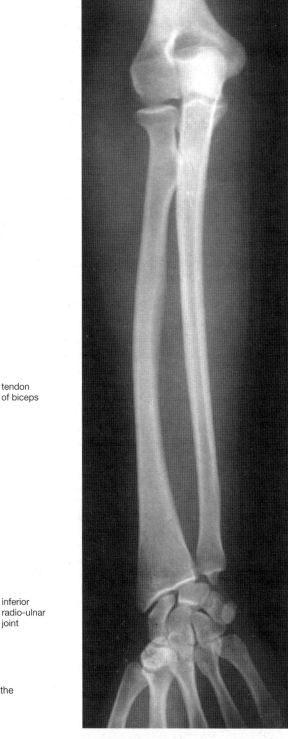

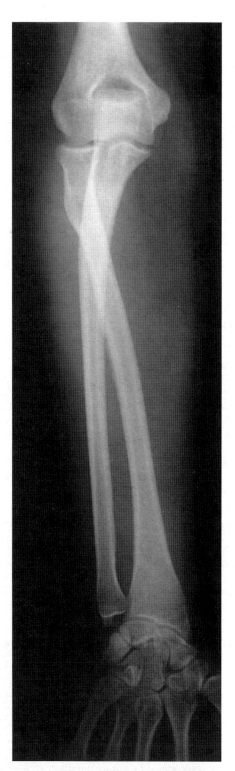

5.5.1 Forearm supinated (AP).

5.5.2 Forearm pronated (AP).

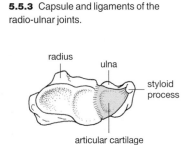

attachment
of capsule
of elbow joint

annular
ligament

oblique cord

interosseous
membrane

tendon
of biceps

inferior
radio-ulnar
joint

attachment of capsule
of wrist joint

5.5.3 Capsule and ligaments of the
radio-ulnar joints.

radius   ulna

styloid
process

articular cartilage

5.5.4 Intra-articular disc of inferior
radio-ulnar and wrist joints.

membrane (5.5.3). Its fibres pass distally from the radius to the ulna. This orientation of the fibres serves to transfer compressive forces transmitted from the hand and radius to the ulna and thence to the humerus. It effectively forms a mobile fibrous, middle radio-ulnar joint.

The **distal radio-ulnar joint** is the articulation between the head of the ulna, the concavity (ulnar notch) on the medial aspect of the distal end of the radius, and the fibrocartilaginous articular disc which unites the two bones (5.5.4). The apex of the triangular disc is attached to the styloid process of the ulna and its base to the ulnar notch on the radius. The distal end of the ulna therefore articulates with the fibrocartilaginous disc and not with the carpus, and the disc separates the synovial cavity of the distal radio-ulnar joint from that of the wrist.

Pronation and supination movements

Pronation

Pronation is produced by muscles which pull the lower end of the radius across the ulna. The prime movers are:

- **pronator teres** (5.5.5; median nerve), which arises by two heads from the common flexor origin and from the medial aspect of the coronoid process of the ulna; it passes diagonally to insert halfway down the shaft of the radius;
- **pronator quadratus** (5.5.5; median nerve) attached across the distal ends of the radius and ulna.

When the elbow is fully extended, pronation relies on pronator quadratus; only when the elbow is semi-flexed can pronator teres exert a strong pronator action.

Supination

Supination is produced by muscles which can return the pronated radius to the 'anatomical position'.

These are:

- **biceps** (5.4.12, 5.5.11; musculocutaneous nerve) which, through its insertion into the bicipital tuberosity on the radius, is a powerful supinator when the elbow is semi-flexed, but has only a weak action if the elbow is fully extended.
- **supinator** (5.5.6, 5.5.14; radial nerve), which has deep fibres originating from the ulna just behind the superior radio-ulnar joint (supinator crest) and more superficial fibres arising from the lateral epicondyle. Its fibres wrap around the back of the radius to insert (adjacent to pronator teres) into the shaft of the radius.

MOVEMENTS OF THE WRIST

Living anatomy

Hold your right forearm in the supine position, with the elbow semi-flexed. With your left hand hold the distal ends of the radius and ulna so that they cannot move.

Qu. 5C *What movements can you perform at the wrist joint, and what is their extent?*

All movements of the wrist joint are, in fact, accompanied by small sliding movements of the synovial intercarpal joints. What you experience is the combined movement.

Now repeat the movements against resistance and note the long tendons standing out on the front (5.5.7) and back of the wrist.

Wrist joint

The wrist (radio-carpal) joint is a synovial ellipsoid joint. The distal end of the radius and the articular disc articulate with the proximal row of carpal bones [scaphoid, lunate, triquetral; see **5.5.8** (wrist abducted), **5.5.9** (wrist adducted)].

The triangular intra-articular disc is interposed between the distal end of the ulna and the carpus

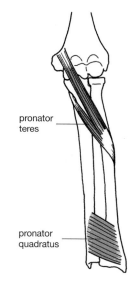

pronator teres

pronator quadratus

5.5.5 Pronator muscles.

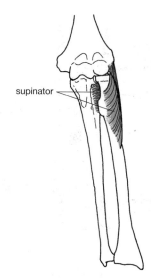

supinator

5.5.6 Supinator.

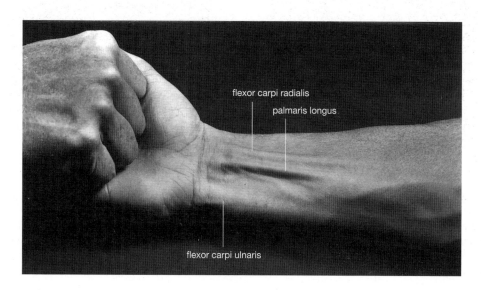

flexor carpi radialis

palmaris longus

flexor carpi ulnaris

5.5.7 Long flexor tendons demonstrated by flexion of wrist against resistance.

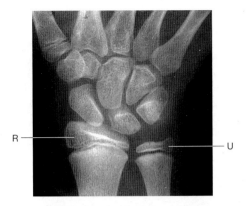

5.5.8 Immature wrist joint with hand abducted; distal epiphyses of radius (R) and ulna (U).

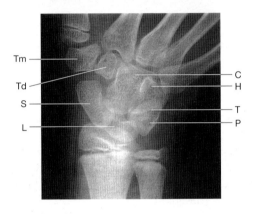

5.5.9 Immature wrist joint with hand adducted; trapezium (Tm), trapezoid (Td), capitate (C), hamate (H), pisiform (P), triquetral (T), lunate (L), scaphoid (S).

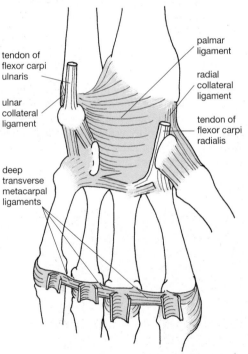

5.5.10 Capsule and ligaments of wrist, carpal, and metacarpo-phalangeal joints.

(hence the wrist joint is more specifically termed the radio-carpal joint).

Qu. 5D *From radiographs 5.5.8 and 5.5.9 determine which carpal bones articulate with the radius when the hand is adducted, and with the articular disc when the hand is abducted.*

The joint capsule (**5.5.10**) is attached proximally around the articular margins of the distal ends of the radius and ulna; and distally to the proximal row of carpal bones. It is strengthened by dorsal and palmar ligaments and by collateral ligaments which are attached from the styloid process of the ulna to the pisiform and triquetral, and from the styloid process of the radius to the scaphoid.

Wrist movements: muscles and their innervation

Flexion

Flexion of the wrist is produced by muscles which lie in the anterior compartment of the forearm and pass anterior to the wrist joint before reaching their insertions (**5.5.11**, **5.5.12**). Some are superficially placed, taking origin largely from a '**common flexor origin**' on the anterior aspect of the medial epicondyle of the humerus. Two (flexor digitorum profundus and flexor pollicis longus) arise deeply from the radius or ulna and the interosseous membrane.

These anterior compartment muscles form two functional groups: one group acts only on the wrist; the other acts primarily on the fingers but can also have a flexor action on the wrist. All are supplied by either the median or the ulnar nerve.

Flexor muscles which act only on the wrist (**5.5.11**) are:
- **flexor carpi radialis** (median nerve), which inserts into the bases of the second and third metacarpal bones;
- **flexor carpi ulnaris** (ulnar nerve), which arises from both the common flexor origin and the posterior subcutaneous border of the ulna, and inserts via the pisiform (sesamoid) bone into the base of the fifth metacarpal and the hook of the hamate bone.

Between these two lies:
- **palmaris longus** (an insubstantial muscle which is not always present), which crosses the mid point of the wrist and inserts into the thick, tough fascia (palmar aponeurosis) which lies beneath the skin of the palm.

Flexor muscles which act primarily on the fingers, but have an additional action on the wrist are:
- **flexor digitorum superficialis** (**5.5.11**), which lies a little deeper than the other superficial forearm flexor muscles—it ends in four tendons which cross the wrist and palm to insert into the base of the middle phalanges of each finger;
- **flexor digitorum profundus** (**5.5.12**), which also gives four tendons that insert into the base of the distal phalanges of the fingers;
- **flexor pollicis longus** (**5.5.12**) which inserts into the distal phalanx of the thumb.

The tendons of all these muscles, except those of flexor carpi ulnaris and palmaris longus, pass beneath the flexor retinaculum (**5.5.11**; p. 92), which keeps them in place, before they enter the palm.

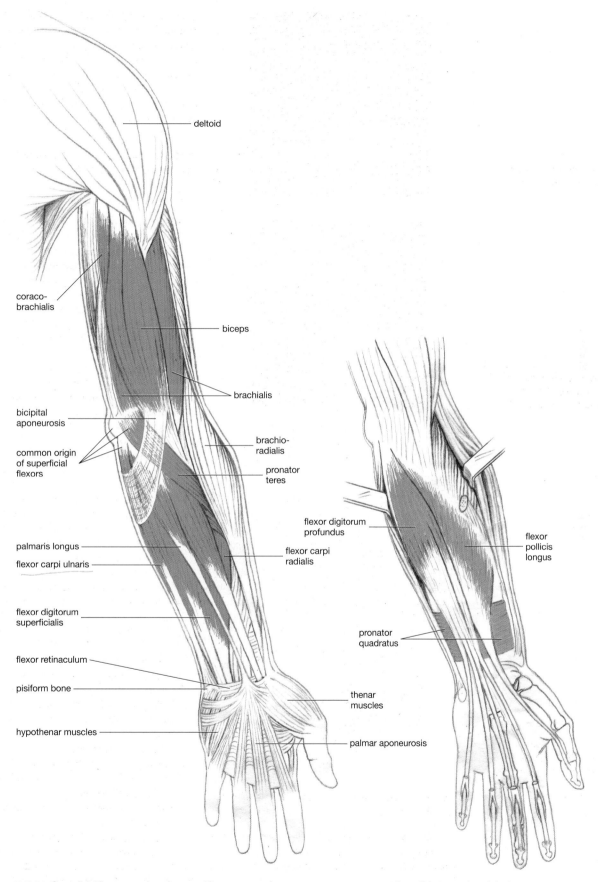

deltoid

coraco-
brachialis

biceps

brachialis

bicipital
aponeurosis

brachio-
radialis

common origin
of superficial
flexors

pronator
teres

flexor digitorum
profundus

flexor
pollicis
longus

palmaris longus

flexor carpi ulnaris

flexor carpi
radialis

flexor digitorum
superficialis

pronator
quadratus

flexor retinaculum

pisiform bone

thenar
muscles

hypothenar muscles

palmar aponeurosis

5.5.11 Superficial flexor muscles of arm and forearm.

5.5.12 Deep flexor muscles of the forearm.

Flex your wrist against resistance again and identify the tendons of these muscles on the anterior aspect of your wrist (**5.5.7**). Accidental deep cuts on the anterior aspect of the wrist are common and it is important to be able to distinguish these tendons and the nerves (p. 117, 118), which may also be damaged.

The anterior (flexor) compartment also contains pronator quadratus (see above).

Extension

Extension of the wrist is produced by muscles of the posterior (extensor) compartment of the forearm, which pass dorsal to the wrist joint before inserting into either the carpus or the fingers (**5.5.13**). A **common extensor origin** is situated on the *anterior* aspect of the lateral epicondyle of the humerus (cf. the common flexor origin); it gives origin to the more superficial extensor muscles. Muscles situated deeply in the posterior compartment and attached to the forearm bones and the interosseous membrane act on the index finger and thumb. All are supplied by the radial nerve, either through its trunk or its deep branch.

'Tennis elbow'

The condition commonly called 'tennis elbow' (but seldom associated with the sport) is an inflammation of the tendons (tendinitis) attached to the common extensor origin. Its cause is unknown. A similar condition ('golfer's elbow') involves the common flexor origin at the medial epicondyle.

As in the anterior compartment of the forearm, the muscles in the posterior compartment form two functional groups. Some act only at the wrist:

- **extensor carpi radialis longus** and **brevis** (**5.5.13**; radial nerve) which arise, respectively, from the lateral supracondylar ridge and common extensor origin on the humerus and insert into the base of the second and third metacarpals;
- **extensor carpi ulnaris** (radial nerve, deep branch), which arises from the common extensor origin and inserts into the base of the fifth metacarpal.

These three powerful extensors of the wrist act synergistically with the long *flexors* of the fingers in the power grip (p. 90). This grip can therefore be weakened by forcibly flexing the wrist joint.

Muscles which act primarily on the fingers (**5.5.13**, **5.5.14**; see Section 6) but which can also extend the wrist are: **extensor digitorum** and **extensor digiti minimi,** which lie superficially; **extensor indicis** and **extensor pollicis longus,** which lies deeply. The tendons of **abductor pollicis longus** and **extensor pollicis brevis** cross the radial side of the wrist to reach their insertions and play no part in extension of the wrist.

The posterior compartment of the forearm also contains **supinator** (see above). The tendons of all the posterior compartment muscles which act on the carpus or fingers pass deep to, and are held in place by, the extensor retinaculum (**5.5.13**; p. 92).

Abduction and adduction

Abduction of the wrist is produced by the combined action of flexor carpi radialis and extensor carpi radialis longus and brevis.

Qu. 5E *Which muscles will adduct the wrist?*

Circumduction and fixation

Circumduction of the wrist is produced by the sequential action of all carpal flexors and extensors. Note that the flexors and extensors of the wrist are inserted, symmetrically, into the bases of the second, third, and fifth metacarpals. When they contract together the wrist is **fixed** so that delicate movements of the fingers can occur from a stable base.

Imaging the wrist

Revise the radiographs of the forearm and hand **5.5.1** and **5.5.2** (p. 78) which show the forearm in supination and pronation.

On radiographs **5.5.15** and **5.5.16** note the angle of slope of the distal articular surface of the radius in relation to its long axis in both antero-posterior (AP) and lateral views. In the antero-posterior view, a line joining the tip of the styloid process of the radius to the tip of

---

Wrist fractures

A **Colles' fracture**, named after the surgeon who described the injury long before X-rays were discovered, is the most common fracture occurring at the wrist (**5.5.17, 5.5.18**). During a fall on the outstretched hand, especially in the aged, in whom the bones are weaker, the strength of the palmar part of the wrist joint capsule causes the upward, backward, and lateral displacement of the distal part of the radius.

This displaces the articular surface of the radius. It is important that the angulation is corrected if full movement of the wrist is to be restored.

Falls on the outstretched hand commonly produce two other injuries. The **scaphoid**, which transmits the main force to the radius, can fracture across its waist (**5.5.19**). Because its blood supply enters from distally, the fracture may heal badly or the proximal part of the bone in the wrist joint may undergo avascular necrosis. For this reason the fracture must be immobilized carefully.

The lunate bone, which articulates with the anterior sloping articular surface of the radius (**5.5.20**) may dislocate forward into the carpal tunnel and compress its contents (see p. 84).

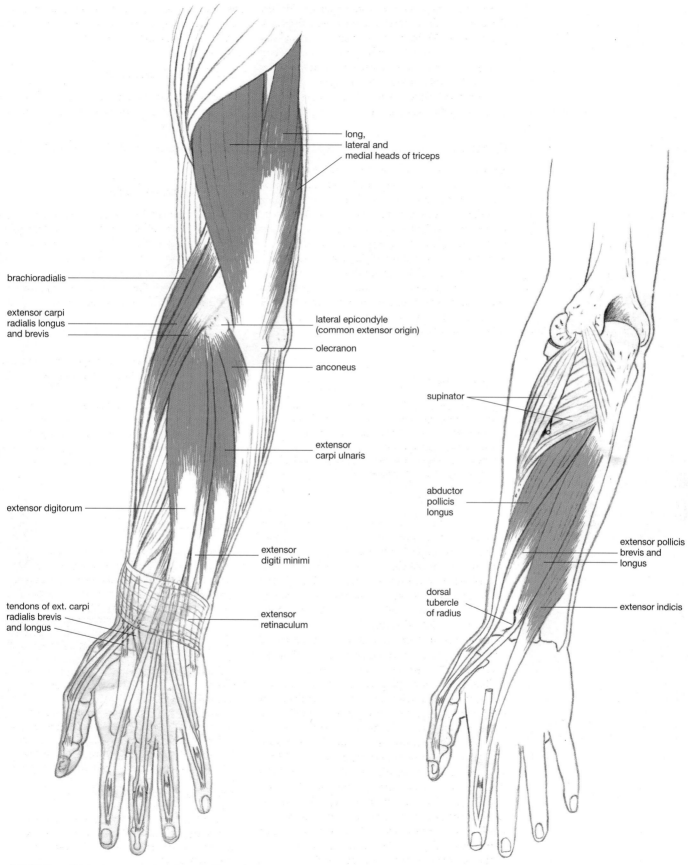

long,
lateral and
medial heads of triceps

brachioradialis

extensor carpi
radialis longus
and brevis

lateral epicondyle
(common extensor origin)

olecranon

anconeus

supinator

extensor
carpi ulnaris

abductor
pollicis
longus

extensor digitorum

extensor pollicis
brevis and
longus

extensor
digiti minimi

tendons of ext. carpi
radialis brevis
and longus

dorsal
tubercle
of radius

extensor indicis

extensor
retinaculum

5.5.13 Superficial extensor muscles of arm and forearm.

5.5.14 Deep extensor muscles of forearm.

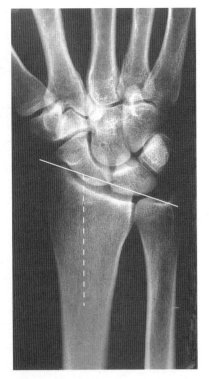

5.5.15 Left wrist joint (AP). See text for explanation of lines.

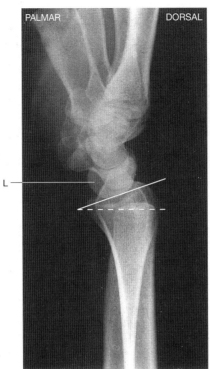

5.5.16 Wrist joint (lateral). See text for explanation of lines.

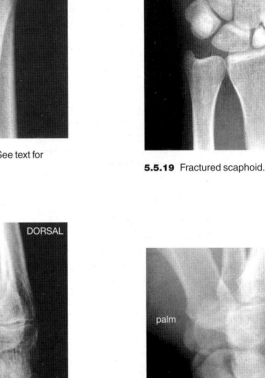

5.5.19 Fractured scaphoid.

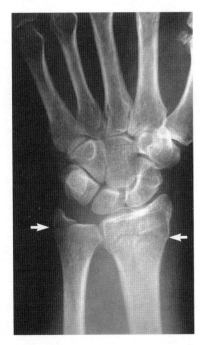

5.5.17 Fractured lower end of radius and ulna (Colles' fracture; AP).

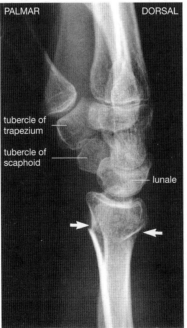

5.5.18 Colles' fracture (lateral) to show the marked posterior angulation of the articular surface of the radius. Compare with **5.5.4**.

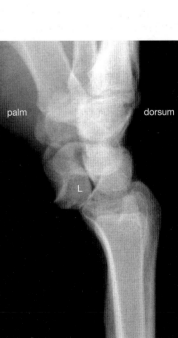

5.5.20 Dislocated lunate, lateral view. The lunate has become detached from its proximal and distal articulations, rotated by 90°, and now lies in the palm beneath the flexor retinaculum.

Table 5.5.1 Radio-ulnar and wrist joints: movements, principal muscles, and their innervation.

Movement	Principal muscles	Peripheral nerve	Spinal root origin
Supination	Biceps	Musculocutaneous nerve	C 5, 6
	Supinator	Radial nerve (deep branch)	C 6, 7
Pronation	Pronator teres	Median nerve	C 6, 7
	Pronator quadratus	Median nerve	C 7, 8
Flexion	*Common flexor origin muscles*		
	flexor carpi radialis	Median nerve	C 6, 7
	flexor carpi ulnaris	Ulnar nerve	C 7, 8
	(palmaris longus)	Median nerve	C 6, 7
	Long digital flexors (Table 5.6.1)	Median and ulnar nerves	C 6, 7
Extension	*Common extensor origin muscles*		
	extensor carpi radialis longus and brevis	Radial nerve (trunk and deep branch*)	C 6, 7
	extensor carpi ulnaris	Radial nerve (deep branch*)	C 7, 8
	Long digital extensors (Table 5.6.1)		
Abduction	Flexor carpi radialis	Median nerve	C 6, 7
	Extensor carpi radialis longus and brevis	Radial nerve	C 6, 7
	Abductor pollicis longus and brevis	Radial nerve (deep branch*)	C 7, 8
Adduction	Flexor carpi ulnaris	Ulnar nerve	C 7, 8
	Extensor carpi ulnaris	Radial nerve (deep branch*)	C 7, 8

* The deep branch of the radial nerve is also called the posterior interosseous nerve from its position in the extensor compartment posterior to the interosseous membrane.

the styloid process of the ulna lies at an angle of about 75° to the long axis of the shaft of the bones, the articular surface facing toward the ulna. In the lateral view, a line joining the margins of the carpal articular surface of the radius usually slopes about 11° to the antero-posterior axis, facing anteriorly.

Questions and answers

Qu. 5A *Against resistance, is pronation or supination the stronger? Why do screws have right-hand threads?*

Answer Supination. Therefore, screws always have right-hand threads. Biceps is a powerful supinator of the semi-flexed elbow, in addition to the supinator muscle.

Qu. 5B *Through which finger does the axis of movement pass in this free movement?*

Answer The normal axis passes through the middle finger. To achieve this the lower end of the ulna moves slightly laterally, largely due to the contraction of anconeus. This enables a grip to be maintained on fixed objects (e.g. a door knob) while the forearm and hand are rotating.

Qu. 5C *What movements can you perform at the wrist joint, and what is their extent?*

Answer At the wrist joint, movements at the radio-carpal and intercarpal joints combine to permit flexion (90°) and extension (80°), abduction (10°) and adduction (45°), and circumduction (a mixture of the other movements) to occur, but no rotation.

Qu. 5D *From radiographs 5.5.8 and 5.5.9 determine which carpal bones articulate with the radius when the hand is adducted, and with the articular disc when the hand is abducted.*

Answer During adduction the lower end of the radius articulates with the lunate and scaphoid. During abduction, it articulates only with the scaphoid.

Qu. 5E *Which muscles will adduct the wrist?*

Answer Both flexor and extensor carpi ulnaris adduct the wrist.

Joints and movements of the fingers and thumb

Joints and movements of the fingers and thumb

The hand, which can be moved to almost any position with respect to the body, is adapted to grip and manipulate objects of various shapes and sizes. Hand movements are also an important part of the non-verbal language that people use to signal to one another. The skin of the hand, and particularly that over the pads of the fingers, is richly supplied with sensory receptors and nerves (p. 11, 19). The hand should, therefore, also be thought of as an actively exploratory sensory organ.

Living anatomy

Natural posture of the hand

Rest the back of your hand on a flat surface and note that the index, middle, ring, and little fingers are progressively more flexed. The axis of the thumb, and therefore also of its movements, lies at right angles to the other digits (i.e. its nail is directed laterally). This is the natural position of the hand. It enables the thumb to contact (oppose) each of the fingers for grip and manipulation.

A deep laceration which severs long flexor tendons to the digits will distort the pattern, and the injury can be diagnosed on sight.

Movements of the fingers and thumb

Movements of the digits (**5.6.1**) do not occur at single joints, but rather involve co-ordinated movements at many of the joints of the hand.

The functional axis of the hand passes through the centre of the palm and middle finger. Abduction and adduction of the fingers are related to this plane. The middle finger can therefore only be abducted from the midline.

Qu. 6A *What movements can you make at the metacarpo-phalangeal joints and the interphalangeal joints, and what is their extent?*

Flex the thumb across the palm and then extend it; abduct it at right angles away from the index finger and then adduct it to its original position. Now approximate the pads of the thumb and little finger; this movement of **opposition** is, with respect to its range, unique to humans. It is achieved by a combination of movements which effectively rotate the thumb at its carpo-metacarpal joint.

Qu. 6B *Why is the ability to oppose the pads of the thumb and the fingers of such importance to humans?*

Grasp the head of each metacarpal in turn and assess its mobility. The metacarpal of the thumb (first) is the most mobile, followed by the fifth and fourth; the second and third metacarpals are, however, practically immobile. This varied pattern of mobility of the metacarpal heads allows the palm to be curved around an object it is holding.

Qu. 6C *During the evolutionary development of opposition and other manipulative movements of the hand and fingers, evolution of the neural control of these movements was taking place. What might this involve?*

Grips

First pick up a heavy tool such as a hammer and note the position of your hand and wrist. This is the **power grip** (**5.6.2**): the handle of the tool is gripped firmly between the opposed thumb and thenar eminence on one side and the four fingers on the other. The wrist is extended by about 45° and, if forcibly flexed, the grip becomes much weaker and can be broken.

Pick up a briefcase by its handle. Your hand will be making a **hook grip** (**5.6.3**), in which the handle of the case is supported by the flexed fingers. The thumb may be opposed, but this is not essential, and the wrist is not extended.

Pick up a pen as if you were about to write with it; this is the **precision grip** (**5.6.4**). The pen is held between the opposed thumb and forefinger and supported against the middle finger; the ring and little fingers are flexed.

Finally, hold a key as if you were about to insert it into a lock. Your hand adopts the **key grip** (**5.6.5**), by

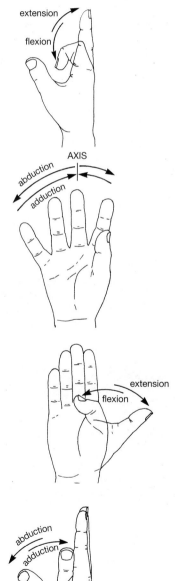

5.6.1 Movements of the fingers and thumb.

5.6.2 Power grip.

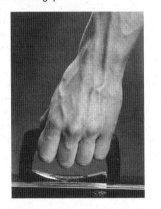

5.6.3 Hook grip.

5.6.4 Precision grip.

5.6.5 Key grip.

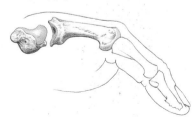

5.6.6 Carpo-metacarpal ('saddle') joint of thumb.

which the object is gripped between the opposed thumb and the radial side of the flexed index finger.

There are, of course, many variations on these basic grips.

The 'layers' of the hand

Production of the various grips involves the muscles and tendons in the hand. These are said to form four layers:

- The most superficial (first layer; see **5.6.8**) comprises short muscles of the thumb and little finger. They form the thenar eminence ('ball' of the thumb) and hypothenar eminence.
- Beneath them, lying centrally in the palm, are the long flexor tendons and the lumbrical muscles that arise from them (second layer; see **5.6.8**).
- The adductor of the thumb (see **5.6.19**) lies deep to the long tendons (third layer).
- The palmar and dorsal interosseous muscles form the deepest (fourth) layer (see **5.6.17**, **5.6.18**).

All the muscle tissue is situated either on the palmar aspect of, or between, the metacarpal bones; only tendons are found on the dorsum of the hand.

Joints of the carpus, fingers, and thumb

Review the radiological appearance of the bones and joints of the hand (see **5.1.10–5.1.13**) and be sure you can identify individual carpal bones.

Intercarpal joints

Adjacent carpal bones articulate by plane synovial joints which enable small sliding movements to occur. Significant amounts of movement occur only between the proximal and distal row of carpal bones. Movements at this **mid-carpal joint** complement those occurring at the wrist.

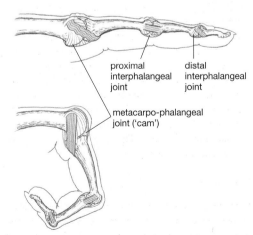

5.6.7 Metacarpo-phalangeal ('cam joint') and interphalangeal joints in flexion and extension.

Carpo-metacarpal joints

Clench your fist hard and observe the movements of your knuckles, which reflect movements occurring at synovial joints at the base of the second to fifth metacarpals. Of these, only the fourth and fifth metacarpals move to any extent, to enhance the grip.

The **carpo-metacarpal joint of the thumb** (**5.6.6**) is a synovial 'saddle' joint specialized to allow opposition of the thumb. The articular surfaces on both the trapezium and the base of the first metacarpal are concave in one axis and convex in the other (like a rider in a saddle).

Metacarpo-phalangeal joints

Metacarpo-phalangeal joints are condylar synovial joints (**5.6.7**). If the metacarpo-phalangeal joints of the index, middle, ring, and little fingers are extended, a certain amount of side-to-side movement of the fingers can occur. This is described as abduction and adduction in relation to the axis through the middle finger (**5.6.1**). When the metacarpo-phalangeal joints are flexed, however, these movements are greatly restricted. This is because the head of the metacarpal is a condyle (i.e. in lateral profile it is shaped like a cam).

The collateral ligaments of each joint pass from dorsally on the head of the metacarpal to the base of the proximal phalanx. When the metacarpo-phalangeal joints are extended, these ligaments are lax and abduction and adduction movements are possible. In flexion, the collateral ligaments are tightened, thereby preventing side-to-side movements. This increases the stability of grip, particularly when a power grip is required.

Strained thumb metacarpo-phalangeal joint

A common injury on dry-ski slopes is a strain or rupture of the collateral ligaments of the metacarpo-phalangeal joint of the thumb. This is caused by the thumb becoming trapped in the matting and forced back in extension during a fall.

Qu. 6D *How could you confirm damage to the ligaments?*

The heads of metacarpals 2–5 are held together by a **deep transverse metacarpal ligament** (see **5.5.10**) attached to the palmar aspect of the metacarpo-phalangeal joints.

Interphalangeal joints

These are synovial hinge joints (**5.6.7**). Their collateral ligaments are taut throughout the range of flexion and extension and no adduction or abduction is possible.

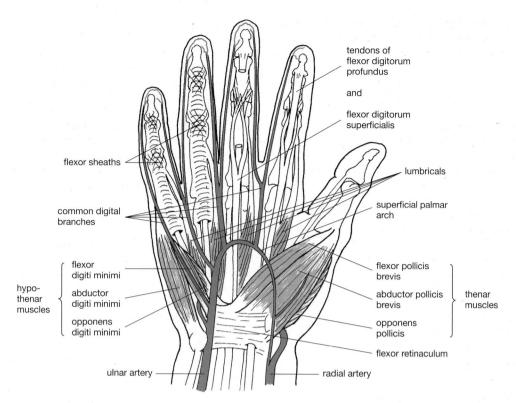

5.6.8 Superficial aspect of palm.

Immobilization of an injured hand in plaster

If an injured hand is immobilized with the metacarpo-phalangeal joints fully extended, the collateral ligaments may shorten in their relaxed state. The patient may then find it impossible to make a satisfactory grip because the collateral ligaments become too taut, limiting full flexion. Therefore, if a hand has to be immobilized in plaster due to injury, the metacarpo-phalangeal joints of the ulnar four digits are positioned in nearly full flexion to prevent shortening of the collateral ligaments, and a normal range of movement should return when the plaster is removed.

Therefore, after injuries, the fingers are best immobilized so that the metacarpo-phalangeal joints are flexed by 80°, and the interphalangeal joints by 10°.

Movements of the digits: muscles and their innervation

Movements of the digits do not occur at single joints but involve co-ordinated movements of many joints of the hand. Look at **5.6.9**, a lateral radiograph of the index finger, and you will see that the heads of the metacarpals and the proximal and middle phalanges are curved to permit flexion and extension.

Flexion

Flexion of the fingers depends to a large extent on muscles of the forearm with long tendons that cross the wrist joint, palm and metacarpo-phalangeal joints to insert into the palmar aspect of the phalanges. The main **flexors** are:

- **Flexor digitorum superficialis** (**5.6.8**, **5.6.10** see **5.5.11**; median nerve). Its four tendons pass beneath the flexor retinaculum, those to the middle and ring fingers lying superficial to those to the index and little fingers. They cross the palm and, opposite the metacarpo-phalangeal joints, each divides to allow the tendon of flexor digitorum profundus to pass through, before partially reuniting and inserting into the base of the middle phalanx.
- **Flexor digitorum profundus** (**5.6.8**, **5.6.11**; median and ulnar nerves) arises deep in the forearm. Its tendons pass beneath the flexor retinaculum and through the palm beneath those of the superficial flexor; they each pass through the division in the superficial flexor tendon to insert into the base of the

5.6.9 Lateral radiograph showing interphalangeal joints of index finger.

distal phalanx. In the palm, a small, slender **lumbrical** muscle arises from the radial side of each tendon (**5.6.8**, **5.6.11**) and passes into the finger web to insert into the base of an extensor expansion. The parts of the profundus muscle and the radial two lumbricals which act on the index and middle fingers are supplied by the median nerve; those which act on the ring and little fingers are supplied by the ulnar nerve.

- Both the **lumbricals** and the **interossei** (see below) cross the metacarpo-phalangeal joints to insert into the base of the extensor expansions which cover the dorsum of the fingers. They therefore have a flexor action on the metacarpo-phalangeal joints.

Extension

Extension of the fingers depends largely on muscles of the posterior compartment of the forearm, the tendons of which cross the wrist and the dorsum of the hand to insert into **extensor expansions** (**5.6.12**). These tendinous expansions, which cover the proximal

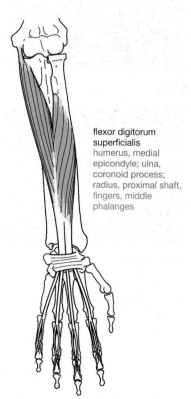

flexor digitorum superficialis
humerus, medial epicondyle; ulna, coronoid process; radius, proximal shaft, fingers, middle phalanges

5.6.10 Flexor digitorum superficialis.

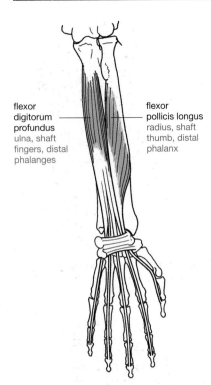

flexor
digitorum
profundus
ulna, shaft
fingers, distal
phalanges

flexor
pollicis longus
radius, shaft
thumb, distal
phalanx

5.6.11 Flexor digitorum profundus; flexor pollicis longus.

phalanx, are attached to the dorsal aspects of the middle and distal phalanges. They extend the interphalangeal and metacarpo-phalangeal joints. The muscles are named according to their actions: **extensor digitorum**, **extensor indicis**, **extensor digiti minimi**; all are supplied by the deep branch of the radial nerve.

In addition to the long tendons, the small muscles of the palm (lumbricals and interossei) which insert into the base of the extensor expansions, extend the middle and distal interphalangeal joints.

Avulsed extensor tendon—'mallet finger'

If an extensor tendon is torn from its insertion to the distal phalanx by a strong flexion force on the distal interphalangeal joint when the extensor tendon is under strain, then the condition of 'mallet finger' results (**5.6.13**). The terminal interphalangeal joint is flexed about 45° and, although it will flex both actively and passively and extend passively, the patient cannot straighten the joint actively.

Qu. 6E *An elderly man who has arthritic changes in his wrist suddenly finds that he is unable to extend the terminal phalanx of his thumb. What might have happened?*

Testing finger flexor muscles

When the integrity of an individual muscle is in question a simple specific test of its function is useful. To test flexor digitorum superficialis acting on a finger, ask a colleague to lay a supinated hand on a flat surface. Keep the distal interphalangeal joints of the other fingers in extension (by holding a ruler or your index finger horizontally across them). Flexion of the free finger can be easily performed only if flexor digitorum superficialis is intact.

Qu. 6F *What simple test could you devise to test the integrity of flexor digitorum profundus?*

Control and lubrication of tendon movement

At the wrist, the long flexor tendons are firmly held in place by the **flexor retinaculum** (**5.6.8**), a thick, strong band of fibrous tissue attached to the pisiform and hook of hamate medially and to the tubercle of the scaphoid and ridge of the trapezium laterally. Identify these bony prominences in your hand and mark the position of the retinaculum; it lies distal to the distal skin crease of the wrist.

The flexor retinaculum converts the concavity of the palmar surface of the carpus into a channel, the **carpal tunnel** (**5.6.14**). Passing through the tunnel are the long flexor tendons to the thumb and fingers, together with the median nerve. The tendon of flexor carpi radialis passes through a separate compartment.

In the fingers each pair of tendons (superficialis and profundus) enters a **fibrous flexor sheath**—a tunnel of fibrous tissue attached to the sides of the phalanges of the fingers and thumb (**5.6.8, 5.6.12**). These hold the tendons firmly against the shafts of the proximal and middle phalanges and joints, but have more flexible parts which ensure that finger movements are not impeded.

As the tendons pass through both the flexor retinaculum and the fibrous flexor sheaths, their movement is facilitated by **sheaths of synovial membrane** and fluid around them. Under the flexor retinaculum the tendons of flexor carpi radialis and flexor pollicis longus each have their own synovial sheath. The long flexor tendons to the fingers, however, are surrounded by a **common flexor sheath** (**5.6.15**). This extends from 3 cm proximal to the wrist to the middle of the palm, where it terminates, except for an extension around the tendons to the little finger which continues throughout their length, extending into the fibrous flexor sheath. Separate synovial sheaths surround the tendons in the fibrous flexor sheaths of the index, middle, and ring fingers. Within the sheaths the tendons receive a small blood supply carried by bands of synovial membrane (vincula).

Qu. 6G *What might be the danger if a deep wound of the little finger became septic?*

The **extensor retinaculum** (**5.6.16**) is thinner than the flexor retinaculum. It stretches across the back of the wrist and converts the grooves on the dorsum of the distal end of the radius into separate channels for the long extensor tendons and their synovial sheaths. It is attached medially to the pisiform bone and hook of the hamate (as is the flexor retinaculum) but laterally to the radius.

As on the flexor aspect of the wrist, the tendons of extensor digitorum lie within a common synovial sheath beneath the extensor retinaculum, but almost

fibrous flexor sheath
extensor expansion
palmar interosseous
lumbrical
tendon of flexor digitorum profundus
tendon of extensor digitorum

5.6.12 Lateral view of right index finger. Note the insertion of lumbrical and interosseous tendons into the dorsal extensor expansion; also the flexor tendons and fibrous flexor sheath.

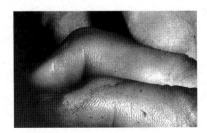

5.6.13 'Mallet finger'.

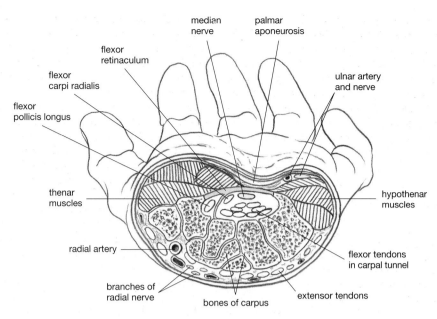

5.6.14 Carpal tunnel and contents (tendon sheaths not shown); transverse section.

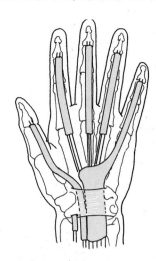

5.6.15 Synovial sheaths of long flexor tendons and flexor retinaculum.

all the other tendons have separate sheaths (**5.6.16**). None of these sheaths extends into the fingers.

Qu. 6H *Why is the extensor retinaculum not attached to the dorsal aspect of the ulna?*

Flexion of the metacarpo-phalangeal joint with extension of the interphalangeal joint

Certain manipulations require the ability to flex the fingers at the metacarpo-phalangeal joints, at the same time extending them at the interphalangeal joints. The attachments of the interossei and lumbricals to the lateral angles of the extensor expansions extend the interphalangeal joints by pulling on the extensor expansion, but flex the metacarpo-phalangeal joints because the wings of the expansions wrap around the proximal phalanges so that the tendons pull on the palmar side of the metacarpo-phalangeal joint (**5.6.12**).

Abduction and adduction of the fingers

The functional axis of the hand runs from the centre of the palm distally through the middle finger (**5.6.17**).

Abduction of the index, middle, and ring fingers away from the midline axis is produced by the larger **dorsal interossei** (**5.6.17**; ulnar nerve) which arise from the adjacent sides of the metacarpals and also insert into the extensor expansions and proximal phalanges. The thumb and little finger have separate abductor muscles.

Adduction of the index, ring, and little fingers toward this axis occurs at the metacarpo-phalangeal joints. It is produced by the **palmar interossei** (**5.6.18**; ulnar nerve), each of which arises from a metacarpal and inserts into the dorsal extensor expansion ('wing tendons') and the adjacent base of the proximal

phalanx of the same digit (**5.6.12**). The thumb has its own adductor (see **5.6.19**).

Examine **5.1.13** again and note how the heads of the metacarpals are curved on each side to permit abduction and adduction of the fingers. Compare this with the shape of the distal ends of the phalanges.

Movements of the little finger

In addition to movements produced by the long flexor and extensor tendons, the little finger is controlled by small muscles which form the **hypothenar eminence** (**5.6.8**, **5.6.19**; ulnar nerve). Three muscles lie superficially in the palm, each arising from the flexor retinaculum and adjacent carpal bones. **Abductor digiti minimi** and **flexor digiti minimi** both insert into the ulnar side of the base of the proximal phalanx of the little finger. The deeper **opponens digiti minimi**, which inserts into the ulnar border of the relatively mobile fifth metacarpal, slightly opposes the pad of the fifth finger toward that of the thumb.

A small muscle—palmaris brevis—inserts into the skin of the hypothenar eminence and helps deepen the palm.

Movements of the thumb

The position of the thumb, which lies at right angles to the plane of the fingers, and the ability to oppose the pad of the thumb to that of any other finger, is of great importance to humans. No other animal has the ability to perform fine manipulatory movements to anywhere near the same extent.

In injuries of the hand involving the loss of a part or all of the thumb, a prime aim of surgeons is to fashion, from the remaining tissues, a prosthesis which can

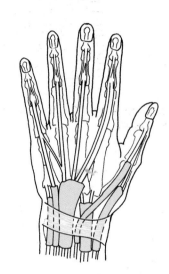

5.6.16 Synovial sheaths of extensor tendons and extensor retinaculum.

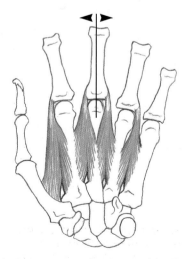

5.6.17 Dorsal interossei (attachments to extensor expansions not shown).

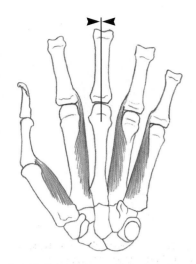

5.6.18 Palmar interossei (attachments to extensor expansions not shown).

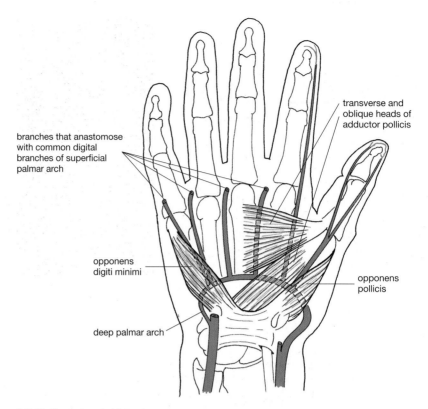

5.6.19 Deep aspect of the palm.

substitute for a thumb and restore opposition and thereby the ability to grip.

Three muscles which form the fleshy **thenar eminence** all arise from the flexor retinaculum and adjacent carpal bones (**5.6.8**, **5.6.19**). Both **abductor pollicis brevis** and **flexor pollicis brevis** attach to the radial side of the base of the proximal phalanx of the thumb. As in the hypothenar eminence, the deeper **opponens pollicis** attaches to the radial margin of the thumb metacarpal, effectively medially rotating it on the saddle-shaped first metacarpo-phalangeal joint (**5.6.6**).

Opposition is a composite movement consisting of circumduction which has the effect of medially rotating the metacarpal on the trapezium at the saddle joint (see **5.6.6**).

All three muscles of the thenar eminence are supplied by a branch of the median nerve, which is at risk with penetrating injuries into the palm (p. 117).

An additional short muscle controlling the thumb, which is very important in grip, is **adductor pollicis** (**5.6.19**; ulnar nerve). This originates deeply from the shaft of the third metacarpal and from the base of the second and third metacarpal bones around the flexor carpi radialis tendon insertion. It pulls the abducted thumb toward the palm.

Extend your thumb forcibly. You will find that the tendon of **extensor pollicis longus** stands out (**5.6.20**; radial nerve). This arises from the ulna deep in the forearm; its tendon hooks around the dorsal (Lister's) tubercle of the radius, where it is held in place by the extensor retinaculum, and inserts into the distal phalanx of the thumb, which has no extensor expansion (**5.6.16**; see **5.5.14**).

More laterally are the tendons of **extensor pollicis brevis**, which inserts into the base of the proximal phalanx of the thumb, and **abductor pollicis longus**, which inserts into the base of the thumb metacarpal (**5.6.20**, see **5.5.14**; all supplied by the radial nerve).

Between these two groups of tendons is a triangular depression.

Qu. 6I *Why is the depression known as the 'anatomical snuff-box'? Which carpal bone forms its base?*

Qu. 6J *A middle-aged woman, who had been doing extensive pruning in her garden, complains of pain on the lateral side of the wrist. Examination reveals some swelling and tenderness over the styloid process of the radius. What might be the cause, and how could you test your diagnosis simply?*

Fascia and fascial spaces of the hand

It is important for grip that the hairless skin of the palm is firmly tethered to the underlying tissues. This is achieved by strong fibrous connections between the skin and the fibrous tissue of the palm. Where the connections are particularly strong the prominent palmar creases are formed. The pressure of the grip must be distributed evenly; therefore the fat beneath the skin is divided into multiple small loculi surrounded by fibres.

The fibrous tissue is particularly prominent in the centre of the palm, where it forms the **palmar**

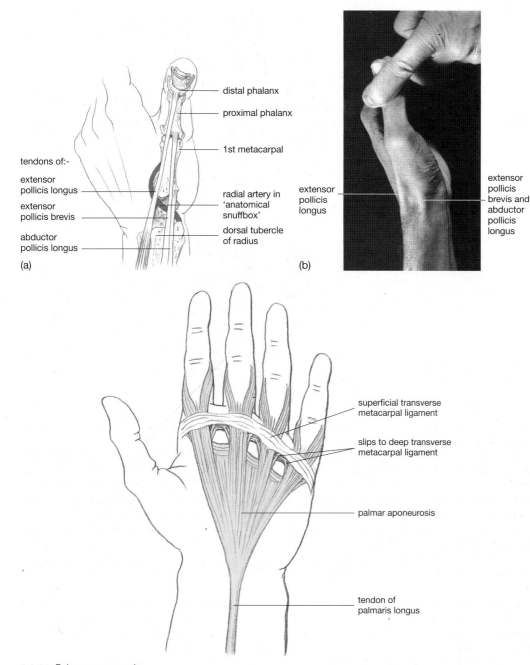

(a)

distal phalanx

proximal phalanx

1st metacarpal

radial artery in 'anatomical snuffbox'

dorsal tubercle of radius

tendons of:-

extensor pollicis longus

extensor pollicis brevis

abductor pollicis longus

(b)

extensor pollicis longus

extensor pollicis brevis and abductor pollicis longus

5.6.20 'Anatomical snuff-box' and long tendons extending and abducting the thumb.

superficial transverse metacarpal ligament

slips to deep transverse metacarpal ligament

palmar aponeurosis

tendon of palmaris longus

5.6.21 Palmar aponeurosis.

aponeurosis (**5.6.21**, see **5.6.24**) which protects the underlying nerves, vessels, and tendons. This merges with the flexor retinaculum and is derived from palmaris longus (the muscle itself may not be present) which forms four superficial tendinous slips; one for each finger. Each slip is attached to the fibrous flexor sheath of a finger and to the deep transverse metacarpal ligament which unites the heads of the metacarpals. Other fibres pass along the sides of the proximal phalanges to the base of the middle phalanges. On either side of the central aponeurosis, the fascia covering the thenar and hypothenar eminence is very thin.

At the roots of the fingers a thin superficial transverse metacarpal ligament stretches across the palm in the superficial fascia, attached to the skin of the finger clefts. Vessels and nerves supplying the fingers pass between the superficial and deep transverse metacarpal ligaments.

From the medial border of the palmar aponeurosis a **medial palmar septum** (see **5.6.24**) passes deeply between the hypothenar muscles and the long flexor tendons to the little finger to attach to the fifth metacarpal. Similarly, from the lateral border of the aponeurosis a **lateral palmar septum** passes between the three superficial muscles and the tendon of flexor pollicis longus to attach to the first metacarpal. These two septa separate the thenar and hypothenar eminence compartments from the palmar spaces.

Dupuytren's contracture

For unknown reasons, the palmar aponeurosis is commonly affected by a dense fibrosis which affects particularly the fibres passing to the little and ring fingers (5.6.22). The fibrous tissue becomes thickened and causes a flexion contracture of the metacarpo-phalangeal and proximal interphalangeal joints. This may cause severe deformity and require operative excision of the thickened, contracted aponeurosis.

Between the palmar aponeurosis and the metacarpal bones with their attached interosseous muscles, the central part of the palm contains the long flexor tendons and lumbrical muscles, the superficial palmar arterial arch (p. 103), and the digital vessels and nerves. A thin **intermediate palmar septum**, which usually forms an effective barrier to pus when the palm is infected, passes between the long flexor tendons of the index and middle fingers to attach to the shaft of the third metacarpal alongside adductor pollicis. This creates a **thenar space** containing the long flexor tendons of the thumb and index finger, and a **middle palmar space** containing the tendons of the middle, ring, and little fingers (5.6.23, 5.6.24). Distally, these spaces extend into the sides of the fingers along the lumbricals.

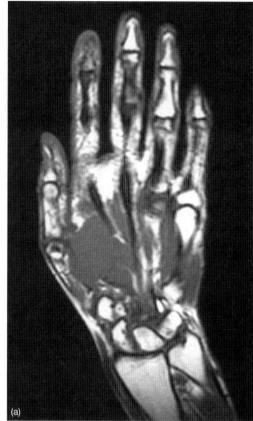

(a)

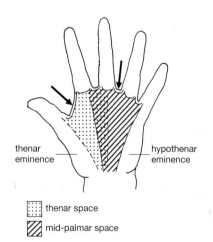

5.6.22 Dupuytren's contracture.

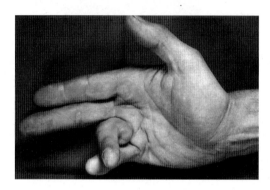

thenar eminence   hypothenar eminence

▦ thenar space
▨ mid-palmar space

(b)

5.6.25 MRIs of the hand in (a) longitudinal and (b) transverse section. Identify the muscles indicated in the transverse section.

5.6.23 Palmar fascial spaces.

5.6.24 Cross-section of palm showing palmar fascial spaces.

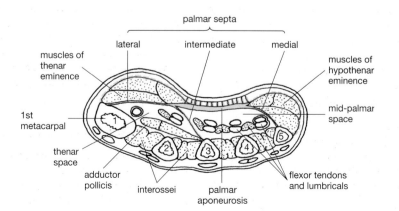

palmar septa

muscles of thenar eminence

lateral   intermediate   medial

muscles of hypothenar eminence

1st metacarpal

mid-palmar space

thenar space

adductor pollicis   interossei   palmar aponeurosis

flexor tendons and lumbricals

Table 5.6.1 Movements of fingers and thumb: principal muscles and their innervation.

Movement	Principal muscles	Peripheral nerve	Spinal root origin
Index, middle, ring, and little fingers			
Flexion (mcp and ip†)	Flexor digitorum superficialis	Median nerve	C 6, 7
	Flexor digitorum profundus		
	to index and middle finger	Ulnar nerve	C 8, T1
	to ring and little finger	Median nerve	C 6, 7
	Flexor digiti minimi	Median nerve	C 6, 7
Extension (mcp and ip)	Extensor digitorum, extensor indicis, extensor digiti minimi	Radial nerve (deep branch)	C 7, 8
Abduction (mcp)	Dorsal interossei	Ulnar nerve (deep palmar branch)	C 8, T1
Adduction (mcp)	Palmar interossei	Ulnar nerve (deep palmar branch)	C 8, T1
Flexion of mcp + extension of ip	Interossei	Ulnar nerve (deep palmar branch)	C 8, T1
	Lumbricals	median and ulnar nerves	C 8, T1
Thumb			
Flexion	Flexor pollicis longus* and brevis	Median nerve (in forearm* and palm)	C 8, T1
Extension	Extensor pollicis longus and brevis	Radial nerve	C 8, T1
Abduction	Abductor pollicis longus	Radial nerve	C 8, T1
	Abductor pollicis brevis	Median nerve in palm	C 8, T1
Adduction	Adductor pollicis	Ulnar nerve (deep palmar branch)	C 8, T1
Opposition	Opponens pollicis	Median nerve (in palm)	C 8, T1

† mcp, Metacarpo-phalangeal joint; ip, interphalangeal joints.

Qu. 6K *By what routes might infected fluids in the thenar space and mid-palmar space be drained surgically?*

Qu. 6L *Look again at 5.1.13. What is the small ovoid opacity situated just to the right of the metacarpophalangeal joint of the thumb?*

Imaging the hand

Conventional radiography of the hand shows the bones well, but MRI is needed if the soft tissues are to be visualized. **5.6.25a, b** show longitudinal and transverse sections through the hand. Compact bone on the bone surfaces and fluid appear black; fat in the bone marrow and elsewhere appears white, the muscles appear grey; flexor tendons can just be seen in the sheath in the palm. The transverse section shows the palmar spaces well; compare it with **5.6.24.**

Questions and answers

Qu. 6A *What movements can you make at the metacarpo-phalangeal joints and the interphalangeal joints, and what is their extent?*

Answer Flexion (90°), extension (5°), abduction and adduction (40°) can occur at the metacarpophalangeal points, while a combination of these movements produces circumduction. Only flexion (90°) and extension (which returns the flexed joint to the anatomical position, but not beyond) occurs at the interphalangeal joints.

Qu. 6B *Why is an ability to oppose the pads of the thumb and the fingers of such importance to humans?*

Answer It helps to provide humans with the ability to manipulate even very small objects with exquisite precision.

Qu. 6C *During the evolutionary development of opposition and other manipulative movements of the hand and fingers, evolution of the neural control of these movements was taking place. What might this involve?*

Answer It might have involved parallel evolution of mechanisms concerned with the conduction and modification of sensory information reaching the brain; conscious appreciation of what is being held and the use to which it can be put; correlation, integration, and modification of appropriate behavioural and motor responses.

Qu. 6D *How could you confirm damage to the ligaments?*

Answer By testing the ranges of flexion, extension, abduction and adduction at the metacarpophalangeal joint of the injured thumb, and comparing them with those of the uninjured side.

Qu. 6E *An elderly man who has arthritic changes in his wrist and hand suddenly finds that he is unable to extend the terminal phalanx of his thumb. What might have happened?*

Answer The tendon of extensor pollicis longus has probably been disrupted as a result of arthritic changes causing the development of a rough bony spur at the wrist.

Qu. 6F *What simple test could you devise to test the integrity of this muscle (flexor digitorum profundus)?*

Answer To test the integrity of flexor digitorum profundus, lay the dorsum of the hand on a flat surface and prevent the middle finger from moving by applying light pressure to its middle phalanx; an intact muscle will flex the terminal phalanx.

Qu. 6G *What might be the danger if a deep wound of the little finger became septic?*

Answer If the synovial tendon sheath of the little finger is infected, the infection might well spread to the common flexor synovial sheath with which it is connected. This is a serious development because fibrous adhesions can form between the inflamed tendon sheath and the tendons, limiting their movement.

Qu. 6H *Why is the extensor retinaculum not attached to the dorsal aspect of the ulna?*

Answer Because if it were, pronation and supination would be limited.

Qu. 6I *Why is the depression known as the 'anatomical snuff-box'? Which carpal bone forms its base?*

Answer Snuff-takers have used this convenient depression on the lateral aspect of the wrist as a receptacle from which to inhale snuff (powdered tobacco, which provides a source of nicotine). The scaphoid bone forms its base.

Qu. 6J *A middle-aged woman, who had been doing extensive pruning in her garden, complains of pain on the lateral side of the wrist. Examination reveals some swelling and tenderness over the styloid process of the radius. What might be the cause? and how could you test your diagnosis simply?*

Answer Inflammation of the tendon sheath of abductor pollicis is a possible cause of the trouble. This can be verified by abducting the thumb against resistance. This will increase pain in the region of the styloid process of the radius where the tendon can be palpated.

Qu. 6K *By what routes might infected fluids in the thenar space and mid-palmar space be drained surgically?*

Answer An incision into the web between the thumb and index finger (**5.6.23**, arrow) permits drainage of the thenar space. An incision into the web between the middle and ring fingers (**5.6.23**, arrow) permits drainage of the mid-palmar space.

Qu. 6L *Look again at **5.1.13**. What is the small ovoid opacity situated just to the right of the metacarpophalangeal joint of the thumb?*

Answer A sesamoid bone in the tendons of abductor pollicis and flexor pollicis brevis.

Blood supply and lymphatic drainage of the upper limb

Blood supply and lymphatic drainage of the upper limb

The arterial supply to each upper limb is derived primarily from a single artery, the subclavian artery, and its veins drain into the subclavian vein. Because of the accessibility of the upper limb, its vessels are often used to assess the state of the vascular system. Pulsations in the radial artery at the wrist are used to determine the rate and strength of the heart beat, and arterial blood pressure is still often measured by a sphygmomanometer cuff placed around the upper arm. Similarly, the superficial veins of the limb are frequently used for intravenous injections and infusions. The lymphatics of the upper limb are much less obvious in health. They drain both the upper limb and the breast.

Living anatomy

The pulsations of the **arteries** to the upper limb can be felt at certain points along their course, where they can be compressed against bone (5.7.1).

Stand behind a colleague and feel for the pulsation of the **subclavian artery** as it crosses the first rib, by pressing your index finger downward between the clavicle and the upper border of the scapula in the front of the neck. It is possible to compress the artery against the first rib if there is severe haemorrhage from the arm, but this is painful because large nerve trunks lie close to the artery as it enters the axilla.

Place the flat of your hand against the upper and medial aspect of the arm with your fingers as high in the apex of the axilla as possible. To feel pulsation of the **axillary artery** press laterally against the medial aspect of the upper end of the humerus.

The **brachial artery** can be felt against the mid-shaft of the humerus, and also where it lies on the medial side of the biceps tendon as it crosses the front of the elbow. It may (rarely) be necessary to compress the brachial artery in the upper arm if severe haemorrhage is occurring distally and direct pressure has failed to stop the bleeding. This is best done by squeezing the brachial artery against the mid-shaft of the humerus (usually by applying a tourniquet).

Feel the pulsation of the **radial artery** at the wrist and note the consistency of its wall by compressing the artery against the flattened distal end of the radius. Count the pulsations of the artery for 1 minute to determine the pulse rate, and note whether the pulse is regular. The pulsations of the radial artery can also be felt where it crosses the floor of the 'anatomical snuff-box' (p. 95). Feel also for the **ulnar artery** as it crosses the flexor retinaculum.

Qu. 7A *What do the walls of the radial artery consist of? Why are the walls of arteries thicker and more elastic than those of veins?*

The brachial artery at the front of the elbow, is a convenient site at which to measure the blood pressure. The artery is constricted in the upper arm by a pneumatic tourniquet cuff connected to a manometer; the cuff is inflated until the vessel is occluded and the radial pulse has disappeared. A stethoscope is then placed over the brachial artery just medial to the tendon of biceps and the compression of the tourniquet is slowly released until the sound of pulses of blood flowing through the artery is first heard; this indicates the systolic blood pressure. As the compression is released further, the sounds at first increase and then quite suddenly disappear, when blood flow becomes continuous. The point at which the sounds disappear indicates the diastolic blood pressure.

Examine the pattern of **superficial veins** which form an arch on the back of the hand and wrist, and trace the arch on either side to the **cephalic** and **basilic veins** (5.7.2). Grip the upper arm firmly to prevent venous return and examine the cubital fossa at the front of the elbow to locate a vein running diagonally across the fossa. This is the **median cubital vein** (5.7.3) which links the basilic and cephalic veins and which also receives blood from deep tissues of the forearm. It is often used for intravenous injections and infusions. Beware, the ulnar artery may be anomalously superficial in this position.

Qu. 7B *How would you decide whether what you feel is artery or vein?*

Place your right index finger on the distal end of one superficial vein on the forearm and occlude it. With the index finger of the other hand, express the blood from the proximal end of the vein. The vein is likely to remain empty. William Harvey (1628) used this simple experiment to demonstrate that venous blood was returned to the heart through veins which contained valves.

Intravenous procedures

Medical practice often requires access to the venous bloodstream to withdraw blood or to introduce fluids or drugs (and very occasionally for parenteral feeding). It is essential therefore to have a sound working knowledge of where superficial veins can be identified as being well anchored in the dermis. A common site for venepuncture is the cubital fossa (5.7.2), where the median cubital vein crosses from the cephalic to the basilic vein. For long-term catheterization, veins on the back of the hand or in the forearm are used in order to allow the patient more freedom of elbow movement. Blood samples from newborn babies can be taken from the superior sagittal sinus (Vol. 3), which lies deep to the soft anterior fontanelle between the frontal and parietal bones of the skull.

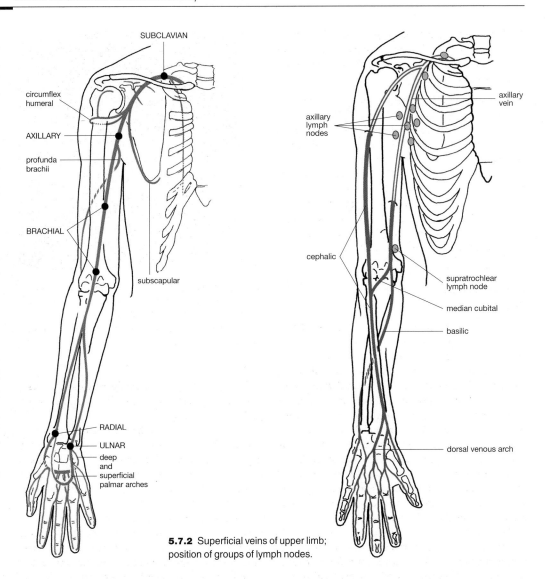

5.7.1 Major arteries of upper limb:
● pressure points for arrest of haemorrhage.

5.7.2 Superficial veins of upper limb;
position of groups of lymph nodes.

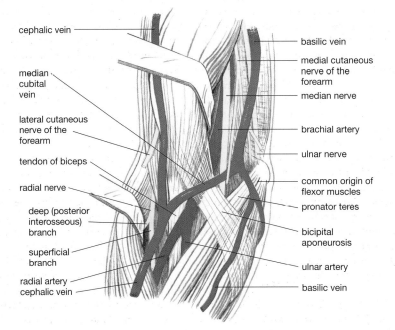

5.7.3 Anterior aspect of elbow; 'cubital fossa'. Note the retraction of biceps and brachioradialis.

Qu. 7C *What would be the explanation if the distal end of the vein was to fill with blood when you removed the pressure of your proximally placed left index finger?*

Using a skin-marking pencil, draw on your arm the course of the major vessels of the upper limb.

Lymphatic vessels and nodes are small and are difficult to locate unless they are inflamed or enlarged. With your colleague's arm resting lightly at his side, try to feel pea-sized lymph nodes in the axilla. The highest (apical) nodes are quite difficult to reach with the tip of the examining finger. Normal lymph nodes often cannot be felt, but a palpable lymph node does not necessarily indicate active pathology; it may be the result of fibrosis of a previously infected node.

Arterial supply to the upper limb (5.7.1)

The subclavian arteries which supply the upper limbs arise from the arch of the aorta. The left subclavian artery arises from the aorta directly, the right subclavian artery arises with the common carotid artery, as the brachiocephalic trunk. Each **subclavian artery** crosses the first rib beneath the clavicle to enter the axilla. It gives branches to the anterior and lateral chest walls and to an anastomosis around the scapula.

As the subclavian artery enters the axilla it is renamed the **axillary artery** (**5.7.4a, b** and see **5.7.8**). Here, the artery is accompanied by the brachial plexus of nerves (p. 112). This neurovascular bundle is packed around with fascia and protected by fat; it also gains protection from the walls of the axilla.

The axillary artery gives branches to the chest wall (**superior** and **lateral thoracic arteries**), which also supply the breast and become enlarged in lactation, and a branch (**thoraco-acromial artery**) which supplies the superficial tissues of the shoulder region anteriorly. It also gives anterior and posterior **circumflex humeral arteries**, which encircle the upper end of the shaft of the humerus, and a **subscapular artery** which runs down the lateral border of the scapula.

As it leaves the axilla at the lower border of teres major, the axillary artery is renamed the **brachial artery**. It passes distally down the medial aspect of the arm between biceps and brachialis. At the front of the elbow it lies quite superficially, medial to the tendon of the biceps, where its pulsations can be felt.

As it leaves the axilla the brachial artery gives off the **profunda brachii artery**, which accompanies the radial nerve in its spiral course around the humerus and supplies muscles of the posterior compartment (triceps) and the elbow joint. The brachial artery also gives small branches which supply the humerus (nutrient artery) and muscles of the anterior compartment.

As the brachial artery passes into the forearm it divides into **radial** and **ulnar arteries** (**5.7.5**) which

continue towards the wrist, lying between the superficial and deep flexor muscles in the anterior compartment of the forearm.

Soon after its origin, the **ulnar artery** gives off a branch which passes deeply and divides to give two interosseous arteries. These run distally on either side of the interosseous membrane to supply the deep tissues of the flexor and extensor compartments of the forearm.

At the wrist the ulnar artery is relatively superficial; it passes into the palm on the radial side of the pisiform bone. Here, it divides into superficial and deep branches; the **superficial branch of the ulnar artery** turns laterally, crosses the long flexor tendons superficially, and anastomoses with a smaller superficial branch of the radial artery to form the **superficial palmar arch** (**5.7.6a, b**). This arch lies at the level of the distal border of the outstretched thumb. The **deep branch of the ulnar artery** passes through the muscles of the hypothenar eminence, then deeply beneath the long tendons to anastomose with a deep branch of the radial artery to form the **deep palmar arch**, which lies at the level of the proximal border of the outstretched thumb (**5.7.1, 5.7.6**).

As the **radial artery** reaches the wrist it gives off a small superficial branch which crosses the muscles of the thenar eminence to anastomose with the superficial branch of the ulnar artery to form the superficial palmar arch. The main radial artery curves dorsally around the lateral aspect of the wrist joint, passing across the floor of the anatomical snuff-box, deep to the long tendons controlling the thumb. It then passes between the two heads of the first dorsal interosseous muscle to reach the palm deep to the long flexor tendons to the fingers. Here, it anastomoses with the deep branch of the ulnar artery to form the **deep palmar arch**.

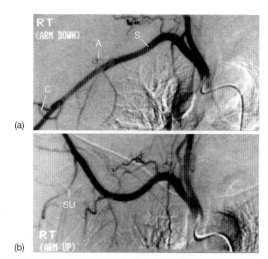

(a)

(b)

5.7.4 Digital subtraction angiograms of subclavian and axillary arteries with: (a) arm hanging down, (b) arm raised vertically above the head. S, subclavian artery; A, acromiothoracic artery; C, circumflex humeral arteries; SU, subscapular artery.

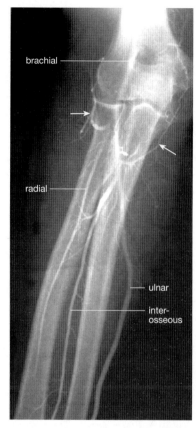

5.7.5 Angiogram showing arteries in the forearm. Arrows indicate recurrent branches contributing to the anastomosis around the elbow.

Fractures of the scaphoid and their consequences

As the radial artery crosses the snuff-box, it lies on the **scaphoid** to which it gives small branches which enter the bone at about its 'waist'. From here, branches pass to its proximal and distal poles. Falls on the outstretched hand not infrequently cause the scaphoid to fracture across its 'waist' (**5.5.19**, arrow). Such fractures may interrupt the blood supply to the proximal pole which then undergoes avascular necrosis.

The presence of a dead proximal pole of the scaphoid in the wrist joint makes movement of the wrist both painful and limited. It is therefore very important to check for scaphoid fractures after such falls and to immobilize the wrist to give a good chance of healing should such a fracture be suspected.

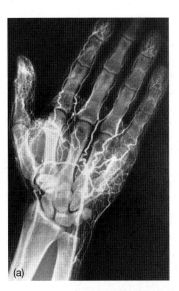

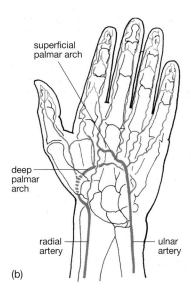

5.7.6 (a) Arteriogram of palmar arterial arches and supply to fingers; (b) labelled key.

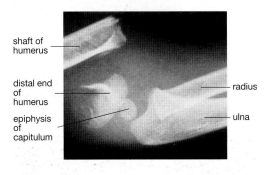

5.7.7 Supracondylar fracture of humerus in a child aged 5 years (note oval epiphysis of capitulum).

The fingers are supplied by **digital arteries** which arise from the superficial palmar arch. They divide opposite the metacarpal heads, and pass along the sides of the fingers to their tips, lying just dorsal to the digital nerves. The deep structures of the palm are supplied by branches of the deep arterial arch.

Arterial anastomoses

Muscles and joints of the upper limb are, in general, supplied by small branches which arise from adjacent arteries. Wherever a considerable amount of movement takes place (at joints or between parts of the body such as the scapula and chest wall), **anastomoses** between branches of nearby arteries will almost certainly be present. These provide a **collateral circulation** which can maintain arterial supply to distal tissues even if flow in the main artery is compromised by the movement.

The anastomoses are most easily seen on arteriograms. **5.7.4**, **5.7.5**, and **5.7.6a** show anastomoses of arteries around the scapula, elbow joint, and in the hand.

Qu. 7D *If someone had sustained a deep cut in the palm of the hand, how could you stop the resultant haemorrhage?*

Venous drainage of the upper limb (5.7.2)

The venous drainage of a limb forms vessels which can be divided into two groups:
- **superficial veins**, which drain the skin and superficial fascia;
- **deep veins**, which drain structures deep to the deep fascia covering the muscles.

Digital veins on the medial and lateral aspects of the fingers drain into a **dorsal venous arch** lying on the back of the hand. This also receives veins from the palm.

Qu. 7E *Why are there no major veins in the palm?*

The medial (ulnar) aspect of the arch is drained by the **basilic vein**. This passes proximally, receiving tributaries from the medial aspect of the forearm. Above the elbow, the basilic vein pierces the deep fascia and is joined by deep veins running with the brachial artery, which have drained the deep structures of the forearm and arm. Together they form the **axillary vein** which lies medial to the axillary artery in the axilla.

The lateral (radial) aspect of the dorsal venous arch is drained by the **cephalic vein**. This passes up the lateral aspect of the forearm and arm, draining its superficial tissues. In the upper part of the arm it lies in the groove between pectoralis major and deltoid, a site at which catheters may be introduced. Just beneath the clavicle it pierces the (clavi-pectoral) fascia which forms the anterior wall of the apex of the axilla and drains into the axillary vein.

The pattern of minor veins is very variable, but there is usually a large connecting vein, the **median cubital vein**, between the cephalic and basilic veins which crosses the cubital fossa (**5.7.3**) at the front of the elbow. Because veins in the cubital fossa are firmly anchored by connective tissue, the median cubital vein is often used to perform a venepuncture.

Deep veins of the hand and forearm are usually found in pairs, **venae comitantes**, accompanying any artery. These small veins eventually unite to form larger vessels which drain into the axillary vein. The axillary vein therefore receives tributaries which correspond to the branches of the axillary artery. The axillary veins continue into the root of the neck as the **subclavian veins**, which join with veins from the head and form the superior vena cava, which returns the blood to the heart.

During exercise or in hot weather the superficial veins of the extremities dilate to aid heat loss by radiation and convection. Under resting conditions when the ambient temperature is cool, the characteristic arrangement of the deep vessels enables heat to be distributed by counter-current mechanisms from the small arteries to their accompanying venae comitantes, thereby helping to protect the core temperature.

Lymphatic drainage of the upper limb

The lymphatic system (**5.7.2, 5.7.8, 5.7.9**) is very difficult to demonstrate in both the living and the dead. The fine **lymph vessels** cannot be felt in the normal healthy state. Likewise, **lymph nodes** are difficult to feel unless they are enlarged. Furthermore, in the elderly, lymph nodes tend to atrophy. The system is, however, extremely important in the spread and control of infection and malignancy.

The lymphatic drainage of the upper limb parallels that of the venous drainage:

- **superficial lymphatics** accompany the large superficial veins and drain the surrounding skin and superficial fascia; they have relatively few connections with the deeper vessels;
- **deep lymphatics** follow the deep blood vessels and drain the deeper tissues.

Lymphatics from the thumb and thumb web, and from the radial part of the forearm and arm, therefore tend to drain along vessels passing with the cephalic vein; those from the ulnar side of the forearm along the basilic vein. (Small supratrochlear lymph nodes may be present on the vessels just above the medial epicondyle.)

Both superficial and deep vessels eventually drain into the **axillary lymph nodes** lying along the axillary artery (**5.7.8, 5.7.9**):

- A lateral group along the axillary artery drains much of the lymph from the arm.
- From there lymph passes to central nodes lying more deeply in the axilla and thence to apical nodes in the apex of the axilla.
- Lymph from the anterior and posterior walls of the axilla drains first to local nodes and from there to central axillary nodes.
- Lymph vessels running with the cephalic vein enter the apex of the axilla with the vein and end in apical nodes there.
- The apical nodes give rise to a **subclavian lymph trunk** which runs with the subclavian artery to end with other lymphatic trunks (in particular the large **thoracic duct** on the left side) by draining

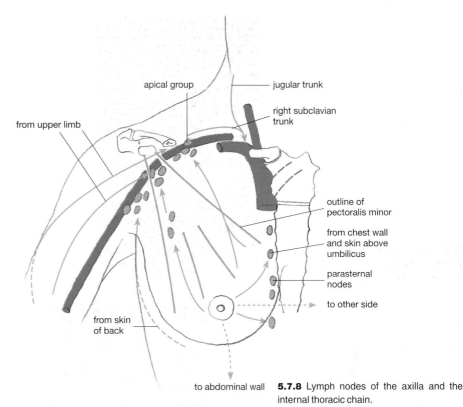

5.7.8 Lymph nodes of the axilla and the internal thoracic chain.

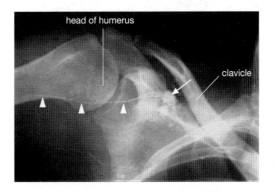

5.7.9 Lymphogram of vessels (arrowheads) and nodes (arrow) of axilla.

into the venous system at the confluence of the subclavian and internal jugular veins at the root of the neck.

In addition to draining the upper limb, axillary nodes also drain the skin and superficial fascia of the trunk above the umbilicus, and the breast.

The **lymphatic drainage of the breast** is very important in breast cancer. Seventy-five per cent of breast lymph normally drains up through the axillary clusters of nodes; 25% (largely from its medial aspect) drains into nodes along the internal thoracic artery in the second to fourth intercostal spaces. The internal thoracic nodes are of importance because they are often involved at an early stage in the spread of breast cancer; they communicate freely across the midline and, from them, cancer cells can spread to the pleural cavity. (The breast and its lymph drainage is considered more fully with the female reproductive

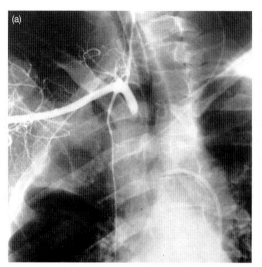

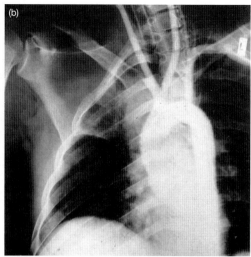

5.7.10 See Qu. 7G.

system, Vol. 2, Ch. 6, Sect. 9) If axillary nodes have to be removed in the treatment of breast cancer, this will almost inevitably interfere with the lymphatic drainage of the upper limb.

Qu. 7F *If you had a septic little finger, where would you be likely to find enlarged lymph nodes?*

Imaging

Review the section in Chapter 3 on the use of contrast media in medical imaging.

Angiograms

Angiograms are radiographs taken after the injection of radiopaque material into the circulation; they can be used to study arteries, veins, or lymphatics.

Arteriograms

Examine the arteriograms of the upper limb (**5.7.4a, b, 5.7.5, 5.7.6a**) and identify as many of the vessels as possible. The anastomoses around the scapula, elbow, and wrist are more easily seen on angiograms than in dissections. **5.7.4a, b** are digital subtraction angiograms showing the subclavian and axillary arteries with the arm by the side, and raised. Note how the axillary artery is bent after it has passed between the first rib and the clavicle; also the vessels taking part in the anastomosis around the scapula. In angiogram **3.10** identify the circumflex humeral vessels, the profunda brachii, radial, ulnar, and interosseous arteries; note too the anastomoses around the joints.

Lymphograms

Lymphograms (**5.7.9**) can be prepared by taking radiographs after injection of radiopaque material into small lymphatic vessels which have previously been made visible by the subcutaneous injection of patent blue dye which is taken up by the lymphatics.

Lymphangiograms can be used to detect larger vessels, lymph nodes, and sites of blockage of lymphatic drainage. Lymph nodes can also be detected by the injection of radioactive colloids, which are phagocytosed by macrophages which sequester in the nodes.

Questions and answers

Qu. 7A *What do the walls of the radial artery consist of? Why are the walls of arteries thicker and more elastic than those of veins?*

Answer An outer layer of connective tissue containing vessels and nerves (tunica adventitia); a middle layer of smooth muscle and elastic tissue (tunica media); and an inner connective tissue and endothelial layer (tunica intima). The walls are more elastic to maintain the higher blood pressure in the arteries and smooth the pulse pressure.

Qu. 7B *How would you decide whether what you feel is artery or vein?*

Answer An artery transmits the pulsations of the blood derived from the contraction of the ventricles of the heart (systole).

Qu. 7C *What would be the explanation if the distal end of the vein was to fill with blood when you removed the pressure of your proximally placed left index finger?*

Answer A deep vein or veins is connecting with the superficial vein.

Qu. 7D *If someone had sustained a deep cut in the palm of the hand how could you stop the resultant haemorrhage?*

Answer First, by direct pressure on the palm of the hand (after first checking that no sharp object is still embedded there) and by elevating the limb. If this fails, then compression of the artery proximal to the injury is required. A tourniquet can be applied to the upper arm, or the axillary or subclavian arteries can be compressed. It is essential that a tourniquet be applied for a minimum period only (less than 30 min), or tissue death might occur.

Qu. 7E *Why are there no major veins in the palm?*

Answer Because grip creates pressures in the palm which would occlude the veins. Therefore venous blood from the palm drains through to the dorsum of the hand.

Qu. 7F *If you had a septic little finger, where would you be likely to find enlarged lymph nodes?*

Answer Lymph from the little finger drains along the course of the basilar vein to nodes in the axilla; possibly a gland close to the medial epicondyle would also be enlarged.

Qu. 7G *Where was the site of arterial obstruction?*

Answer The arterial obstruction lies at the junction of the right subclavian artery with the common carotid artery.

Innervation of the upper limb

Innervation of the upper limb

The somatic nerve supply to the upper limb is derived, on each side, from the fourth to the eighth cervical and first thoracic spinal nerve roots; these supply the motor innervation to the muscles, and the sensory innervation to the skin, muscles, joints, and other deep tissues. The somatic nerves are essential to the stretch reflex and other reflexes involved in posture of the limb and its withdrawal from painful stimuli. The upper limb also receives postganglionic sympathetic fibres from the sympathetic chain; these control the blood vessels, sweat glands, and pilo-arrector muscles.

During development, each segment of skin, and the muscles producing each movement of a joint, become supplied by a particular nerve root or group of roots (dermatome for the skin; myotome for the muscles; see **5.8.3**, **Table 5.8.1**). The brachial plexus redistributes bundles of nerve fibres from the individual spinal nerve roots, to form nerves which contain fibres from the appropriate nerve roots for the particular muscle or area of skin to be supplied.

The muscles of the flexor compartments of the arm and forearm, and the skin over them, are all supplied by anterior divisions of the trunks of the brachial plexus. These anterior divisions form the lateral cord and the medial cord of the plexus. These cords give branches which supply the muscles forming the anterior wall of the axilla, and three main nerves—the musculocutaneous nerve, the median nerve, and the ulnar nerve—which pass down the limb to distribute fibres to the flexor muscles and skin and to the joints over which the muscles act.

The muscles of the extensor compartments of the arm and forearm and the skin over them are all supplied by fibres in posterior divisions of the trunks of the brachial plexus. The posterior divisions of all three trunks unite to form the posterior cord of the plexus. From the posterior cord arise nerves which supply the muscles of the posterior wall of the axilla and deltoid, and the radial nerve which supplies the extensor compartments of the arm and forearm, and a narrow strip of skin on the extensor surface of the limb and hand. These nerves also supply posterior aspects of all the joints of the upper limb.

Living anatomy

Extend your neck and bend it laterally to one side. Press firmly with your fingers just above the clavicle, moving from lateral to medial. Deep to the skin you will feel a number of thick bundles of nerves (pressing on them will give an odd sensation!). These are a part (the 'trunks') of the brachial plexus. Their relatively superficial position means that they can be damaged by penetrating injuries. Equally, if the head and shoulder are moved violently apart, as can happen in a motor cycle injury, for example, the nerve roots or trunks can be pulled and torn, creating particular groups of disabilities depending on exactly which fibres have been damaged.

A knowledge of the position of the brachial plexus in the neck is important for any anaesthetist who is required to 'block' nerves or inject radiopaque material into arteries in the vicinity.

The median and ulnar nerves can be felt as part of the neurovascular bundle running down the medial aspect of the arm. At the elbow, the ulnar nerve is readily palpable as it passes behind the medial epicondyle. At the wrist, the median nerve can be rolled under the fingers to the radial side of the tendon of palmaris longus, just proximal to the main skin crease at the wrist. In the palm, you may be able to feel the ulnar nerve as it crosses the hook of the hamate.

The radial nerve is not very easily palpable in any part of its course as, for the most part, it lies deeply embedded in muscle. You may, however, be able to roll it under your finger as it enters the cubital fossa lateral to the tendon of biceps.

Brachial plexus

The **brachial plexus** (**5.8.1**, **5.8.2**) is an arrangement of nerves which distributes motor and sensory fibres to particular nerves that supply muscle groups, joints, and skin of the upper limb.

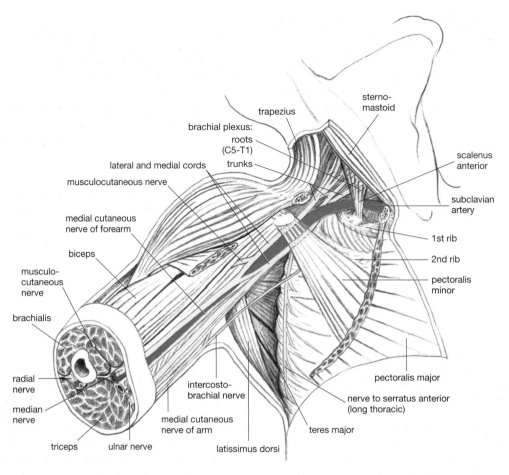

5.8.1 Axilla, to expose the neurovascular bundle, the axillary vein and most of pectoralis major has been removed and pectoralis minor has been divided. To show the origins of the plexus from between the scalene muscles, the clavicle has been divided and sternomastoid reflected.

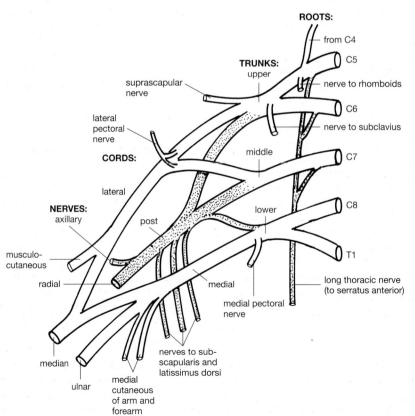

5.8.2 Brachial plexus: schematic diagram of roots, trunks, cords, and branches.

It is usually formed in the neck from **cervical spinal nerves C5–C8** and the **first thoracic nerve T1** which arises in the thorax [occasionally it is derived either from higher (C4–C8) or lower (C6–T2) spinal nerves; it is then said to be 'prefixed' or 'postfixed'].

Spinal nerves are formed by the union of **ventral (motor)** and **dorsal (sensory) spinal nerve roots** which emerge from the spinal cord within the spinal canal and unite in an intervertebral foramen. On each dorsal root in the intervertebral foramen is a **dorsal root ganglion**, which contains the cell bodies of the peripheral sensory fibres. The cell bodies of the somatic motor and autonomic neurons are situated in the spinal cord.

Immediately distal to the foramen, each spinal nerve divides into an **anterior** and a **posterior primary ramus**. Posterior primary rami supply extensor muscles of the spine and skin of the back. The anterior primary rami of C5–T1 form the brachial plexus. Its various parts are termed:

- **roots**
- **trunks**
- **divisions**
- **cords**.

Like any other arrangement of nerves or vessels, the brachial plexus commonly does not appear as in text-book diagrams. This does not mean that the nerve fibres reach the wrong targets, only that they reach them by a different route.

The **roots** of the brachial plexus (**5.8.1**, **5.8.2**) are formed from the anterior primary rami of C5–T1 spinal nerves. As the roots emerge from the intervertebral foramina, they lie between and are protected by muscles of the neck attached to the anterior tubercles (scalenus anterior) and posterior tubercles (scalenus medius and posterior) of the transverse processes of the cervical vertebrae (see Vol. 3, Ch. 6, Sect. 12). The first thoracic nerve (T1) passes upward from the chest cavity, crossing the neck of the first rib behind the subclavian artery, to join the C8 root in the base of the neck.

Branches from the roots of the plexus supply the scalene muscles (segmentally); subclavius (C5, C6); the rhomboid muscles via a nerve (C5) that passes dorsally through levator scapulae to reach the back; and serratus anterior via the **nerve to serratus anterior** (long thoracic nerve; C5, C6, C7), which crosses the first rib beneath the trunks of the plexus and runs down over the digitations of serratus anterior on the side of the chest wall. This nerve is vulnerable in operations for removal of the breast (mastectomy) and axillary lymph nodes draining the breast (see **5.8.4**).

Qu. 8A *What would be the result if the following nerve structures were cut: (a) the ventral root of C5 spinal nerve; (b) the anterior primary ramus of C5 spinal nerve; (c) the long thoracic nerve?*

The **trunks** of the brachial plexus are formed from the union of its roots. They pass downward and laterally over the first rib, enclosed, with the subclavian artery, in a sheath of prevertebral fascia. The usual pattern is:

- C5 and C6 roots join to form the **upper trunk**;
- C7 root alone forms the **middle trunk**;
- C8 and T1 roots join to form the **lower trunk**.

The **suprascapular nerve** (C5, C6) arises from the upper trunk and passes backward across the neck to reach the suprascapular notch, through which it passes to supply supraspinatus and infraspinatus.

Qu. 8B *What actions would be lost if the suprascapular nerve was damaged?*

Beneath the clavicle, nerve fibres in each of the three trunks of the plexus are redistributed into **anterior divisions** and **posterior divisions** (which supply, respectively, the flexor and extensor muscles and skin). These divisions then recombine to form the cords of the brachial plexus.

The three **cords** of the brachial plexus are named according to their position relative to the mid-part of the axillary artery:

- the **lateral cord** gives: a branch to pectoralis major (lateral pectoral nerve); a musculo-cutaneous nerve which passes through coracobrachialis; and a contribution to the median nerve.
- the **medial cord** gives branches which pass between the axillary artery and vein: a branch which supplies pectoralis major and minor (medial pectoral nerve); a small medial cutaneous nerve of the arm and a larger medial cutaneous nerve of the forearm; a contribution to the median nerve; and the ulnar nerve.
- the **posterior cord** lies behind the axillary artery on the posterior wall of the axilla. It gives branches to the muscles of the posterior wall of the axilla (subscapularis, teres major, and latissimus dorsi); an axillary (circumflex) nerve, which passes backward to leave the axilla between subscapularis and teres major, immediately below the shoulder joint; and a radial nerve which runs downward through the axilla to pass between the long and medial heads of triceps into the posterior compartment of the arm.

Motor distribution of the plexus

Every muscle has a nerve supply derived from one or more segments of the spinal cord. Memorizing the root values of the nerve supply to individual muscles is unnecessary; they can be looked up in a reference textbook. What is more, they can be determined by remembering certain broad principles, because muscles are innervated according to the movement they produce. Also, the movement of a joint is tested much more easily than the action of any particular muscle, so that, by analysing which movements are impaired after an injury, the level of neurological involvement of the plexus or spinal cord can be determined.

Each spinal nerve supplies certain functional groups of muscles. **Table 5.8.1** indicates the principal nerve roots responsible for particular movements of the upper limb. The pattern of arrangement of the supply to the muscles is quite different from that of the supply to the

Table 5.8.1 Main spinal nerve roots supplying the movements of the upper limb.

	Movement	Main nerve roots
Shoulder	Abduction, lateral rotation	C 5
	Adduction, medial rotation	C 6, 7, 8
Elbow	Flexion	C 5, 6
	Extension	C 7, 8
Forearm	Supination	C 6
	Pronation	C 7, 8
Wrist	Flexion and extension	C 6, 7
Digits	Long flexors and extensors	C 7, 8
Hand	Intrinsic muscles	C 8, T1

skin. In general, more distal muscle groups are supplied by more caudal spinal nerves; and opposing movements of a joint are supplied by adjacent spinal segments.

The 'reflex jerks' of the arm are stretch reflexes produced by tapping muscle tendons. Any reflex jerk depends upon the integrity of:

- afferent nerves from tendon and muscle receptors to the spinal cord;
- efferent motor pathways from the cord to the muscles concerned;
- the degree of central excitation of motor neurons in the part of the spinal cord at which the reflex connections occur.

Testing the reflex jerks

Analysis of reflexes is an important part of clinical assessment of the nervous system. The reflex jerks should always be compared on the two sides of the body.

The biceps jerk and the triceps jerk are the two most commonly examined in the upper limb; their root value can be found in **Table 5.4.1** and **5.8.1**.

Sensory distribution of the plexus

The sensory distribution of the roots of the plexus provides another method of determining the level of a neurological lesion. The loss of sensation in the arm may be caused by damage to a peripheral nerve, to part of the plexus, or to a segment of the spinal cord; each will produce a characteristic pattern of sensory loss.

The area of skin supplied by one dorsal spinal nerve root is known as a **dermatome**. **5.8.3** shows a dermatome map of the upper limb produced from an analysis of the results of injuries. Because dermatomes overlap, and no two people are precisely alike, dermatome maps differ in detail. Therefore the general principles are important:

- progressively more caudal spinal segments supply the pre-axial border of the limb, the digits, and the post-axial border;
- the middle nerve of the plexus (C7) supplies the middle digit;

Testing sensory root deficits in the limbs

The division of the supply between non-adjacent dermatomes (axial lines) is more pronounced on the flexor than on the extensor surface of the limbs. This is made use of when testing patients for the 'sensory level' of a spinal nerve lesion. The ability to perceive sensation should always be tested *across* the axial line on the flexor surface of the limb, i.e. from lateral to medial in the upper arm (C5 to T1) and then the forearm (C6 to C8).

During recovery after an injury, the supply from intact dermatomes may invade the periphery of anaesthetic areas. Thus, when one spinal nerve is lesioned, the neatly defined area of anaesthesia suggested by **5.8.3** is rarely the final result.

- overlap of supply is least between non-adjacent (C5 and T1, C6 and C8) segments, but is considerable between territories supplied by adjacent spinal nerves.

Autonomic nerve supply to the upper limb

The **autonomic nerve** supply to vascular smooth muscle, sweat glands, and arrector pili muscles (attached to skin hairs) of the upper limbs consists of postganglionic **sympathetic** fibres only. The cell bodies of preganglionic neurons supplying the upper limb are situated in the upper thoracic segments of the spinal cord in a lateral horn of grey matter. Their myelinated fibres (white rami communicantes) pass into the ventral spinal nerve roots but leave them just outside the vertebral column to enter the sympathetic chain—a system of interconnected ganglia and nerve fibres lying vertically on either side of the vertebral column. The preganglionic neurons synapse on ganglion cells in the inferior cervical ganglion and first thoracic ganglion (which may be fused to form a 'stellate' ganglion) and in the middle cervical ganglion (Vol. 3, Ch. 6, Sect. 12). Unmyelinated postganglionic axons (grey rami communicantes) mostly rejoin the ventral roots and are distributed with the branches of the brachial plexus; some, however, pass directly on to the subclavian artery and are distributed via the arterial tree.

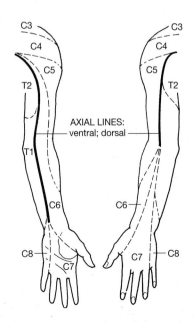

5.8.3 Dermatomes of upper limb: note the axial lines.

Damage to the brachial plexus

By combining anatomical knowledge with the findings on examination of sensory loss, muscle paralysis, and reflex loss, a clinician can usually determine the level of a neurological lesion.

Most damage to the brachial plexus occurs as a result of severe traction injuries. Motorcycle accidents are a common cause. The rider hurtles through the air and either strikes some object with his shoulder or lands, forcing the side of his head and shoulder apart. The stretching of the roots of the plexus that occurs can tear the roots in sequence from above downward. Damage to the upper roots can also occur during delivery of a baby if too much traction is applied to the head while the shoulder is retained in the birth canal.

The lower part of the brachial plexus can be injured in the opposite way, by sudden powerful traction of the arm above the head, as for instance when someone tries to break a fall by holding on to an object above their head.

If only the **upper trunk** of the brachial plexus is involved, muscles innervated by C5 and C6 will be paralysed and eventually waste. The most important are the clavicular head of pectoralis major, deltoid, supraspinatus and infraspinatus, brachialis and biceps, brachioradialis, supinator and extensor carpi radialis longus. The arm hangs by the side, the elbow cannot be flexed, the arm is medially rotated, and the forearm is pronated. This appearance has been called the 'waiter's tip' or 'crafty smoke' position (Erb's palsy). Damage to C5 and C6 will also cause loss of sensation over deltoid (C5) and the lateral aspect of the upper limb (C6).

If the **middle trunk** (C7) of the plexus is involved (usually it is damaged with the upper roots) the following muscles are also paralysed: serratus anterior, latissimus dorsi, teres major, triceps, the middle fibres of pectoralis major, pronator teres, flexor carpi radialis, flexor digitorum superficialis, extensor carpi radialis longus and brevis, extensor digitorum and extensor digiti minimi. There is 'winging' of the scapula (**5.8.4**), loss of extension of the elbow, and radial deviation of the wrist, with some weakness of power grip due to loss of extension of the wrist and fingers.

Qu. 8C *If the C7 root of the plexus was damaged, what sensory loss would you expect to find and how could you most easily test it?*

If only the **lower trunk** of the plexus is injured, muscles innervated by C8 and T1 will be paralysed. These are: all the muscles of the flexor compartment of the forearm except pronator teres and flexor carpi radialis, and the intrinsic muscles of the hand. The paralysis is much the same as would be produced if the median and ulnar nerves were divided; the ability to grip is lost. In the longer term, the muscles will waste and a claw-like deformity, similar to that caused by damage to the ulnar nerve, will result. The skin of the little finger, and the ulnar side of the palm and forearm is insensitive. If T1 and T2 nerve roots are both injured, this will cut off the sympathetic supply, not only to the upper limb, but also to the head and neck on the side of the lesion, resulting in 'Horner's syndrome' (Vol. 3, Ch. 6, Sect. 12).

If the **whole brachial plexus** is injured, the arm hangs uselessly from the shoulder, and is entirely insensitive except for the skin over the upper part of the shoulder (supplied by fibres from supraclavicular branches of the cervical plexus; C4) and the medial aspect of the upper arm (supplied by the intercosto-brachial nerve; T2). Such an injury defies treatment. However, paralysed upper limbs can be supported by splints which can be manoeuvred by the patient. Also, recent attempts have been made to stimulate the muscles in a paralysed arm in a manner that can be controlled by computer to produce movement

Qu. 8D *What other disabilities would you expect to be able to elicit if the entire plexus was injured?*

Do remember that it is not necessary to commit these lists of paralysed muscles to memory. **Table 5.8.1** is provided so that you can work out which spinal nerve root supplies which muscle.

Supply to the flexor compartment

The muscles of the flexor compartment and the flexor skin are all supplied from branches of the lateral and medial cords of the plexus.

Lateral cord

The **lateral cord** of the brachial plexus is formed from the anterior divisions of the upper and middle trunks. It lies lateral to the axillary artery. It has three branches:
- the **lateral pectoral nerve**, which passes forward to the anterior wall of the axilla to supply pectoralis major;
- the **musculocutaneous** nerve;
- a contribution to the **median nerve**.

Medial cord

The **medial cord** is formed mainly from the anterior division of the lower trunk, but also gains C7 fibres. It lies medial to the axillary artery. It has five branches, which all emerge between the axillary artery and vein:
- the **medial pectoral nerve**, which supplies pectoralis minor and major;
- the small **medial cutaneous nerve of the arm**, which supplies skin of the medial side of the arm above the elbow;

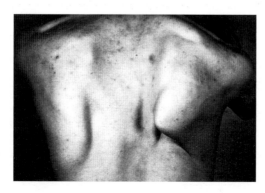

5.8.4 'Winged scapula', demonstrated by pushing forward against resistance.

- the larger **medial cutaneous nerve of the forearm**, which passes distally in the subcutaneous fascia to supply the medial aspect of the forearm from elbow to wrist;
- a contribution to the **median nerve**;
- the **ulnar nerve**.

Musculocutaneous nerve

The **musculocutaneous nerve** (5.8.5, 5.8.6) supplies:
- the muscles of the flexor (anterior) compartment of the arm;

Neurological complications of a cervical rib

If a rib or fibrous band develops with the last cervical vertebra, it can exert pressure on the lower trunk of the brachial plexus. This trunk contains fibres which supply the small muscles of the hand, so damage to the root will cause weakness and wasting of the small muscles of the hand. There is likely to be sensory loss on the medial aspect of the forearm and hand. In addition, the autonomic fibres to the blood vessels of the upper limb may be irritated or damaged, causing vascular changes which will be noticed predominantly in the hand.

- the skin over the lateral aspect of the forearm. It leaves the axilla, supplies and pierces coraco-brachialis, then lies between biceps and brachialis, supplying both.

Having supplied the three muscles, it emerges from the lateral border of biceps just above the elbow, where it is renamed the **lateral cutaneous nerve of the forearm**. This supplies the skin on the front and back of the lateral (radial) side of the forearm down to the thenar eminence (5.8.6).

Qu. 8E *What disabilities would result from damage to the musculocutaneous nerve as it leaves the lateral cord?*

Median nerve

The **median nerve** (5.8.7, 5.8.8) is formed in the axilla by contributions from both the lateral and medial cords. It therefore carries fibres from all the roots of the brachial plexus.

Branches given off in the forearm supply:
- most of the muscles of the flexor (anterior) compartment (but not flexor carpi ulnaris or the ulnar half of flexor digitorum profundus);
- the skin of the palm.

Branches in the hand supply:
- the lateral two lumbricals;

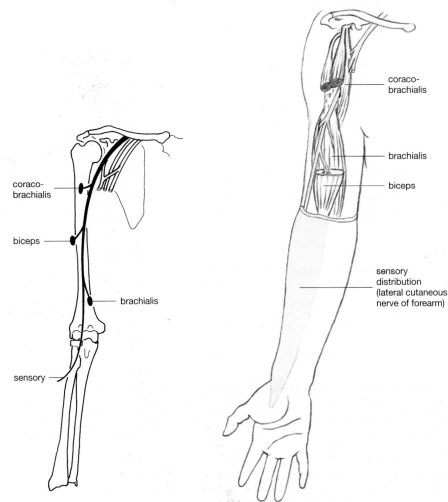

5.8.5 Musculocutaneous nerve: supply to muscles.

5.8.6 Course of musculocutaneous nerve; supply to skin.

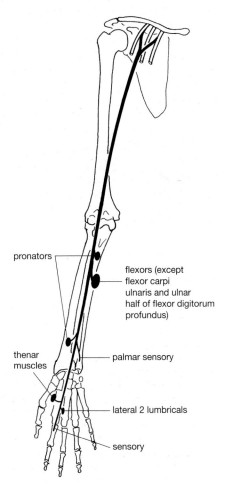

5.8.7 Median nerve: supply to muscles.

- the muscles of the thenar eminence;
- skin over the palmar surface and the nail beds of the lateral (radial) $3\frac{1}{2}$ (or, sometimes $2\frac{1}{2}$) digits.

It crosses either in front of, or occasionally behind, the axillary artery, and passes distally along the medial aspect of the humerus in the groove between biceps and brachialis. At the front of the elbow it lies medial to the brachial artery and the tendon of biceps. It then enters the forearm by passing between the two heads of origin of pronator teres. Here it gives off a deep branch (anterior interosseous nerve) which passes with the interosseous branch of the ulnar artery to the deep muscles of the forearm.

The median nerve is well protected in this part of the forearm, lying between the superficial and deep flexor muscles; it continues distally, bound to the deep aspect of flexor digitorum superficialis by fascia, until it reaches the wrist. Before it reaches the wrist, it gives off a slender **palmar cutaneous branch** which passes over the flexor retinaculum to supply the palmar skin.

As the median nerve crosses the wrist joint it lies between flexor carpi radialis and the lateral side of the long tendons of the superficial flexor muscles. The nerve is quite superficial at this point, but immediately passes beneath the flexor retinaculum to enter the carpal tunnel with the long flexor tendons and their synovial sheaths.

As the median nerve emerges from the carpal tunnel it gives a short, thick **recurrent branch** which doubles back and supplies the muscles of the thenar eminence. The main trunk of the nerve divides into **digital branches**, which accompany the digital arteries from the superficial palmar arch, running along the sides of the fingers. They supply the lateral (radial) $3\frac{1}{2}$ digits and the lateral two lumbricals. The digital nerves supply both palmar and dorsal aspects of skin over the terminal phalanx and, therefore, the nail bed.

Qu. 8F *If a finger needs to be anaesthetized, where would you inject the local anaesthetic? Is there a possible danger in this procedure, and if so, what is it?*

Carpal tunnel syndrome

The fibro-osseous carpal tunnel cannot expand, so that if there is swelling of any of its contents, the median nerve will be compressed, **causing carpal tunnel syndrome.** This is characterized by tingling sensations in the thumb, index, and middle fingers, sometimes extending into the forearm, and especially troublesome in the early hours of the morning. Carpal tunnel syndrome can occur in pregnancy when water retention occurs, in rheumatoid arthritis when the carpal joints swell, in repetitive strain injury affecting the synovial sheaths of the long flexor tendons, and often for apparently no reason at all! If symptoms persist, the flexor retinaculum can be surgically divided to relieve the compression.

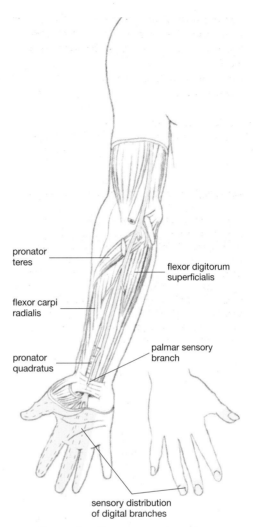

5.8.8 Course of median nerve; supply to skin.

Qu. 8G *If the median nerve is damaged at the elbow or above, what will be the additional effects to those mentioned above?*

Ulnar nerve

The **ulnar nerve** (5.8.10, 5.8.11, 5.8.12) arises in the axilla as the continuation of the medial cord. It supplies:

- flexor carpi ulnaris;
- the ulnar half of flexor digitorum profundus;
- the small muscles of the hand, except those supplied by the median nerve (p. 116);
- the skin of the palmar and dorsal aspects of the ulnar (medial) $1\frac{1}{2}$ (or $2\frac{1}{2}$) fingers.

The ulnar nerve runs distally medial to the axillary artery and then the brachial artery in the anterior compartment of the arm, and then pierces the medial intermuscular septum to enter the posterior compartment. It then passes behind the medial epicondyle, where it can be palpated and can easily be bruised. Such trauma causes a burning or tingling sensation which runs down the forearm to the little and ring fingers—hence the layman's term 'funny bone' for the bone on the medial side of the elbow!

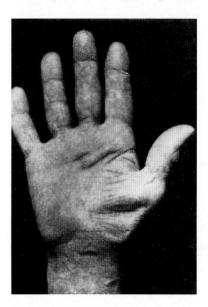

5.8.9 Right median nerve paralysis: note wasting of thenar eminence and position of thumb.

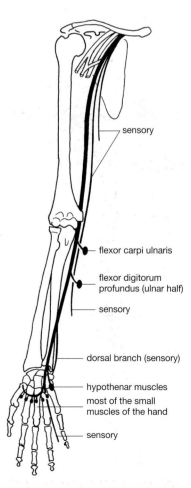

5.8.10 Ulnar nerve: supply to muscles.

Damage to the median nerve

The median nerve is susceptible to damage at two points: it can be damaged just above the elbow by a supracondylar fracture of the humerus (p. 104), and at the wrist by carpal tunnel syndrome, or by penetrating injuries.

If the median nerve is divided at the wrist, or if its compression in the carpal tunnel is sufficiently severe, there will follow:

- **Appearance**—if the nerve damage has been present for some time, the superficial thenar muscles will have wasted, and the thenar eminence will appear 'flat'. Because of the paralysis, the thumb will be lying in the same plane as the palm and the other digits. This appearance is often described as simian (monkey-like) **(5.8.9)**.
- **Motor loss**—loss of power in the thenar eminence muscles will cause weak opposition and therefore a weak pinch grip. The lumbricals of the middle and index fingers will also be paralysed. These effects vary from person to person because some muscles can be supplied from the ulnar nerve.
- **Sensory loss**—loss of sensation over the thenar eminence and flexor aspects of the radial $3\frac{1}{2}$ digits, extending over the tips of the digits to the nail beds **(5.8.8)**. This, combined with the motor loss, will prevent the ability to discriminate between small objects by touch, such as searching for the appropriate coin by feeling in one's pocket. Loss of pain and temperature sensation can be more dangerous; considerable damage can be done inadvertently to a hand lacking sensation.

If the motor supply to the thenar eminence is damaged (by a penetrating or surgical injury to the thenar branch of the median nerve just distal to the flexor retinaculum) opposition, and therefore grip, will be seriously impaired. Some opposition can be restored by transposing a tendon of flexor digitorum superficialis from its normal insertion to the lateral border of the thumb metacarpal.

Effects of an increased carrying angle of the elbow

The ulnar nerve can suffer gradual traction and compression as a result of an increase in the carrying angle at the elbow caused by unequal growth of the epiphyseal plate. If the angle is increased **(5.8.13)** the position of the elbow which results is known as a 'valgus' (bent-outward) deformity (the opposite is 'varus').

Qu. 8H *From a knowledge of its course, how might the ulnar nerve be re-routed to relieve this entrapment?*

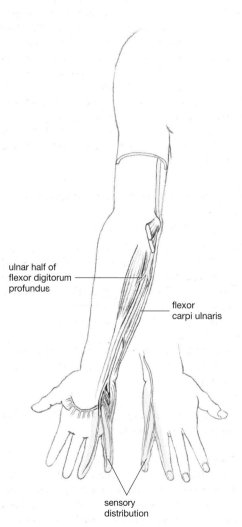

ulnar half of flexor digitorum profundus

flexor carpi ulnaris

sensory distribution

5.8.11 Course of ulnar nerve; supply to skin.

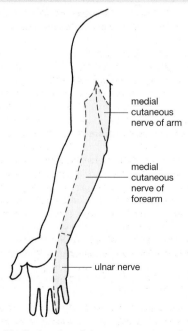

medial cutaneous nerve of arm

medial cutaneous nerve of forearm

ulnar nerve

5.8.12 Distribution of medial cutaneous nerves of arm and forearm and of ulnar nerve.

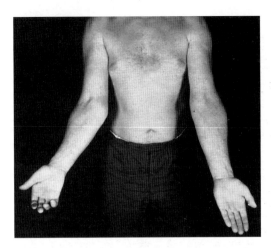

5.8.13 Increased carrying angle ('valgus deformity') of right elbow associated with ulnar nerve damage. Note the 'claw' position of fingers on the affected side.

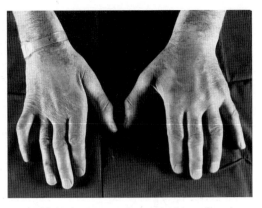

5.8.14 Right ulnar nerve palsy causing 'clawed' hand—note hyperextended metacarpo-phalangeal joints, especially of ring and little fingers.

Passing distally from the medial epicondyle, the ulnar nerve supplies and then pierces flexor carpi ulnaris, to reach the flexor compartment of the forearm. Here, the nerve continues distally under flexor carpi ulnaris, lying on flexor digitorum profundus to which it gives a branch. As it nears the wrist, it gives a **dorsal cutaneous branch**, which passes around the wrist to supply the dorsal aspect of the medial (ulnar) $1\frac{1}{2}$ (or $2\frac{1}{2}$) fingers.

Damage to the ulnar nerve

If the ulnar nerve were damaged at the elbow there would follow:
- Appearance—the ring and little fingers would appear 'clawed' **(5.8.13, 5.8.14)** (see below). If muscle wasting had occurred, the hypothenar eminence would be flattened and the intermetacarpal spaces would appear hollowed on the dorsum of the hand.
- Motor loss—adduction at the wrist would be weak due to paralysis of flexor carpi ulnaris. Flexion of the little and ring fingers would be weak, and the power of abduction and adduction of the fingers would be lost. This is tested by asking the patient to try to hold a piece of paper between extended fingers, or to spread the fingers against resistance. Because the interossei and lumbricals flex the metacarpo-phalangeal joints but extend the interphalangeal joints (p. 92) the action of the long extensor tendons is unopposed and the metacarpo-phalangeal joints become hyperextended. The interphalangeal joints would, however, be flexed (the medial two more than the lateral two).
- Sensory loss—loss of sensation over the palmar and dorsal aspects of the ulnar $1\frac{1}{2}$ (or $2\frac{1}{2}$) fingers.

Qu. 8I *Why are neither the middle nor the index fingers similarly clawed?*

Qu. 8J *How would the results of severance of the ulnar nerve at the wrist differ from those of severance at the elbow?*

As the ulnar nerve crosses the wrist, on the radial side of the tendon of flexor carpi ulnaris, it lies in a small fibrous tunnel superficial to the main part of the flexor retinaculum. When it reaches the muscles of the hypothenar eminence it divides into superficial and deep branches. The **superficial branch** crosses the hook of the hamate and divides into digital nerves, which pass on either side of the little finger and on the ulnar aspect of the ring finger to supply the skin, including the nail beds. The **deep branch** of the ulnar nerve passes through the hypothenar eminence muscles and supplies them. It then turns laterally beneath the long flexor tendons to the fingers, to lie with the deep palmar arterial arch; it supplies most of the small muscles of the hand, i.e. the dorsal and palmar interossei, the medial two lumbricals, and adductor pollicis.

Supply to the extensor compartment

Posterior cord

The **posterior cord** (**5.8.15**, see **5.8.2**) of the branchial plexus is formed from the posterior divisions of all three trunks. It lies first above, then posterior to, the axillary artery. It lies on and supplies the muscles of the posterior wall of the axilla. Its branches are:
- **upper** and **lower subscapular nerves**, which supply subscapularis and teres major;
- the **nerve to latissimus dorsi**, which arises from the cord between the two subscapular nerves;
- the **axillary nerve**;
- the **radial nerve**.

Qu. 8K *Which nerves supply the muscles of the anterior and medial walls of the axilla?*

Axillary nerve

The **axillary nerve** (**5.8.16**) passes dorsally out of the axilla between the lower border of subscapularis and the upper border of teres major. As it does so, it supplies a branch to teres minor and then divides into two terminal branches. The deeper branch passes laterally around

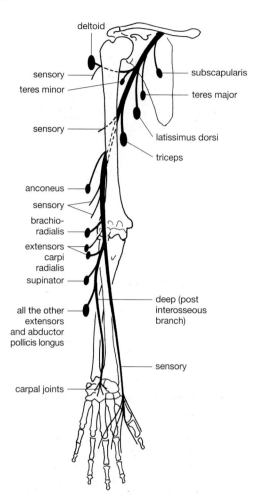

5.8.15 Posterior cord, axillary and radial nerves: supply to muscles.

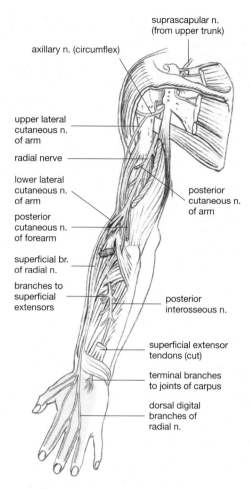

5.8.18 Course of radial nerve; sensory supply (to hand).

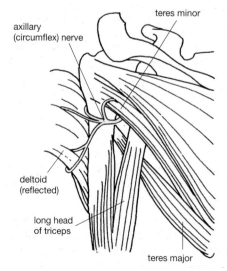

5.8.16 Course of axillary nerve.

5.8.17 Axillary nerve: supply to skin.

the 'surgical neck' of the humerus, deep to deltoid and supplying it. The more superficial terminal branch turns laterally around the posterior border of deltoid, supplying it and a small area of skin over the deltoid tubercle to which the muscle is attached (**5.8.17**).

Axillary nerve damage resulting from shoulder dislocation

As the axillary nerve leaves the axilla it lies immediately inferior to the capsule of the shoulder joint at its loosest and least strong part. When the head of the humerus dislocates, which it usually does in an antero-inferior direction, the axillary nerve is often bruised, if not permanently damaged.

Qu. 8L *What would be the result of damage to the axillary nerve? How could you assess the damage in someone with a dislocated shoulder?*

Radial nerve

The **radial nerve** (**5.8.15**, **5.8.18**, **5.8.19**) supplies virtually all the extensor muscles and skin over the posterior aspect of the upper limb.

The radial nerve leaves the axilla and passes posteriorly between the long and medial heads of triceps into the posterior compartment of the arm. As it does so, it gives off the small **posterior cutaneous nerve of the arm**, which supplies a small area of skin on the back of the arm. The radial nerve then spirals laterally around the shaft of the humerus, following the radial groove and lying on the uppermost fibres of the medial head of triceps; these muscle fibres often protect the nerve from injury if the bone is fractured at this level. In the arm, the radial nerve supplies branches to the three heads of triceps (these are given off early and not usually damaged by a mid-shaft fracture of the humerus) and to a small muscle, anconeus (**5.5.13**).

As the nerve approaches the lateral intermuscular fibrous septum—which it pierces to enter the anterior compartment—it gives off a small cutaneous branch which supplies the lower lateral aspect of the arm (lower lateral cutaneous nerve of the arm), and a larger cutaneous branch, the **posterior cutaneous nerve of the forearm**, which passes distally to supply the skin on the posterior aspect of the forearm.

After the radial nerve has entered the anterior compartment of the arm it supplies the muscles arising from the lateral supracondylar ridge of the humerus (brachioradialis and extensor carpi radialis longus). It lies under cover of these muscles on the lateral side of the elbow and is thus well protected.

As the radial nerve continues distally it lies on the anterior aspect of a muscle (supinator) which wraps around the head of the radius. At this point the radial nerve divides into a superficial and a deep branch. The **deep branch of the radial nerve (posterior interosseous nerve)** supplies the superficial extensors arising from the common extensor origin. It then supplies and pierces supinator, winding laterally around the neck of the radius to reach the posterior compartment of the forearm. Here, it supplies all the remaining forearm extensor muscles.

The **superficial branch of the radial nerve** lies anterior to supinator then passes distally through the anterior compartment of the forearm, lying between brachioradialis and the deeper muscles of the forearm (in particular, flexor pollicis longus). As it approaches the wrist, the nerve passes dorsally deep to the tendon of brachioradialis and then breaks up into superficial **dorsal digital branches** which supply the skin of the lateral $3\frac{1}{2}$ (or $2\frac{1}{2}$) digits on the back of the hand as far as the distal phalanx. It is possible to feel some of these branches by extending your thumb and palpating over the tendon of extensor pollicis longus, which the nerves cross to reach the fingers.

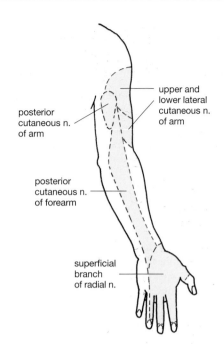

5.8.19 Radial nerve: supply to skin.

Damage to the radial nerve

The radial nerve is susceptible to injury in the upper arm. If long crutches are used incorrectly, the body weight may be taken by the upper bar of the crutch pressing hard into the armpit. However, crutches should be designed so that the body weight is supported by the grip of the hand on a lower bar, or by supporting bars for the forearm. Excessive pressure into the axilla can damage the radial nerve and cause paralysis of the extensor muscles of the forearm, with subsequent 'wrist drop'.

Qu. 8M *If a patient had sustained a fracture of the mid-shaft of a humerus and you suspected damage to the radial nerve, what would you expect to find on examination?*

Rapid clinical assessment of the major nerves of the upper limb

When confronted with a patient who has a badly injured upper limb, it is important to assess the function of the major nerves. However, it is often impossible, or too painful, for the patient to move the forearm, wrist, and fingers, so that reliance must be placed, in the first instance, on sensory function.

A pinprick into the pulp of the terminal phalanx of the index finger will test the presence of median nerve function, and a similar pinprick of the little finger will test ulnar nerve function. Pinprick over the dorsum of the first intermetacarpal space will test the radial nerve, but is not quite so reliable. If extension of the thumb can take place at the interphalangeal joint, then the radial nerve must be intact to the level of the posterior interosseous nerve.

Questions and answers

Qu. 8A *What would be the result if the following nerve structures were cut: (a) the ventral root of C5 spinal nerve; (b) the anterior primary ramus of C5 spinal nerve; (c) the long thoracic nerve?*

Answer (a) Cutting the ventral root of C5 would paralyse the muscles it supplies (deltoid, rhomboid major, subclavius, supraspinatus, and infraspinatus), the principal effects being an inability to abduct the shoulder and to rotate it laterally. The loss of the innervation to a small amount of spinal extensor muscles supplied by the posterior primary ramus would not be obvious.

(b) Cutting the anterior primary ramus of C5 would, in addition to the motor loss described in (a), cause sensory loss in the C5 dermatome, i.e. over the upper lateral part of the arm.

(c) Cutting the long thoracic nerve would cause paralysis of serratus anterior and winging of the scapula (see **5.8.4**, p. 115).

Qu. 8B *What actions would be weakened if the supra-scapular nerve was damaged?*

Answer Abduction of the humerus at the shoulder joint (supraspinatus) and lateral rotation of the shoulder (infraspinatus) would be weak.

Qu. 8C *If the C7 root of the plexus was damaged, what sensory loss would you expect to find and how could you most easily test it?*

Answer Sensory loss (C7 dermatome) would be expected over the front and back of the index, middle, and ring fingers, extending proximally toward the wrist. This is conveniently demonstrated by testing for anaesthesia (cotton wool for light touch; pinprick for pain) at the pad forming the tip of the middle finger.

Qu. 8D *What other disabilities would you expect to be able to elicit if the entire plexus was injured?*

Answer The scapula would be 'winged' (serratus anterior); adduction would be weak (pectoralis major, latissimus dorsi); the limb would be mottled in colour because of lack of control of blood flow to the skin, and sweating reduced (autonomic nervous system).

Qu. 8E *What disabilities would result from damage to the musculocutaneous nerve as it leaves the lateral cord?*

Answer Muscles of the anterior compartment of the arm (biceps, brachialis, coracobrachialis) would be paralysed and flexion at the elbow would be very weak. There would be sensory loss over the lateral aspect of the forearm.

Qu. 8F *If a finger needs to be anaesthetized, where would you inject the local anaesthetic? Is there a possible danger in this procedure, and if so, what is it?*

Answer Anaesthetic should be injected into the webs at the base of the digit (digital block) to reach the digital nerves. Catecholamines can be added to local anaesthetics to reduce blood flow and thereby localize their action; the smooth muscle of the arteries may be hypersensitive to the amines and this could lead to arterial spasm and cutting off of the blood supply to the fingers.

Qu. 8G *If the median nerve is damaged at the elbow or above, what will be the additional effects to those mentioned above?*

Answer Paralysis of the muscles of the anterior compartment of the forearm with the exception of flexor carpi ulnaris. Flexor pollicis longus will be paralysed and thumb flexion is a useful test. Flexion at the wrist,

metacarpo-phalangeal and interphalangeal joints, and abduction (radial deviation) at the wrist will also be weak; but the ulnar nerve contributes to some of these actions.

Qu. 8H *From a knowledge of its course, how might the ulnar nerve be re-routed to relieve this entrapment?*

Answer By relocating the ulnar nerve from its posterior position between the medial epicondyle and the olecranon process, to the anterior surface of the medial epicondyle.

Qu. 8I *Why are neither the middle nor the index fingers similarly clawed?*

Answer Because the lateral two lumbricals, which flex the metacarpo-phalangeal joints and extend the interphalangeal joints of the middle and index fingers, are supplied by the median nerve.

Qu. 8J *How would the results of severance of the ulnar nerve at the wrist differ from those of severance at the elbow?*

Answer The motor component of the ulnar nerve in the forearm supplies flexor carpi ulnaris and that part of flexor digitorum profundus which inserts into the little and ring fingers. Therefore damage to the nerve at the elbow would lead to weak adduction (ulnar deviation) of the wrist and weak flexion of the little and ring fingers, in addition to the defects found after severance of the nerves at the wrist (see text). The dorsal sensory branch of the ulnar nerve passes dorsally in the forearm. The dorso-ulnar aspect of the hand would therefore be insensate after division of the nerve at the elbow, but not at the wrist.

Qu. 8K *Which nerves supply the muscles of the anterior and medial walls of the axilla?*

Answer The muscles of the anterior wall of the axilla (pectoralis major and minor) are supplied by medial and lateral pectoral nerves of the medial and lateral cords of the brachial plexus. Serratus anterior, which forms the medial wall, is supplied by the long thoracic nerve from the roots of C5, C6, C7.

Qu. 8L *What would be the result of damage to the axillary nerve? How could you assess the damage in someone with a dislocated shoulder?*

Answer Deltoid would be paralysed and the shoulder joint could not be abducted more than about 30° (i.e. by supraspinatus). If the arm is dislocated, the integrity of the axillary nerve can be tested by investigating sensation over a small area of skin overlying the insertion of deltoid into the humerus (the 'sergeant's stripes' area).

Qu. 8M *If a patient had sustained a fracture of the mid-shaft of a humerus and you suspected damage to the radial nerve, what would you expect to find on examination?*

Answer Wrist drop, loss of extension of the metacarpo-phalangeal joints of the fingers and loss of active extension of the thumb would be the result of paralysis of the muscles of the posterior compartment of the forearm. Triceps would probably not be impaired because its nerves arise in the axilla and upper arm; some extension of the interphalangeal joints would be possible through the actions of the interossei. Sensory loss in the forearm might be difficult to detect because the supply of the medial and lateral cutaneous nerves of forearm overlap on to its posterior surface, but some loss over the dorsum of the radial side of the hand should be detectable.

The lower limb: introduction

Bipedalism in hominids means that the lower limb has become modified from the general pentadactyl pattern to function in both stance and the many varied forms of locomotion that are undertaken, often on very irregular surfaces. Unlike the arm, the lower limb frequently bears the entire weight of the body and this is regularly taken on just one leg in walking. Moreover, the stresses that the limb has to withstand are often multiplied many times, as on landing after a jump. In adapting to these functions the lower limb has foregone specializations which enable the upper limb to perform precision movements over a wide range. Nevertheless, considerable dexterity can be attained with practice as, for example, in a person unable to use the upper limbs for this purpose.

The weight-bearing function of the lower limb demands that the joints are modified for stability in weight bearing. The weight of the body is transmitted through the shaft of each femur largely to the tibia in the lower leg. This bone, with the fibula, forms a mortice-type joint, transmitting weight on to the talus, the bone which forms the apex of the arch of the foot. Finally, the arch transfers weight forward to the toes and backward to the heel.

The lower limb also requires considerable mobility in locomotion. To achieve this, the neck of the thigh bone has become elongated so that the shaft is offset from the head, an arrangement which also gives greater leverage to muscles acting at the upper end of the femur. Since the presence of the neck increases the distance between the upper ends of the femoral shafts, which are separated more widely than are the feet at ground level, the shafts slope downward and medially.

Furthermore, as a result of the medial rotation of the lower limbs during development, not only are they brought closer together but the powerful extensor muscles of the thigh, leg, and foot are positioned anteriorly, with the big toe lying medially. This is in contradistinction to the upper limb with its manipulative functions, where the flexor muscles face anteriorly and the homologue of the big toe, the thumb, lies laterally. A major advantage which results from the different arrangement of muscles in the lower limb is propulsion, where the combined strength of the extensor muscles can be exerted on the bones and joints to propel the body forward.

While studying the lower limb the anatomical specializations concerned with stance, which consists of weight bearing on one or both legs; with walking, which consists of a stance phase and a swing phase for each limb in turn; and with other forms of gait, such as running and jumping, should be considered carefully (see Chapter 9).

Bones of the pelvic girdle and lower limb

Bones of the pelvic girdle and lower limb

The pelvic girdle has a number of functions. It surrounds and protects the pelvic viscera (see Vol. 2) and also provides a strong bony link between the spinal column and the lower limb for both weight-bearing and locomotion. The limb bones themselves form a series of levers, moved by the muscles and articulating at the joints, a system which is specialized both for weight-bearing when upright and also for locomotion. Its bones are therefore more massive than those of the upper limb but, as in the upper limb, their surface contours and internal architecture reflect the forces to which the bones are subject. Whereas weight-bearing demands stability, locomotion requires the bones to be mobile, but also places additional stresses on the bones. The bones therefore provide an excellent example of the compromise between the requirements of stability and mobility.

Living anatomy

The living anatomy of the skeleton of the pelvic girdle and lower limb is best studied in your own limb, or that of a colleague. Many parts of the bones can easily be felt in the living person. As you study the bones on an articulated skeleton (**6.1.1–6.1.4**), determine which of the bony prominences can readily be palpated in life. In the diagrams that follow, mark the palpable bony structures.

Note also the **orientation** of the bones. When standing, the pelvic girdle is tilted so that its cavity points downward and backward. Confirm on yourself that the anterior superior iliac spines and the anterior surface of the pubis (see **6.1.2b**) are in a vertical plane.

When standing, note that the knees are closer together than the hip joints, so the shaft of each thigh bone (femur) slopes medially as it passes down. Unlike the hand, the foot is at right-angles to the leg bones when standing, so that the posture is upright.

Pelvic girdle

The **pelvic girdle** (**6.1.1**, **6.1.2b**) is an articulated ring of bones surrounding the caudal part of the body cavity. Its main functions are:

- To transmit the combined weight of the head and neck, upper limbs, and trunk to the lower limbs.
- To enable locomotion, by deep synovial ball and socket joints with the heads of the femurs. These joints allow the lower limbs to be sufficiently mobile for locomotion and, at the same time, sufficiently stable to withstand the forces generated by the upright stance and the various forms of locomotion.
- To protect and support the pelvic organs (see Vol. 2).

The pelvic girdle comprises two **hip** (**innominate**) bones joined together anteriorly by a midline cartilaginous joint, the pubic symphysis, and completed posteriorly by the two sacroiliac joints, which articulate with the wedge-shaped **sacrum**. Although the sacroiliac joints are synovial in type, any movement is

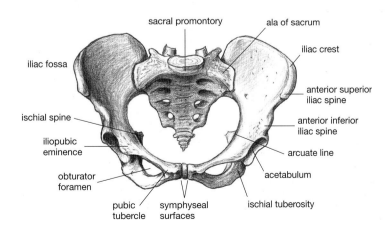

6.1.1 Anterior aspect of adult (female) pelvis.

sacral promontory

ala of sacrum

iliac crest

iliac fossa

anterior superior iliac spine

anterior inferior iliac spine

ischial spine

iliopubic eminence

arcuate line

acetabulum

obturator foramen

ischial tuberosity

pubic tubercle

symphyseal surfaces

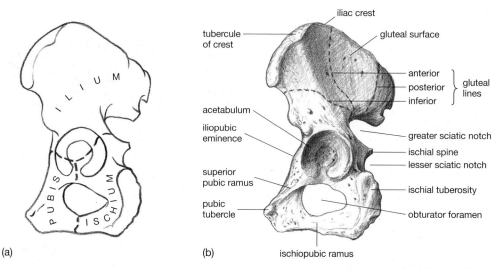

6.1.2 (a) Diagram of pelvis (lateral view) showing fusion lines where the three constituent bones (ilium, ischium, pubis) meet. (b) Lateral aspect of adult pelvis.

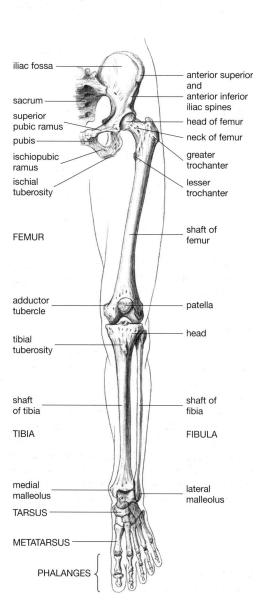

6.1.3 Bones of the lower limb and pelvic girdle: anterior view.

almost entirely prevented by strong ligaments and interlocking articular cartilage contours (p. 206).

Each hip bone is formed from three originally separate bones: the **ilium**, **ischium**, and **pubis**, which meet and fuse at the **acetabulum**, which forms the socket for the head of the femur.

The bony pelvis encloses an upper cavity, the greater pelvis, which is flanked by the blades of the iliac bones; it is demarcated from the narrower, lower part, the lesser pelvis, by the **pelvic inlet** or **brim** (see **6.1.6** of Vol. 2). Because the pelvis is oriented such that the anterior superior iliac spines and the pubic tubercle are in the same vertical plane, the plane of the pelvic inlet is tilted forward by about 60°. The inner surfaces of the pubic bones therefore face upward and help support the weight of the abdominal and pelvic contents.

Aspects of the pelvic girdle are therefore relevant both to the lower limb and to the study of the trunk. This section concentrates on those aspects relevant to the limb; Vol. 2 highlights aspects more relevant to the trunk.

Pubis

Identify the:
- body
- symphysial surface
- pubic crest
- pubic tubercle
- superior and inferior pubic ramus
- pectineal line (the sharp posterior border of the upper aspect of the superior pubic ramus) which extends laterally into the iliopectineal eminence

Ischium

Identify the:
- body
- ramus (joined to the inferior ramus of the pubis)
- ischial tuberosity
- ischial spine
- lesser sciatic notch
- greater sciatic notch

Ilium

Identify the:
- body
- ala (wing)—outer gluteal surface with gluteal lines; inner iliac fossa
- iliac crest and its tubercle
- anterior superior iliac spine
- anterior inferior iliac spine
- posterior superior and posterior inferior iliac spines
- articular surface for sacrum

The **acetabulum**, with its horseshoe-shaped articular surface and acetabular notch, is formed from all three pelvic bones. In life, the acetabular notch is bridged over by a transverse ligament to complete the cup-shaped socket for the head of the femur.

Reinforcements of the bony pelvis

Three **buttresses** of bone resist weight-bearing stresses:
- when standing on both legs, weight is distributed from the sacral articular facet to the acetabulum;
- when supported on one leg, the line of maximum stress is directed vertically upward from the acetabulum to the tubercle of the iliac crest;
- when seated, weight is distributed from the sacral articular facet to the ischial tuberosity.

The **sacrum** is considered with the spine (p. 204).

Bones of the lower limb

Femur

The femur (**6.1.3**, **6.1.4**), like the humerus, is the proximal bone of the limb, capable of moving in any direction relative to the pelvis. More massive than the humerus, it is also characterized by a prominent neck. It slopes medially as it passes down, so that its lower end lies immediately under the head. Identify the:
- head with a small central pit (p. 140)
- neck—note the angles it makes with the shaft
- greater trochanter overhanging the trochanteric fossa
- lesser trochanter
- anterior intertrochanteric line and posterior intertrochanteric crest
- gluteal tuberosity, a rough ridge extending from the base of the greater trochanter to the linea aspera
- shaft with posterior linea aspera (rough line) which divides into the medial and lateral supracondylar lines at its lower end
- popliteal surface
- medial and lateral condyles
- medial and lateral epicondyles
- intercondylar fossa
- groove for the tendon of popliteus on the lateral condyle
- adductor tubercle above medial condyle

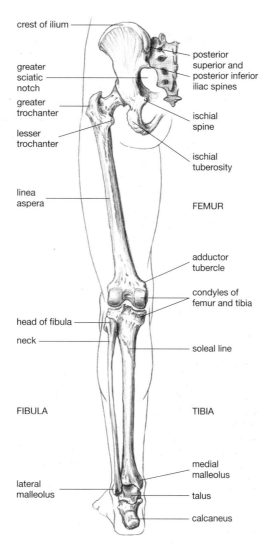

6.1.4 Bones of the lower limb and pelvic girdle: posterior view.

Qu. 1A *What is the functional significance of the neck of the femur? In what way is the neck of the femur comparable with the clavicle?*

Patella

The patella is a sesamoid bone in the tendon of quadriceps femoris. It forms an important part of the mechanism of the knee. Identify the:
- anterior surface
- articular surfaces for the condyles of the femur.

In the leg, the tibia and fibula are, respectively, the equivalent of the radius and ulna. However, rotation of the lower limb during development means that the tibia is placed medially. Unlike the radius and ulna, there is essentially no movement between the tibia and fibula. Also, the tibia bears essentially all the weight.

Tibia

Identify the:
- upper surface ('plateau')

- medial and lateral condyles
- tibial tuberosity
- shaft—with anterior (subcutaneous) border, interosseous border; and medial, posterior, and lateral surfaces
- soleal line
- facets for articulation with the head and lower end of the fibula
- facet for articulation with the upper surface of the talus
- medial malleolus—with facet for the medial side of the talus

Qu. 1B *What is the functional significance of the flat upper surface of the tibia?*

Fibula

Identify the:
- head—with apex and facet for articulation with the tibia
- neck
- shaft—with interosseous border; and lateral, posterior, and medial surfaces
- inferior end—with surface for interosseous ligament and facet for articulation with talus
- lateral malleolus

Tarsus

The foot has to be able to adapt to walking on surfaces that are far from flat. Stability at the ankle demands that there is essentially no movement between tibia and fibula, but the tarsal bones (6.1.5) are adapted to provide joints (principally the subtalar joint) which allow the sole of the foot to point inward (inversion) and outward (eversion), the equivalents of supination and pronation.

  Identify the:
- **talus**—with facets for articulation with the tibia and fibula in the ankle joint, and with the calcaneus and navicular in the subtalar joint
- **calcaneus**—long body with large posterior surface for attachment of calcaneal tendon, facets for articulation with the talus and cuboid; posteriorly placed medial and lateral tubercles on its undersurface, and a large medial protuberance, the sustentaculum tali
- **navicular** and its tuberosity
- **medial**, **intermediate**, and **lateral cuneiform** bones
- **cuboid** with a grooved undersurface

Metatarsus

The metatarsal bones are equivalent to the metacarpals. However, the first metatarsal does not undergo any movement like that of the opposition of the first metacarpal. Each of the five metatarsals has a
- base
- shaft
- head.

The first metatarsal is shortest and stoutest. Two sesamoid bones at its distal end are not usually retained in articulated skeletons. The base of the second metatarsal is long and is held firmly in a mortise between the cuneiform bones, limiting its movement.

Qu. 1C *It is not uncommon for a young adult exposed to unaccustomed prolonged walking (e.g. an army recruit) to complain of a painful foot. The reason is often a fracture ('march fracture') of the shaft of the second metatarsal. Why might this occur?*

Phalanges: proximal, middle, and distal

Again, the phalanges are similar to those in the hand. Each phalanx has a
- base
- shaft
- head.

The great toe, like the thumb, has only two phalanges, which are very strong. In comparison with those of the hand, the middle, and especially the distal, phalanges of the toes are much reduced.

The weight of the body is distributed between the posterior tubercles of the calcaneus and the heads and sesamoid bones of the metatarsals, the intervening bones forming an **arch**.

Qu. 1D *What is the functional significance of the arch of the foot?*

Clinical assessment of leg length

It is often necessary to measure the length of a patient's lower limbs and, if a discrepancy between them is found, to determine the source of the difference.

With a colleague lying supine on a couch, abduct one leg slightly, and then adduct the opposite leg, so that the two limbs again lie parallel to each other, but at an angle to the trunk. The abducted leg will appear longer than the adducted leg. The difference between the 'apparent' lengths of the legs in this position can be measured by first determining the distance between the umbilicus and the medial malleolus of the abducted leg, and subtracting from it the similar measurement of the adducted leg; or by measuring the distance between the two medial malleoli.

Such 'apparent' shortening or lengthening of a leg may occur in a patient whose pelvis is tilted because of a fixed curvature of the spine, or because of an abduction or adduction deformity of one of the hip joints. The difference in leg length is 'apparent' because it is not due to any 'real' difference in the lengths of the legs, but to the position of the legs in relation to the trunk.

The 'real' length of the leg can be measured from a fixed point on the pelvis, such as the anterior superior iliac spine, to the medial malleolus.

Qu. 1E *Suppose there is 3 cm difference between the two sides, how would you tell whether the discrepancy occurs above or below the knee?*

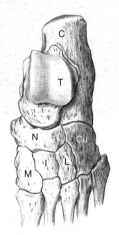

C = calcaneus
T = talus
N = navicular
Cu = cuboid
M = medial cuneiform
I = intermediate cuneiform
L = lateral cuneiform

6.1.5 Tarsal bones: dorsal view.

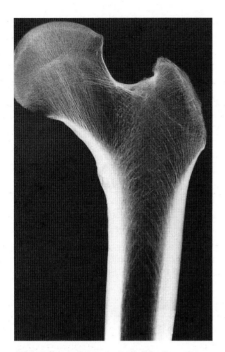

6.1.6 Trabeculae in the upper end of the femur.

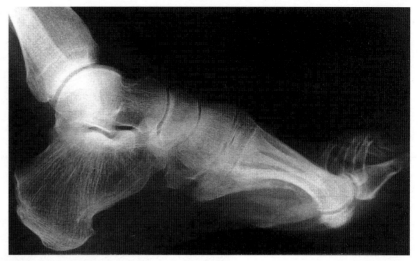

6.1.7 Trabeculae in bones of the foot.

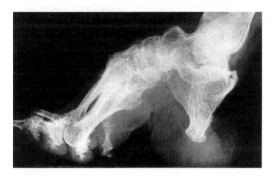

6.1.8 Bones of an oriental foot distorted by binding since birth.

Having identified the bony prominences, note again the overall orientation of the lower limb bones. Viewed antero-posteriorly, the hip, knee, and ankle joints should lie one above the other (**6.1.3**, **6.1.4**, see **8.1**); viewed laterally, the femur and tibia both slope forward at 5° from the vertical, so that the hip joint lies just anterior to the knee and ankle joints (see **8.1**).

Imaging and development of bones of lower limb

Review p. 12, 48, which are as relevant to the lower limb as to the upper limb.

Qu. 1F *Examine 6.1.6, 6.1.7 and comment on the obvious trabecular patterns. 6.1.8 is of an aged oriental woman whose feet were 'bound' from birth.*

Examine **6.1.9**, which is a radiograph of the pelvis and upper end of the femur of an adult. Compare it with **6.1.10**, which is of a newborn baby in which the os innominatus is made up of three separate centres,

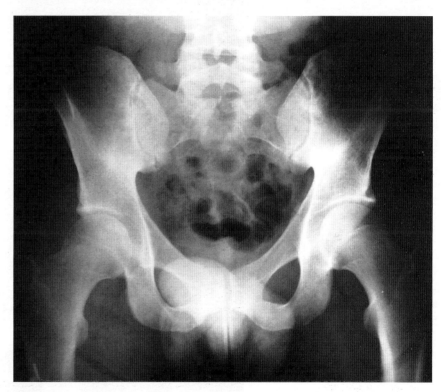

6.1.9 Pelvis and hip joints of adult female.

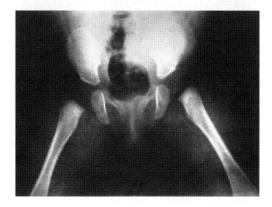

6.1.10 Pelvis and hip joints of neonate.

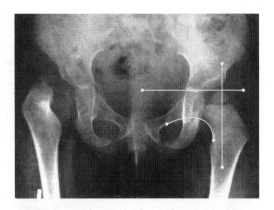

6.1.11 Pelvis and hip joints of child aged 6 months (see text for explanations of lines).

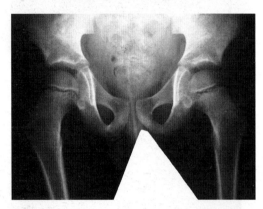

6.1.12 Pelvis and hip joints of child aged 7 years.

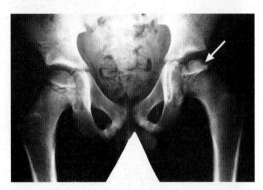

6.1.13 Disordered epiphysis (arrow) of the head of the left femur in a child aged 8 years.

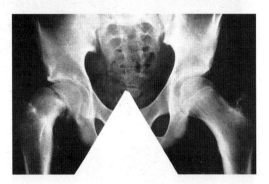

6.1.14 See Qu. 1G.

- On the right side of **6.1.11** a line has been drawn which passes across the pelvis horizontally from one acetabulum to the other, through the points where the three elements of the pelvis meet. A second vertical line from the outer lip of the acetabulum intersects the horizontal line. The centre of ossification of the head of the femur should lie in the lower inner quadrant.

- On the right side of **6.1.11** the curved line connects the inferior aspect of the neck of the femur with the inferior margin of the superior pubic ramus. This line, known as **Shenton's line**, is normally smooth and continuous (see also p. 141; Qu. 2B).

6.1.12 is a radiograph of the pelvis of a child aged 7 years. The centre of ossification of the head of the femur is now much larger, and forms a quite large 'cap' over the upper end of the femur, in the acetabulum. The acetabulum is more fully formed, and the centre of ossification of the greater trochanter is appearing.

Disordered circulation to the developing head of the femur

By the age of 4 years the blood supply to the epiphysis of the head of the femur comes almost entirely from vessels which run upward on the neck of the femur from the trochanteric anastomosis (p. 181). These vessels are vulnerable between the ages of 5 and 10 years. If this blood supply is impaired, the capital epiphysis dies in whole or in part, and the bone which later reforms in the head of the femur may become flattened and misshapen. **6.1.13** shows the result of this condition, known as Perthes' disease. Compare the appearance of the diseased hip with the normal, opposite, hip.

In a 15-year-old boy, the head of the femur is well developed (**6.1.14**), and an obvious growth plate can be seen between the head and neck of the femur.

Slipped upper femoral epiphysis

During adolescence, the great forces that are transmitted from the trunk to the femur must pass through the cartilaginous growth plate of the upper end of the femur. It is therefore not surprising that, in rare instances when the cartilage structure is not entirely normal, the head of the femur can 'slip' on the neck. This can occur either acutely or, more usually, slowly. The head of the femur slips inferiorly (seen on A-P radiographs) and posteriorly (seen on lateral radiographs), so that the leg tends to take up a position of some lateral (external) rotation, with limitation of abduction at the hip joint. The condition is unique to the hip joint. It can cause pain in the hip, or thigh, or be referred to the knee.

A line drawn along the upper margin of the neck of the femur in the normal hip joint should pass through the upper third of the capital epiphysis. This provides a method of recognizing an early stage of slipping of the epiphysis.

Qu. 1G *Examine* ***6.1.14****. Which is the normal side?*

the ilium, the pubis, and the ischium. At this young age the acetabulum is entirely cartilaginous, at the meeting place of its separate elements, and the centre for the head of the femur is not yet visible.

6.1.11 is a radiograph of the hips of a 6-month-old infant; the centre of ossification of the head of the femur is now visible.

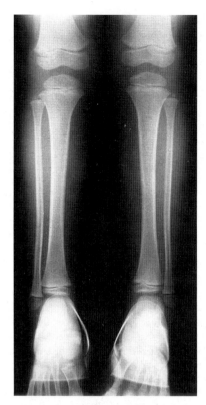

6.1.15 Bones of the leg of child aged 6 years.

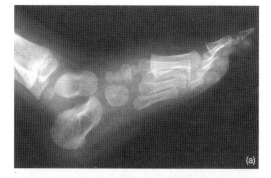

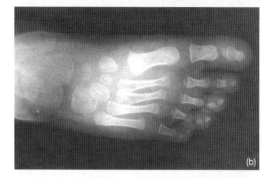

6.1.17 Foot of child aged 5 years:
(a) lateral view; (b) dorsal view.

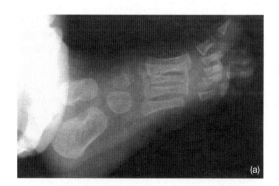

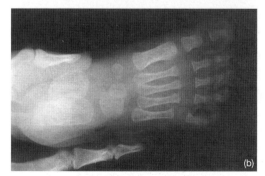

6.1.16 Foot of child aged 18 months: (a) lateral view;
(b) dorsal view. (Note the adult hand holding the foot.)

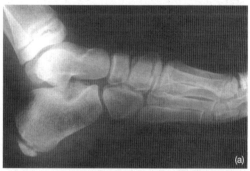

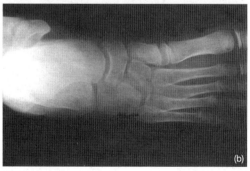

6.1.18 Foot of child aged 11 years:
(a) lateral view; (b) dorsal view.

Examine **6.1.15**, a radiograph of a young person (with plaster casts on both feet). Note the presence of epiphyseal plates at the lower end of the femur and upper ends of the tibia and fibula. Note also that the epiphyseal plate of the lower end of the fibula lies at a lower level than that of the tibia and at the same level as the line of the ankle joint.

For radiographs of the bones comprising the adult knee and ankle see **6.3.6**, **6.3.7**, **6.4.3**, and **6.4.4**.

Examine **6.1.16a,b**, **6.1.17a,b**, and **6.1.18a,b**, which show the feet of children aged 18 months, 4 years, and 11 years, respectively, noting the development of the ossification centres. For a radiograph of an adult foot, see **6.1.7**.

Questions and answers

Qu. 1A *What is the functional significance of the neck of the femur? In what way is the neck of the femur comparable with the clavicle?*

Answer The neck of the femur separates the femoral head from its shaft and greater tuberosity, thereby reducing limitation of movement at the hip joint. The role of the clavicle is comparable in that it acts as a strut by which the upper limb is suspended clear of the trunk to enable a wide range of movements to take place at the shoulder.

Qu. 1B *What is the functional significance of the flat upper surface of the tibia?*

Answer The wide platform-like surfaces of the tibia, which articulate with the condyles of the femur, provide for transmission of the weight of the limb to the lower leg in addition to movements at the knee joint.

Qu. 1C *It is not uncommon for a young adult exposed to unaccustomed prolonged walking (e.g. an army recruit) to complain of a painful foot. The reason is often a fracture of the shaft of the second metatarsal. Why might this occur?*

Answer The base of the second metatarsal is long and is held firmly in a mortise between the medial and intermediate cuneiform bones. This limits its movement, and would account for the frequency with which it undergoes stress fracture as a result of (often) unaccustomed exercise.

Qu. 1D *What is the functional significance of the arch of the foot?*

Answer The arch of the foot, formed by several small bones, well supported by ligaments and muscles, transmits the weight of the body to the ground and provides flexibility while moving over uneven ground. The arch also cushions the impact of foot strike during locomotion.

Qu. 1E *Suppose there is 3 cm difference between the two sides, how would you tell whether the discrepancy occurs above or below the knee?*

Answer It is easiest to determine the exact position of the lower end of the femur when the knee is semiflexed. Therefore, the subject is seated with his/her knees flexed at a right angle. If one femur is shorter than the other, the difference becomes obvious and can be measured from a fixed point on the pelvis. Similarly a difference in length of one shin is obvious, and can be confirmed by a measurement from the joint line of the knee to the medial malleolus.

The tip of the greater trochanter normally lies at the same horizontal level as the centre of the head of the femur. Confirm this on a skeleton, and palpate the greater trochanters. You can judge if they lie at the same level, or measure the distance between the tip of the greater trochanter and the highest point of the iliac crest. If one side is shorter than the other, then the difference in leg length lies in the region of the neck of the femur or hip joint. The angle between the neck of the femur and the shaft could be reduced, the hip joint could be dislocated, or the neck of the femur could be fractured.

The length of the shaft of a femur can be measured from the tip of the greater trochanter to the line of the knee joint. The length of a femur is usually about one quarter of the height of a body.

Qu. 1F *Examine 6.1.6, 6.1.7 and comment on the obvious trabecular patterns. 6.1.8 is of an aged oriental woman whose feet were 'bound' from birth.*

Answer The collagenous fibres on which crystals of bone salts (calcium hydroxyapatite) are deposited are laid down along lines of stresses and strains within the bone. Many of these forces result from weight bearing, though the basic trabecular architecture is genetically determined.

Qu. 1G *Examine 6.1.14. Which is the normal side*

Answer In **6.1.14**, the person's left hip is normal.

Joints and movements of the pelvic girdle and hip

Joints and movements of the pelvic girdle and hip

In sharp contrast to the component parts of the shoulder girdle, which are highly mobile, those of the pelvic girdle are virtually immobile. Thus a stable base is provided for the weight-bearing lower limb, both at rest and during locomotion. The hip and shoulder joints show somewhat greater similarities: each is a synovial ball and socket joint capable of multiaxial movement. The articular contours of the hip joint, however, are far deeper, making it more stable and less likely to dislocate than the shoulder. Inevitably, such differences reduce the mobility of the hip joint, but other modifications have evolved which provide a range of movements for efficient locomotion without compromising its stability.

Living anatomy

Movements of the thigh on the trunk

Move your hip joint and note the type and range of movements that you can perform (see **1.4**). The movements are the same as those at the shoulder joint (i.e. the femur can move in any direction to produce flexion, extension, abduction, adduction, medial and lateral rotation) but the movements are more limited in their range, even in a trained gymnast.

Ask a colleague to lie supine on a couch and to flex a hip until the thigh rests against the trunk. The normal hip joint appears to be able to flex by about 130° but, in fact, the hip joint itself can only flex by 90–100°. To determine how the extra movement is achieved, place your hand in the small of your colleague's back (beneath the lumbar spine). When the movement is repeated, as the hip passes a right angle (90°) you will notice a flattening of the normal gentle forward curve (lordosis) of the lumbar spine. Maximum flexion of the hip therefore involves a considerable rotation of the entire pelvis. This occurs around a transverse axis between the two acetabular fossae.

With a colleague lying on his/her side, pull the uppermost straightened leg backwards. The apparent extension that takes place is again largely due to movement of the pelvis at the lumbar spine rather than at the hip joint.

Bony landmarks of the hip region

Palpate the iliac crest and follow it back to the posterior superior iliac spine, which lies under a dimple on the skin of the back opposite the spinous process of S2.

Sit down on the palms of your hands and feel the bony prominences (ischial tuberosities) on which you sit. Keeping your hands in place stand up and sit down again and note how, when you sit down, the lower border of gluteus maximus (a large, powerful extensor of the hip, which forms the bulk of the buttock) rises to uncover the ischial tuberosities.

The **gluteal region** extends from the iliac crest to the crescentic fold of the buttock. Under the skin is a thick subcutaneous fatty layer, the buttock. The amount of buttock fat is variable, especially in the female. Beneath the fat are the gluteal muscles.

Follow the iliac crest forward to the anterior superior iliac spine. Lying obliquely downward and medial to this landmark is the **inguinal region**, in which the pelvic bone cannot be felt because it is covered by muscles which flex the hip, and the lower extremity of the muscles of the abdominal wall. In the midline, the pubic symphysis is palpable and the bone can be followed laterally to the pubic tubercle and inferiorly along the inferior pubic ramus.

Muscles moving the hip

Step up on to a low stool, and note the contraction of gluteus maximus when you extend the hip joint. Next, stand with both feet together and palpate the muscles just below the anterior part of the iliac crests, then lift one leg off the ground. As you do so, the pelvis is tilted toward the supporting leg by the contraction of these muscles (tensor fasciae latae, gluteus medius and minimus; p. 142) which abduct the pelvis on the femur. Walk forward slowly and note that, with each step, the pelvis is tilted slightly so that the centre of gravity moves over the supporting leg and the non-weight-bearing leg can swing free of the ground (see also **6.2.11**).

Adduct your leg against resistance while palpating the medial aspect of the thigh to feel the contraction of the group of adductor muscles.

Compensation of flexion deformity of the hip

Sometimes, in disease of a hip joint, the capsule contracts from scar tissue so that a flexion deformity develops and the patient cannot extend the hip joint from the flexed to the anatomical position. However, such a flexion contracture can be disguised if the lumbar lordosis increases so that the pelvis is rotated sufficiently to permit the thigh to reach the anatomical position with respect to the trunk (**6.2.1**).

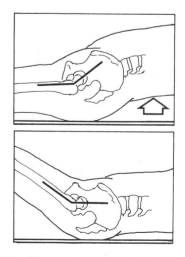

6.2.1 Test to detect fixed flexion deformity of hip joint.

Finally, with your knee joint fully extended, rotate your leg medially and then laterally. All the rotational movement is taking place at the hip joint.

Joints of the pelvic girdle

Pubic symphysis

The **pubic symphysis** is a fibrocartilaginous (secondary cartilaginous) joint which unites the two pubic bones in the midline. It is strengthened by a superior pubic ligament above and an arcuate ligament which spans the pubic arch. Movements at the joint are slight but, during pregnancy, hormones from the placenta cause changes in its connective tissue which increase its mobility somewhat, and allows temporary separation of the two bones.

Sacroiliac joints

The **sacroiliac joints** between the sacrum and ilium are synovial joints, but synovial joints which are adapted to limit movement and permit weight-bearing. Within the joint the irregular surfaces of the articular cartilage interlock, and any movement is limited by strong ligaments in front of and behind the joint. Transmission of weight from the spine on to the forward-sloping superior surface of the sacrum produces a forward rotatory thrust on the sacrum which is resisted not only by the strong iliosacral and iliolumbar ligaments, but also by the (extrinsic) sacrotuberous and sacrospinous ligaments (**6.2.2**).

The hip joint

The hip joint is a ball-and-socket synovial joint between the spherical articular surface on the head of the femur and the horseshoe-shaped articular cartilage lining the upper part of the acetabular fossa (**6.2.3**). The neck and head of the femur point up (the neck makes an angle of 120° with the shaft) and

anteriorly into the acetabular socket (see **6.2.5**, **6.2.20**). To achieve the necessary stability while bearing the substantial loads that the joint bears, the cup-shaped socket is much deeper than that of the shoulder joint, and is further increased by a ring of fibrocartilage around its margin (acetabular **labrum**). Inferiorly and medially, the articulation is not weight-bearing and a pad of fat occupies the centre of the acetabulum.

The **capsule** of the joint (**6.2.4**) is attached proximally to the margins of the acetabulum and to the transverse ligament which bridges the acetabular notch. On the femur it is attached to the intertrochanteric line anteriorly, but around the middle of the neck of the femur posteriorly.

Synovial membrane lines the capsule and all non-articular surfaces within the joint, including the pad of fat and the round ligament of the head.

The capsule is reinforced by an anterior **iliofemoral ligament**; the ligament is shaped like an inverted Y, with its stem attached to the anterior inferior iliac spine, and its two limbs attached to the upper and lower ends of the intertrochanteric line of the femur. The iliofemoral ligament is extremely strong and can act as a fulcrum when a dislocated head of femur is being repositioned (reduced) in the acetabulum. The capsule is also reinforced by the **pubofemoral ligament**, which runs from the iliopubic eminence to the inferior aspect of the neck of the femur. An **ischiofemoral ligament** arises from the ischium behind the acetabulum, but many of its fibres merge into the capsule. The major parts of all three ligaments pass spirally from their origin on the hip bone and therefore limit extension.

The round ligament (ligamentum teres) of the head of the femur links the transverse ligament of the acetabulum and the pit in the head of the femur. The small blood vessel it carries supplies only the small area of the head to which the ligament is attached.

Qu. 2A *With respect to stability and movement, what are the major differences between the synovial 'ball-and-socket' joints of the upper and lower limbs?*

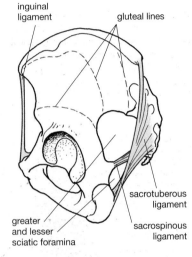

inguinal ligament

gluteal lines

greater and lesser sciatic foramina

sacrotuberous ligament

sacrospinous ligament

6.2.2 Pelvis showing sacrotuberous and sacrospinous ligaments (and also inguinal ligament).

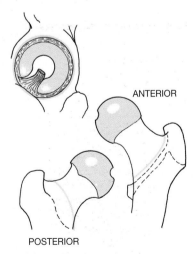

ANTERIOR

POSTERIOR

6.2.3 Attachments of capsule of hip joint.

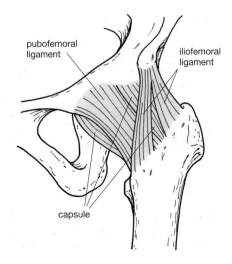

pubofemoral ligament

iliofemoral ligament

capsule

6.2.4 Intrinsic ligaments of hip joint.

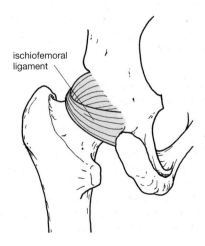

ischiofemoral ligament

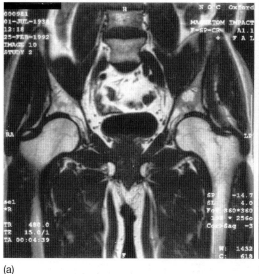

(a)

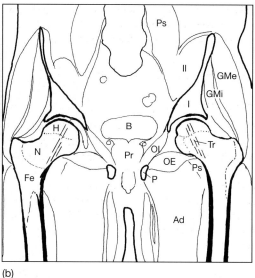

(b)

6.2.5 MRI of hip joint, coronal plane. I, Ilium; P, pubis; H, Head and N, neck of Fe, femur; Tr, Trabeculae strengthening neck of femur; Ps, Psoas; Il, iliacus; GMe, GMi, gluteus medius and minimus; OE, obturator externus; Ad, adductor muscles; B, Bladder; Pr, prostate.

Qu. 2C *Why is there a lower incidence of 'congenital dislocation' of the femur in Nigeria, where many infants are carried with their legs astride on their mother's hip?*

Examine the vertical MRI of the normal pelvis and hip joint (**6.2.5**), noting the articulating surfaces of the head of the femur and acetabulum. MRI studies of the hip joint are particularly useful in conditions where a diminished blood supply to the femoral head leading to ischaemic necrosis of the bone is suspected. As you study the muscles around the hip joint, try to identify them on this image.

Movements of the hip joint: muscles and their innervation

Flexion

Muscles which are attached to the trunk and which cross the hip joint anteriorly to insert into the upper end of the femur flex the hip joint (**6.2.6**):
- **Psoas major** is the most powerful of these. Its tendon, which is separated from the hip joint capsule by a bursa, is joined by fibres of iliacus.

- **Iliacus.**
- **Pectineus** is also a flexor, as is **rectus femoris** (**6.3.17**).
  Psoas is supplied segmentally by lumbar nerves; the other flexors by the femoral nerve.

Extension

Muscles attached to the pelvis which pass behind the hip joint to insert into the femur or bones of the leg must extend the joint:
- **Gluteus maximus** (**6.2.7**: inferior gluteal nerve), a powerful, quadrilateral muscle, is the powerful hip extensor you use to go up stairs or rise from your chair. It inserts partly into the gluteal tuberosity of the femur and partly into the iliotibial tract, which is attached both to the distal end of the femur and to the upper end of the tibia (see below).
- The **hamstring** muscles (**6.2.8**; sciatic nerve), which arise from the ischial tuberosity and pass down behind the knee joint to the tibia and fibula, are primarily flexors of the knee, but also extend the hip joint.

Abduction

Muscles passing from the outer aspect of the ala of the ilium across the lateral aspect of the hip joint to insert into the femur must abduct the hip joint. The principal

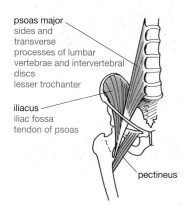

psoas major
sides and transverse processes of lumbar vertebrae and intervertebral discs
lesser trochanter

iliacus
iliac fossa
tendon of psoas

pectineus

6.2.6 Psoas, iliacus, and pectineus.

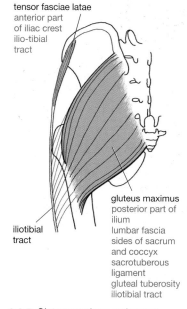

tensor fasciae latae
anterior part of iliac crest
ilio-tibial tract

iliotibial tract

gluteus maximus
posterior part of ilium
lumbar fascia
sides of sacrum and coccyx
sacrotuberous ligament
gluteal tuberosity
iliotibial tract

6.2.7 Gluteus maximus and tensor fasciae latae.

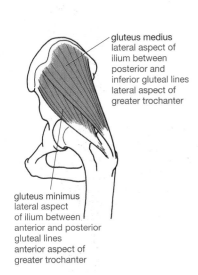

gluteus medius
lateral aspect of
ilium between
posterior and
inferior gluteal lines
lateral aspect of
greater trochanter

gluteus minimus
lateral aspect
of ilium between
anterior and posterior
gluteal lines
anterior aspect of
greater trochanter

6.2.9 Gluteus medius and minimus.

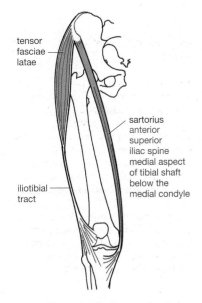

tensor
fasciae
latae

sartorius
anterior
superior
iliac spine
medial aspect of
tibial shaft
below the
medial condyle

iliotibial
tract

6.2.10 Tensor fasciae latae and sartorius.

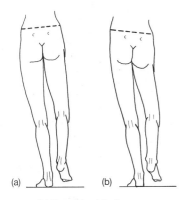

(a)   (b)

6.2.11 (a) Normal pelvic tilt;
(b) Trendelenberg sign.

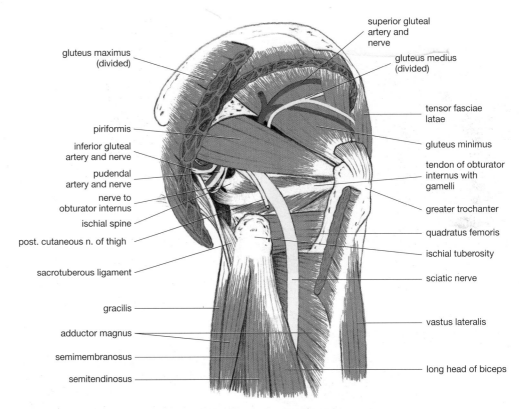

gluteus maximus
(divided)

superior gluteal
artery and
nerve

gluteus medius
(divided)

piriformis

inferior gluteal
artery and nerve

pudendal
artery and nerve

nerve to
obturator internus

ischial spine

post. cutaneous n. of thigh

sacrotuberous ligament

gracilis

adductor magnus

semimembranosus

semitendinosus

tensor fasciae
latae

gluteus minimus

tendon of obturator
internus with
gamelli

greater trochanter

quadratus femoris

ischial tuberosity

sciatic nerve

vastus lateralis

long head of biceps

6.2.8 Deep dissection of gluteal region; gluteus maximus and medius largely removed.

abductors, which are all supplied by the superior gluteal nerve) are:

- **gluteus medius** and **gluteus minimus** (**6.2.9**); both these insert on to the upper aspect of the greater trochanter of the femur;
- **tensor fasciae latae** (**6.2.10**) arises from the iliac crest and inserts into the iliotibial tract.

These muscles can abduct the leg away from the trunk. However, their more important function is to abduct the hip joint when the leg on that side is weight-bearing, and therefore the femur fixed. The abduction tilts the pelvis so that it is raised on the side opposite the weight-bearing limb (**6.2.11a**), enabling the non-weight-bearing leg to swing forward, e.g. when walking (Chapter 7).

If this mechanism fails (**6.2.11b**), either because the muscles are paralysed or because the joint is dislocated, then the pelvis will tilt in the opposite direction (Trendelenberg sign). If the foot is to clear the ground, greater flexion of the knee is needed. Also, if the abnormal pelvic tilt is marked, a considerable degree of lateral flexion of the spine is needed to maintain an upright position of the trunk. This produces a waddling gait known as the Trendelenberg gait.

The **iliotibial tract** is a thickened band of fibrous tissue derived from the tough investing fascia of the thigh (**fascia lata**). Its upper end gives attachment to both tensor fasciae latae and gluteus maximus; its lower end attaches to the lateral condyle of the femur and to a facet on the anterior aspect of the upper end of

the tibia. Through it, these muscles stabilize the pelvis not only on the femur, but also on the tibia and leg.

During relaxed standing, the knee is not 'locked' in full extension; in this position, line of pull of the iliotibial tract across the knee allows the tone in gluteus maximus to hold the knee in its extended position.

Adduction

Muscles attached to the pubic bone which insert into the shaft of the femur pull the leg toward the midline of the body (adduct it). The adductor group of muscles, all of which are supplied by the obturator nerve, comprise:

- **adductor longus** (**6.2.12**);
- **adductor brevis** (**6.2.13**);
- **gracilis** (**6.2.13**); and much of
- **adductor magnus** (**6.2.14**).

Adductor longus, which is attached by a tendon to the body of the pubis immediately beneath the pubic tubercle, is easily palpable high on the medial aspect of the thigh, especially if the leg is adducted and/or medially rotated against resistance.

Adductor magnus has both an adductor part, which arises from the ischiopubic ramus, and a hamstring part, which arises from the ischial tuberosity. The muscle passes laterally and downward to insert into the whole length of the linea aspera and the upper end of the medial supracondylar line. Here it forms a fibrous arch attached distally to the adductor tubercle on the medial condyle. Between the arch and the bone, the

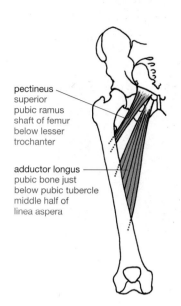

6.2.12 Adductor longus and pectineus.

pectineus
superior
pubic ramus
shaft of femur
below lesser
trochanter

adductor longus
pubic bone just
below pubic tubercle
middle half of
linea aspera

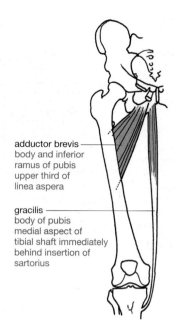

6.2.13 Adductor brevis and gracilis.

adductor brevis
body and inferior
ramus of pubis
upper third of
linea aspera

gracilis
body of pubis
medial aspect of
tibial shaft immediately
behind insertion of
sartorius

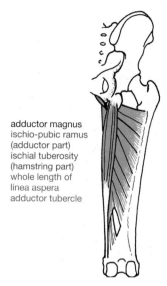

6.2.14 Adductor magnus.

adductor magnus
ischio-pubic ramus
(adductor part)
ischial tuberosity
(hamstring part)
whole length of
linea aspera
adductor tubercle

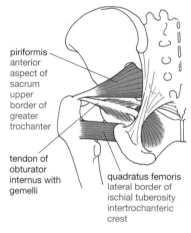

6.2.15 Piriformis, obturator internus with gemelli, quadratus femoris.

piriformis
anterior
aspect of
sacrum
upper
border of
greater
trochanter

tendon of
obturator
internus with
gemelli

quadratus femoris
lateral border of
ischial tuberosity
intertrochanteric
crest

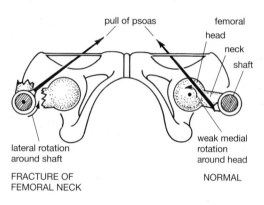

6.2.16 Diagram (viewed from feet) to show the line of pull of iliopsoas, with neck of femur either intact or fractured.

pull of psoas

femoral
head
neck
shaft

lateral rotation
around shaft

weak medial
rotation
around head

FRACTURE OF
FEMORAL NECK

NORMAL

Fracture of the neck of the femur

If the neck of the femur is broken, the shaft of the femur is free to rotate about its own longitudinal axis without constraint from the hip joint. Under these conditions, powerful muscles, such as psoas major produce lateral rotation of the femoral shaft, aided by muscles such as gluteus maximus and unopposed by any effective medial rotators.

Patients with a fractured neck of femur therefore classically present with the uninjured leg in the normal position, and the injured leg in marked lateral rotation (**6.2.16**, **6.2.17**, **6.2.18**).

femoral artery and vein pass from the extensor (anterior) to the flexor (posterior) compartment of the thigh.

Qu. 2E *What actions other than adduction might any of these muscles perform?*

Medial and lateral rotation

Neither medial nor lateral rotation of the hip is a powerful movement. However, both movements occur with each step, as the pelvis swings (p. 216). An understanding of how muscles produce these rotational movements is complicated by the presence of the femoral neck. The neck offsets the shaft and greater trochanter (to which the muscles are attached) from the axis of hip rotation, which, in the standing position, passes vertically down through the centre of the femoral head to the lateral femoral condyle. In the upright posture, muscles which pass in front of the axis produce medial rotation, even if, like adductor longus, they are attached to the posterior aspect of the femur; muscles that pass behind the axis produce lateral rotation.

The principal medial rotators of the hip are:
- adductor longus;
- tensor fasciae latae;
- anterior fibres of gluteus medius.

The most powerful lateral rotator is gluteus maximus (inferior gluteal nerve); the other lateral rotators are short postural muscles which lie deep in the gluteal region (**6.2.15**) and are supplied by small branches of the sacral plexus. They are:
- piriformis, which leaves the pelvis through the greater sciatic foramen;

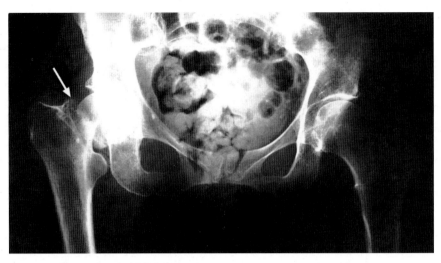

6.2.17 Radiograph of fractured neck of right femur.

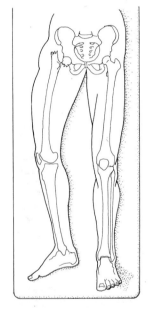

6.2.18 Position of legs in recumbent patient after fracture of neck of right femur.

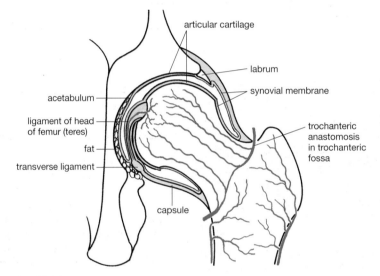

6.2.19 Blood supply to hip joint.

- obturator internus, which leaves the pelvis through the lesser sciatic foramen beneath the ischial spine; two small muscles (gemelli) insert into its tendon;
- quadratus femoris.

Blood and nerve supply to the hip joint

The acetabulum receives small blood vessels from surrounding arteries. The obturator artery gives a small branch which runs along the round ligament of the head, but does not contribute significantly to the supply of the femoral head.

The principal blood supply to the head of the femur is derived from vessels which run up its neck beneath the synovial membrane and fibrous bands (retinacula) continuous with the attachment of the capsule. The

vessels arise from a vascular anastomosis in the trochanteric fossa (p. 181) and enter foramina round the articular margin of the head.

The hip is innervated from the femoral, obturator and gluteal nerves.

Table 6.2.1 Hip joint: movements, principal muscles, and their innervation.

Movement	Principal muscles	Peripheral nerve	Spinal root origin
Flexion	Psoas major	Ventral rami of lumbar nerves	L 1, 2, 3
	Iliacus	Femoral nerve	L 2, 3
	Rectus femoris	Femoral nerve	L 2, 3, 4
	Pectineus	Femoral nerve	L 2, 3, 4
Extension	Gluteus maximus	Inferior gluteal nerve	L 5, S1, 2
	Hamstrings	Sciatic nerve (tibial component)	L 5, S1, 2
Adduction	Adductors longus, brevis, magnus, and gracilis	Obturator nerve	L 2, 3, 4
Abduction	Gluteus medius and minimus	Superior gluteal nerve	L 4, 5, S1
	Tensor fasciae latae	Superior gluteal nerve	L 4, 5, S1
Medial rotation	Tensor fasciae latae	Superior gluteal nerve	L 4, 5, S1
	Gluteus medius and minimus	Superior gluteal nerve	L 4, 5, S1
	Adductor longus	Obturator nerve	L 2, 3, 4
Lateral rotation	Obturator externus	Obturator nerve	L 2, 3, 4
	Sartorius	Femoral nerve	L 2, 3, 4
	Quadratus femoris	Sacral plexus	L 4, 5, S1
	Obturator internus	Sacral plexus	L 5, S1, 2
	Gluteus maximus	Inferior gluteal nerve	L 5, S1, 2

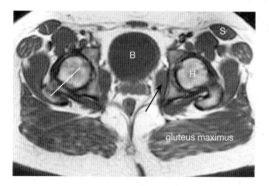

6.2.20 MRI of hip joint of adult male, axial plane. H, Head of femur, B, full bladder; S, sartorius; black arrow, obturator internus.

Imaging the hip joint

The hip joint is very commonly involved in pathological processes which require surgery. Imaging the hip is therefore an important procedure. Conventional radiographs show only the bones; CT and MRI can also show the muscles. **6.2.5** and **6.2.20** show, respectively, coronal and axial views through the hip joint.

6.2.5 shows the upward orientation of the neck of the femur. **6.2.20** shows that the neck of the femur also points anteriorly (white line) into the acetabular fossa. The fovea and part of the round ligament can be seen on the right side of the image. Gluteus maximus lies posteriorly; obturator internus winds posteriorly round the ischium to insert into the trochanteric fossa; sartorius lies anteriorly. Try to identify the other muscles. Within the pelvis the bladder is full; the seminal vesicles and rectum lie behind it. The tip of the coccyx is in the midline posteriorly.

Questions and answers

Qu. 2A *With respect to stability and movement, what are the major differences between the synovial 'ball-and-socket' joints of the upper and lower limbs?*

Answer The articular facets of the shoulder joint enable a wide range of movement to take place, stability in this joint depends on ligaments and, particularly, on the rotator cuff muscles. The articular facets of the hip joint, on the other hand, provide a much greater degree of stability, commensurate with weight-bearing locomotion, and therefore a smaller degree of movement.

Qu. 2B *On the left side of 6.1.11 draw the line described on p. 134 and illustrated on the right side of 6.1.11. Which hip is dislocated?*

Answer The head of the femur on the patient's right side is dislocated; Shenton's line is discontinuous.

Qu. 2C *Why is there a lower incidence of 'congenital dislocation' of the femur in Nigeria, where many infants are carried with their legs astride on their mother's hip?*

Answer Treatment of congenital dislocation of the hip is to place the infant in a plastic cast with both hips abducted. In Nigeria, babies are often carried astride their mother's hip (i.e. with both legs abducted); therefore congenital dislocation is less often apparent in that country.

Qu. 2E *Use 6.2.8 to consider what structures might be damaged by the bony fragment, and what might be the effect of such damage.*

Answer Posterior dislocation of the hip must break off the posterior margin of the acetabulum. The sciatic nerve lies behind this and can be damaged by bone fragments. Car drivers involved in frontal collisions are at risk, but the injury has become less common thanks to the wearing of seat belts which prevent the knees from hitting the dashboard, forcing the femur backward.

Qu. 2D *What actions other than adduction might any of these muscles perform?*

Answer The adductor muscles can also medially rotate the thigh; adductor magnus acting as a hamstring extends the thigh; gracilis flexes and can medially rotate the knee joint.

The knee joint and its movements SECTION 3

The knee joint and its movements   SECTION 3

We spend part of our time moving about in various ways, and at other times we stand still for quite prolonged periods. Therefore, the knee joint has to act both as a part of the lever system that propels us during locomotion, and also as part of a weight-bearing pillar that can be held in a stable, extended position with the minimum amount of muscular effort. It might appear at first sight that the knee joint needs only to flex and extend, and would therefore be similar in structure to the elbow, in which the bony articulation between the humerus and ulna restricts movement to this plane. However, the articular surfaces of the femur and tibia are far less congruent than those between the ulna and humerus. The two condyles of the femur are rounded, but the upper articular surface of the tibia is a horizontal plateau.

Stability of the knee joint depends largely on a powerful anterior 'extensor mechanism' consisting of the quadriceps muscle, in the tendon of which is set a large sesamoid bone, the patella, which also articulates with the femoral condyles. Further support comes from the ligaments, which all become taut in full extension, when a small degree of rotation of the femur produces the locking that stabilizes the knee. When the knee is flexed, a considerable amount of passive rotation of the joint is possible. When excessive, such rotation is a major cause of injury to the knee.

Living anatomy

Ask an adult colleague to stand upright and examine both knees. The patellae should face forward and the centre of the knee joint should lie vertically beneath that of the hip joint. In children up to the age of 4 years the knees are often in contact when the feet are up to 10 cm apart ('knock knees'). This 'valgus' deformity usually disappears with time.

Define, on your own and on a colleague's flexed or extended knee, the following parts of the joint:
- the outline of the patella, especially its medial border;
- the articular margin of each femoral condyle;
- the margin of the anterior part of each tibial condyle;
- the joint line anteriorly, medially, and laterally. To do this, sit with your knees bent at right angles. Feel for the lowest point on the patella then run your fingers laterally while gently flexing and extending your knee. The margin of the femoral condyle and the joint line should be easily felt. On the medial side, the broad, flat medial ligament makes the underlying structures more difficult to feel;
- the medial and lateral epicondyles of the femur;
- the tibial tuberosity.

Move your own knee. Its main movement is flexion and extension and it therefore appears to be a simple hinge joint. However, more subtle movements take place which cannot easily be observed in the living, and the joint is therefore classified as a compound hinge joint.

Extend your knee against resistance while palpating the anterior aspect of your thigh to feel the contraction of quadriceps femoris (**6.3.1**), the homologue of triceps in the arm. Note the muscular bulges formed by parts of quadriceps proximal to and on either side of the patella; that on the medial side is the more pronounced. This is because the shaft of the femur slopes upward *and laterally* from the condyles, and so the patella has a tendency to dislocate laterally.

Compare the size of this prominences on the two sides and see if you can detect a difference. Also measure the circumference of the thigh at two different levels above the patella. Often the dominant thigh (as for kicking) will be measurably larger than the other.

> ### Wasting of quadriceps
>
> Wasting of quadriceps is an early physical sign of disease of the knee joint. This is often apparent first in the diminished prominence of the part of quadriceps (vastus medialis) just above the medial aspect of the knee. A decrease in the strength of this muscle also occurs with prolonged bed rest, and is one of the reasons why people feel 'wobbly' when they first get up again.

Extend one knee fully with the foot on the ground. You may be able to detect that, as full extension is

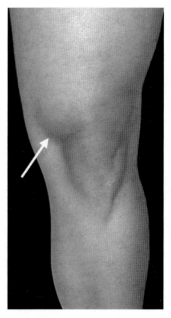

6.3.1 Extension of the knee against resistance. Prominent vastus medialis fibres (arrow) help stabilize the patella.

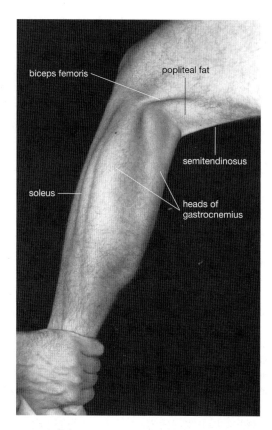

6.3.2 Flexion of the knee against resistance. This outlines the diamond-shaped popliteal fossa which lies behind the knee between the hamstring tendons and the two muscular heads of gastrocnemius.

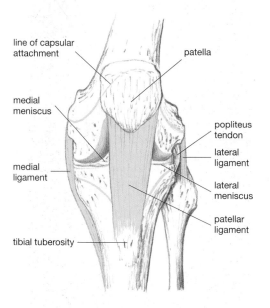

6.3.3 Knee joint: anterior view showing capsule attachments and ligaments.

contraction can be felt if you sit down, palpate the mid-point of your groin, and then lift your leg from the floor, flexing the hip.

Flex your knee against resistance and palpate the contraction of the 'hamstrings' at the back of the thigh (**6.3.2**). Follow the muscles down to the region behind the knee (the popliteal fossa). You should be able to make out two tendons on its medial aspect (semimembranosus and semitendinosus), which attach to the tibia, and one on its lateral aspect (biceps femoris), which attaches to the head of the fibula. If you extend your hip joint against resistance, you can confirm that the hamstrings are also active in this movement (p. 141).

You can show that some **rotation** can occur at the knee by standing with your right foot firmly on the floor and the right knee semi-flexed. Swing your hips from side to side and note that passive rotation occurs at the knee. Now sit and lift your foot from the ground. The leg can be rotated on the femur by about 20°; in either direction. If you feel behind the knee, you can feel the hamstrings contract alternately on the medial and lateral sides.

Qu. 3A. *Imagine a footballer who goes to kick a ball with his right foot, when the left knee is semi-flexed. If the kick is powerful, a considerable rotational force will be exerted on the left knee. When you have studied them, consider what ligaments and what other structures might be damaged.*

With two hands, grasp the lower leg of a seated colleague just below the knee and try to move the upper end of the tibia backward and forward on the femur. No such movement (subluxation) should be possible (see **6.3.8**).

The knee joint

The knee joint is a compound hinge, synovial joint, capable primarily of flexion and extension; small active and passive rotation movements also occur.

Its articular surfaces are the medial and lateral **condyles** of the femur and the tibial plateau, and the posterior surface of the patella, all of which are covered with articular hyaline cartilage (**6.3.3**, **6.3.4**, **6.3.5**). The femoral and tibial surfaces are partly separated by two fibro-cartilaginous **menisci** (**6.3.9**, see below).

Examine antero-posterior (**6.3.6**) and lateral (**6.3.7**) radiographs of an adult normal knee joint. Note the smooth contours of the upper aspects of the tibial condyles. Note also that the fibula takes no part in the joint.

The **capsule** of the knee joint is attached above to the posterior aspect of the femoral shaft above the condyles, and below to the margins of the tibial condyles. Anteriorly the capsule is replaced by the patella, the sesamoid bone of the quadriceps tendon. The knee joint is therefore protected anteriorly by the 'extensor mechanism', which consists of the quadriceps tendon, the patella, and the patellar tendon which passes down to insert into the tuberosity of the tibia. Fascial expansions (retinacula) which extend laterally on to the tibial condyles provide further support to the joint.

approached, the femur rotates medially on the tibia by a few degrees. This rotation is caused by the sequential tightening of ligaments around the knee. With all the ligaments taut, the knee is '**locked**' and virtually no muscular effort is needed to support the body. However, before the fully extended knee can be flexed, it is actively '**unlocked**' by a muscle (popliteus; see below) which rotates the femur laterally on the tibia.

One head of quadriceps femoris (rectus femoris) arises from the pelvis and also flexes the hip. Its

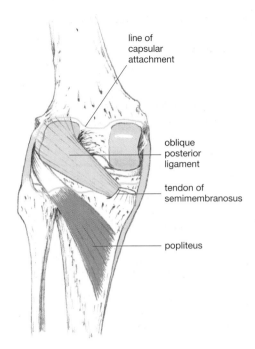

6.3.4 Knee joint: posterior view showing oblique posterior ligament and attachment of popliteus.

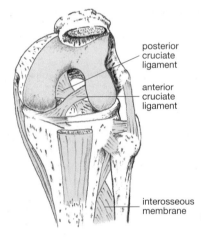

6.3.5 Cruciate ligaments, anterior view.

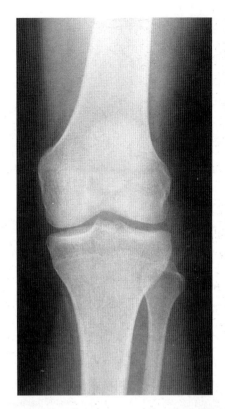

6.3.6 Knee joint (AP).

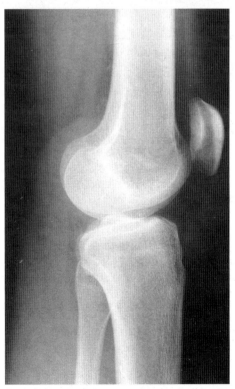

6.3.7 Knee joint (lateral).

As in any hinge joint, strong **collateral ligaments** strengthen the medial and lateral aspects of the capsule. The **medial ligament** is a broad band which extends between the medial epicondyle of the femur and the antero-medial aspect of the tibia well below the medial tibial condyle. The medial meniscus is strongly attached to its inner aspect. The **lateral ligament** is more round and rope-like; it extends between the lateral epicondyle of the femur and the head of the fibula. The lateral meniscus is not attached to it.

The obliquely running **posterior ligament** spreads upward and laterally from the posterior aspect of the medial tibial condyle (close to the insertion of semimembranosus). It reinforces the capsule against torsional stresses and limits the rotation of the femur that occurs as the knee 'locks'.

The **cruciate ligaments** (**6.3.5**) are two thick, rounded cords which lie centrally within the capsule, but outside the synovial cavity. The **anterior cruciate ligament** is attached anteriorly to the upper aspect of

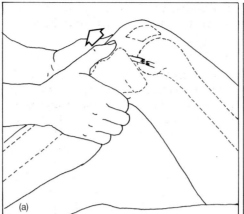
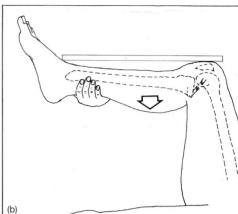

6.3.8 (a) Anterior 'drawer' test; (b) 'sag' test.

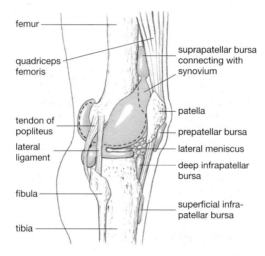

femur

quadriceps femoris

tendon of popliteus

lateral ligament

fibula

tibia

suprapatellar bursa connecting with synovium

patella

prepatellar bursa

lateral meniscus

deep infrapatellar bursa

superficial infra-patellar bursa

6.3.9 Synovial membrane and bursae of knee.

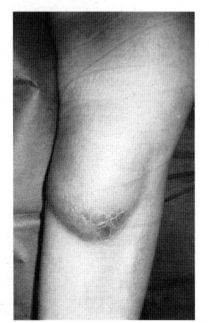

6.3.10 Swollen prepatellar bursa.

the tibia and passes upward and backward to the inner aspect of the lateral femoral condyle. The **posterior cruciate ligament** is attached to the posterior aspect of the upper surface of the tibia; it passes upward and forward to the inner aspect of the medial femoral condyle. The two ligaments therefore cross one another.

Ruptured cruciate ligaments

The cruciate ligaments play a very important part in the stability of the knee joint. If the anterior cruciate ligament is ruptured, the tibia can be moved forward with respect to the femur (the 'anterior drawer' test; **6.3.8a**). If the posterior cruciate ligament is ruptured, the leg will sag visibly if supported horizontally at the ankle (**6.3.8b**).

Synovial membrane lines the capsule and all surfaces not covered by articular cartilage. It covers the anterior and lateral, but not the posterior, surfaces of the cruciate ligaments and therefore does not line the entirety of the posterior aspect of the capsule. Anteriorly, it lines the patellar retinacula. It also extends above the patella to form a **suprapatellar bursa** (**6.3.9**), which allows the quadriceps muscle to slide freely over the femur.

An intra-capsular **fat pad** covered with synovial membrane lies below the patella and extends laterally as two wing-like alar folds. It increases the area of synovial membrane, helps distribute synovial fluid, and fills spaces in the joint which change in shape during movement.

Other bursae around the knee are not normally connected with the joint cavity. In front of the patella is the **prepatellar bursa**, and in front of and behind the patellar tendon are superficial and deep infrapatellar bursae. There are also bursae behind the knee associated with tendons inserted there.

Swellings associated with the knee joint

When a knee swells, either because inflammation has caused an effusion of fluid or trauma has caused bleeding into the joint, the swelling is diffuse and extends proximally above the patella because it extends into the suprapatellar bursa. Gentle squeezing on either side of the patella will therefore move the fluid swelling into and expand this bursa.

By contrast, a swelling that results from inflammation of the prepatellar bursa ('housemaid's knee'; **6.3.10**) or of the superficial infrapatellar bursa ('clergyman's knee') are confined to the front of the knee and do not communicate with the joint cavity.

Behind the knee, the bursa between the medial head of gastrocnemius and the capsule can enlarge to form a cyst.

The fibrocartilaginous **menisci** (**6.3.11**) are attached to the irregular central part of the tibia by each of their two horns. Peripherally they are attached by coronary 'ligaments' to the capsule. The majority of the menisci rely on synovial fluid for nutrition. However, they gain a small blood supply from the capsule so that, when damaged menisci are removed, their peripheral parts may subsequently regrow. The medial meniscus is firmly attached to the medial ligament of the knee, whereas the lateral meniscus is not attached to the lateral ligament but to the tendon of popliteus, which helps to control its movements. **6.3.12** is an arthrogram of a knee into which air has been introduced to delineate the meniscus.

Torn menisci

Severe strain, usually rotational, on a meniscus can cause a crescentic, or sometimes transverse, split in the fibrocartilage. This occurs more frequently in the medial meniscus, possibly because it is attached to the medial ligament of the knee and therefore presumably not as mobile as the lateral meniscus, which is controlled by popliteus (see below). The detached piece of meniscus may move into the centre of the joint and prevent the knee from extending fully. Such 'locking' of the knee which follows an (often sporting) injury must not be confused with the 'locking' mechanism which occurs naturally on full extension (see below).

Qu. 3B *If a rugby player sustained an injury to a knee and on examination it was found that the flexed lower leg could be moved backward and forward on the femur more easily than on the uninjured side, what would be the most likely cause?*

Qu. 3C *If another player complained of pain in the left knee, which he was unable to straighten, what structure might have been damaged?*

'Locking' and 'unlocking' of the knee

When we stand normally at rest, the knee is nearly fully extended, and almost no muscular action in quadriceps is needed for stability (see p. 215). In addition, a mechanism has evolved which 'locks' the knee in the fully extended state, enabling it to act, when necessary, as a very rigid prop.

As the joint approaches full extension, the femur undergoes a few degrees of medial rotation on the tibia which is fixed by contact of the foot with the ground. The rotation occurs because, as extension proceeds, the crossed anterior and posterior ligaments unwind, so that the medial femoral condyle moves backward on the tibia. Further extension and rotation is prevented by tightening of all the ligaments, including the oblique posterior ligament. In this position the joint is most stable. Flexion of the fully extended, 'locked' knee is facilitated by the contraction of popliteus.

Popliteus (**6.3.13**; tibial nerve) is attached so that it can laterally rotate both the lateral condyle of the femur and the lateral meniscus on the tibia, thereby 'unlocking' the joint. It arises from the posterior aspect of the tibia above the soleal line and its tendon passes through the joint capsule and into the knee joint, attaching first to the lateral meniscus and then to a pit on the lateral condyle of the femur.

Movements of the knee joint: muscles and their innervation

Flexion

Muscles attached to the pelvis or femur which pass downward posterior to the knee joint to either the tibia or fibula must **flex** the joint. The principal flexors are the 'hamstring' muscles which lie in the posterior compartment of the thigh (**6.3.14**, **6.3.15** and see **6.2.14**; sciatic nerve). They all arise from the ischial tuberosity and, therefore, also extend the hip.

- **Semimembranosus** originates by a 'membranous' aponeurosis and inserts into the grooved posterior aspect of the medial condyle of the tibia.
- **Semitendinosus** ends in a long tendon which passes downward superficial to semimembranosus then descends well below the level of the joint, to insert into the upper end of the shaft of the tibia behind sartorius and gracilis.
- **Biceps femoris** has a long head which arises from the ischial tuberosity and a short head which arises from the linea aspera. It passes down on the lateral aspect of the popliteal fossa to insert into the head of the fibula.

The part of adductor magnus which arises from the ischial tuberosity (**6.2.14**) is also considered to be a hamstring, but it attaches distally to the adductor tubercle on the femur and, therefore, has no action on the knee joint.

Hamstring injuries in sport

Injuries to one or other hamstring muscles ('torn hamstring') are relatively common and usually associated with sudden explosive exertion. They are therefore relatively common in sprinters, who suddenly pull up in the middle of a race, clutching the back of their thigh and limping off.

Extension

Muscles attached to the pelvis or femur which pass anterior to the knee joint to insert into the tibia must **extend** the knee. The extensors all lie in the anterior compartment of the thigh and are known as 'quadriceps' because of its four components (**6.3.16**, **6.3.17**; femoral nerve):

- **rectus femoris** arises from the anterior inferior iliac spine and the ilium just above the acetabulum;
- **vastus intermedius** arises from the front and sides of the femoral shaft;
- **vastus medialis** arises from a line on the medial aspect of the shaft which continues from the medial intertrochanteric line down the linea aspera;
- **vastus lateralis** arises from the lateral part of the intertrochanteric line, the base of the greater trochanter and the linea aspera.

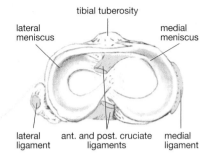

6.3.11 Menisci and attachments of cruciate ligaments of left knee viewed from above.

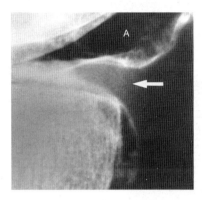

6.3.12 Arthrogram showing lateral meniscus (arrow) and air (A) introduced into joint cavity.

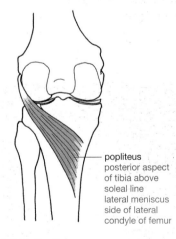

6.3.13 Popliteus.

popliteus
posterior aspect of tibia above soleal line
lateral meniscus
side of lateral condyle of femur

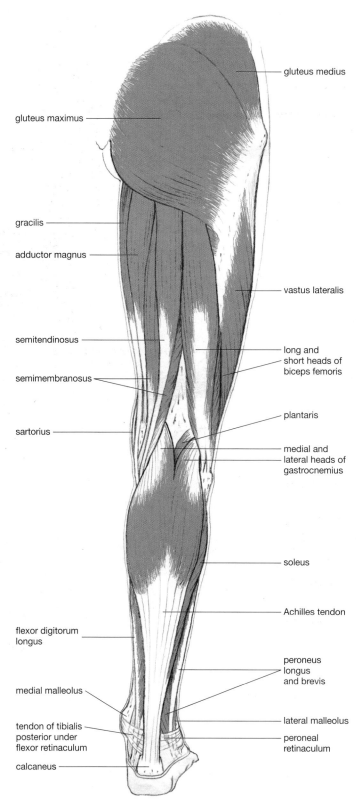

6.3.14 Muscles at the back of the lower limb.

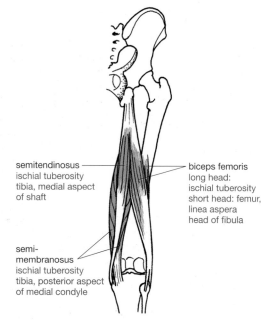

6.3.15 Hamstring muscles.

All four muscle bellies insert into the quadriceps tendon, which inserts into the upper margin of the patella and, via the patella and patellar tendon, to the tibial tuberosity. The fibres of vastus medialis, which make a bulge on the medial side of the knee, insert directly into the medial aspect of the patella.

Traction injury of the insertion of the quadriceps tendon (Osgood–Schlatter's disease)

This condition is common, and usually affects adolescents after strenuous activity. There is pain and a tender lump below the knee and over the tibial tuberosity. The apophysis into which the tendon inserts has been pulled away from the main part of the tibial shaft.

The line of pull of quadriceps is along the line of the shaft of the femur. Although the tibia is oriented vertically, the femur is not, and so quadriceps tends to pull the patella somewhat laterally. This tendency is counteracted by both the greater anterior projection of the lateral femoral condyle, and also by the lower fibres of vastus medialis, which insert into the medial aspect of the patella.

Dislocation of the patella

If the patella is smaller and slightly higher than normal, or if there is a tendency to 'knock knee', the patella can suffer recurrent dislocation, moving laterally so that it 'jumps over' the lateral condyle. When this occurs, quadriceps is reflexly inhibited and the patient's knee 'collapses'.

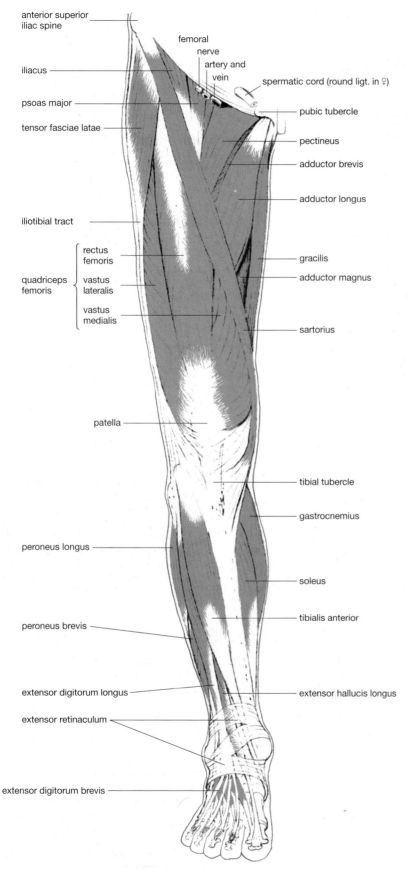

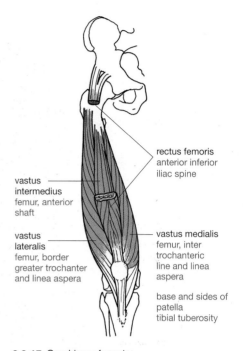

6.3.17 Quadriceps femoris.

6.3.16 Muscles of the front of the lower limb.

The unstable knee

The quadriceps, the patella, and their ligaments are collectively referred to as the **'extensor mechanism of the knee'** to emphasize the unity of function of the separate parts. The stability of the knee joint depends on it. If quadriceps is weakened, the knee will easily give way, causing a fall. If the extensor mechanism is subjected to excessive strain, the tibial tuberosity can be avulsed from its bed, or the lower pole of the patella pulled off; or the patella can fracture. Such injuries usually occur in younger age groups. In the elderly, however, the quadriceps tendon is more likely to give way, so that the patient cannot fully extend the knee against gravity.

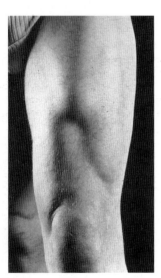

6.3.18 See Qu. 3F.

6.3.19 (a) Sagittal and (b) coronal MRIs of knee joint: Q, quadriceps tendon; Pa, patella; PT, patellar tendon; F, femur; T, tibia; E, epiphyseal line in femur/tibia; Fa, fat pad in knee joint; AC, anterior cruciate ligament; PC, posterior cruciate ligament; Pop, popliteal vessels; P, popliteus; G, gastrocnemius; LM, lateral meniscus; MM, medial meniscus; IT, iliotibial tract; VM, vastus medialis; VL, vastus lateralis.

Rotation

Active rotation of the knee occurs when popliteus laterally rotates the femur in 'unlocking' the knee; the medial rotation of 'locking' is essentially passive. The rotation that can occur in the semiflexed knee is usually passive but can be produced by alternate contraction of the medial and lateral hamstrings.

Qu. 3D *Which muscle of quadriceps group acts on the hip joint, and what movement does it produce?*

Qu. 3E *Why is the attachment of vastus medialis to the medial surface of the patella so important?*

Qu. 3F *Examine 6.3.18. The patient complained of pain in the thigh during a rugby match. What has happened?*

Sitting cross-legged

To sit in this position, the hip joint is flexed, abducted and laterally rotated, and the knee is flexed. Many of the muscles acting on the hip and knee take part in this movement, but one in particular—**sartorius**—moves the thigh into this position (see **6.2.10**; femoral nerve).

Stabilizing the pelvis over the tibia

Consider the attachments of sartorius, gracilis, and semitendinosus. All insert into the medial aspect of the upper end of the tibia, but their attachments on the pelvis are very widely separated—from the anterior superior iliac spine, the body of the pubis, and the ischial tuberosity. These long parallel muscles are thought to act like guy-ropes on a tent, stabilizing the pelvis in relation to the tibia. Similarly, the attachment of the ilio-tibial tract to the tibia allows gluteus maximus to stabilize the extended knee.

Blood and nerve supply to the knee joint

The knee joint receives numerous small vessels (genicular arteries) from an anastomosis formed by all the nearby arteries. One, the middle genicular artery, passes through the posterior part of the capsule to supply the cruciate ligaments.

All nerves which supply muscles acting on the knee also supply the knee joint (femoral, sciatic, obturator). Particularly important are branches from the nerve to vastus medialis (femoral nerve). Pain from a diseased hip joint can be referred to the knee.

Imaging the knee

Magnetic resonance images are used in the evaluation of many disorders of the knee. **6.3.19** and **6.3.20** are MR images of the knee in three different planes. Use these to review the structures of the knee joint. The cruciate ligaments, menisci, and the tendon of popliteus are well visualized by this method.

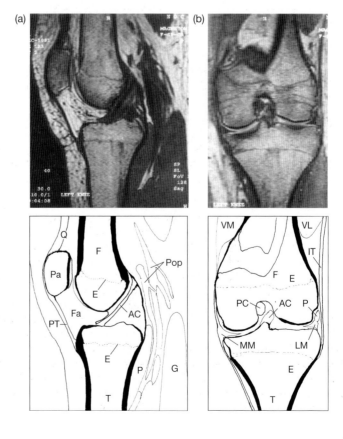

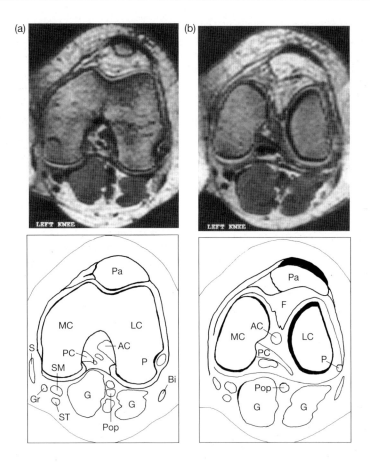

(a)   (b)

6.3.20 Transverse MRIs of knee joint, (a) at higher plane than (b). Labels as **6.3.19** and MC, medial condyle; LC, lateral condyle; S, sartorius; Gr, gracilis; ST, semitendinosus; SM, semimembranosus; Bi, biceps femoris.

Table 6.3.1 Knee joint: movements, principal muscles, and their innervation.

Movement	Principal muscles	Peripheral nerve	Spinal root origin
Extension	Quadriceps femoris	Femoral nerve	L 2, 3, 4
Flexion	Hamstring muscles (semimembranosus, semitendinosus, biceps femoris)	Sciatic nerve (tibial component)	L 5, S1, 2
Rotation	Alternate hamstring muscles	Sciatic nerve (tibial component)	L 4, 5, S1
	Popliteus (unlocking)	Tibial nerve	L 5, S1, 2

Note: because of the rotation of the limb, extension of the knee is supplied by higher segments than flexion. Compare Table 5.3.1.

The MR images also show other soft tissues, such as the vessels. When you have studied the vessels of the lower limb (Section 6), identify them on the images.

Fine flexible endoscopes can be inserted into the cavity of the knee joint to examine the menisci and other intracapsular structures.

Questions and answers

Qu. 3A. *Imagine a footballer who goes to kick a ball with his right foot, when the left knee is semi-flexed. If the kick is powerful, a considerable rotational force will be exerted on the left knee. When you have studied them, consider what ligaments and what other structures might be damaged.*

Answer It is most likely that the medial meniscus of the supporting knee has been torn. The meniscus is held by the medial collateral ligament and is subject to rotational stress as the momentum of the body attempts to rotate the femur on the supporting tibia. A second possibility is that one or other cruciate ligament has been ruptured. The 'anterior drawer' or 'sag' tests would indicate which of the two was damaged. A further possibility is that the medial or lateral collateral ligaments of the knee have been torn; this possibility can be tested by palpation and determining the degree to which abduction/adduction of the tibia on the femur can occur in the damaged limb compared to the uninjured limb.

Qu. 3B *If a rugby player sustained an injury to a knee and on examination it was found that the flexed lower leg could be moved backward and forward on the femur more easily than on the uninjured side, what would be the most likely cause?*

Answer It is likely that one or other of the cruciate ligaments have been ruptured. The 'anterior drawer' or 'sag' tests would indicate which of the two has been damaged.

Qu. 3C *If another player complained of pain in the left knee, which he was unable to straighten, what structure might have been damaged?*

Answer It is likely that a piece of meniscus has become detached, and free within the synovial cavity. This can then become trapped between the femoral and tibial articular surfaces as they become more congruent during extension.

Qu. 3D *Which muscle of quadriceps group acts on the hip joint, and what movement does it produce?*

Answer All muscles of the quadriceps group extend the knee; rectus femoris also stabilizes the hip joint and assists iliopsoas in flexing it.

Qu. 3E *Why is the attachment of vastus medialis to the medial surface of the patella so important?*

Answer The attachment of vastus medialis to the medial aspect of the patella helps to prevent a tendency to lateral displacement of the patella, which results from the angulation of the femoral shaft on the tibia.

Qu. 3F *Examine 6.3.18. The patient complained of pain in the thigh during a rugby match. What has happened?*

Answer Rectus femoris has ruptured.

Joints of the lower leg and their movements

Joints of the lower leg and their movements

As we walk, the foot has to act as a lever to propel the body forward. The fulcrum of that lever is the ankle joint, which therefore has to be very stable, and capable of transmitting the entire body weight from the tibia to the talus. Movements at the ankle joint are therefore essentially restricted to flexion and extension. Unlike the forearm, the tibia and fibula are held together very firmly and move very little on one another. The movements in the lower limb equivalent to pronation and supination in the upper limb, are restricted to joints within the foot.

Living anatomy

Examine the range of movement of your ankle. When standing, the foot is at right angles to the leg. It can be flexed (plantar-flexed) by about 60° and extended (dorsiflexed) by only about 15°. On a skeleton, note that the superior articular surface of the talus, which articulates with the tibia and fibula, is wider anteriorly than posteriorly. Therefore, when the foot is extended (as in walking up hill) the ankle is more stable than when flexed (as in walking down hill), when a small amount of abduction and adduction is possible. Move your foot and discover whether movements other than flexion and extension occur at the ankle. Inversion or eversion of the foot occur only at the subtalar and transverse tarsal joints.

Palpate the front of your leg to feel the sharp anterior margin of the tibia (shin); trace it upward and downward and note that the subcutaneous surface of the tibia extends from the knee to the medial malleolus. Now palpate the lateral malleolus and try to trace the fibula upward; it is largely encased in muscle.

Palpate the muscle group between the tibia and fibula anteriorly and note its contraction when the ankle is extended (dorsiflexed), when the foot is inverted, and when the toes are extended against resistance (**6.4.1**). At the front of the ankle identify the tendons of **tibialis anterior** medially and **extensor hallucis longus** and **extensor digitorum longus** more laterally. Palpate the area immediately lateral to the tendon of extensor digitorum longus and again extend your toes against resistance to feel the contraction of a small muscle—**extensor digitorum brevis**.

Get a colleague to stand and take his weight on one leg, rising on to the toes. In the calf the two bellies of **gastrocnemius** stand out superficially, and **soleus** bulges beneath on either side of them, especially distally (see **6.3.2**). Both muscles end in the **calcaneal (Achilles) tendon**, which is attached to the calcaneus at the heel, and is very easily seen and felt.

Tibio-fibular joints

The head of the fibula articulates with the posterolateral aspect of the lateral condyle of the tibia. This **superior tibio-fibular joint** is a plane synovial joint which permits the fibula to rotate slightly as the talus moves in the ankle joint (see below). The shaft of the tibia is united for most of its length to the fibula by

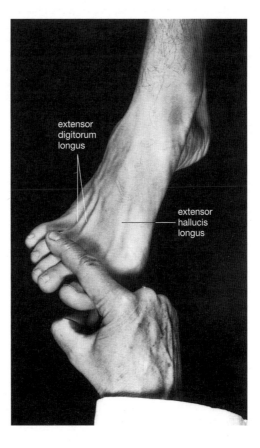

6.4.1 Extension of toes against resistance.

extensor digitorum longus

extensor hallucis longus

Rupture of the calcaneal (Achilles) tendon

The calcaneal tendon transmits very considerable forces and is the thickest tendon in the body. Despite its thickness, it can be weakened by calcification or degeneration, and sudden contractions of the powerful gastrocnemius and soleus muscles can rupture it. This can occur, for example, during violent movement in a game of squash. The tendon often snaps audibly and this, combined with the sudden pain, can make the sufferer believe that they have been struck on the ankle.

The integrity of the calcaneal tendon can be tested by squeezing the calf from side to side with the ankle relaxed ('squeeze test'). If the tendon is intact, then the foot passively plantar-flexes with each squeeze and returns to the resting position when the pressure is relaxed. If the tendon is ruptured no such movement occurs.

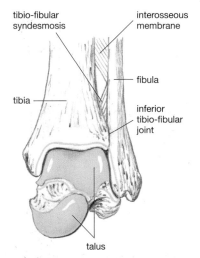

6.4.2 Anterior attachments of capsule of left ankle joint, and inferior tibio-fibular joint.

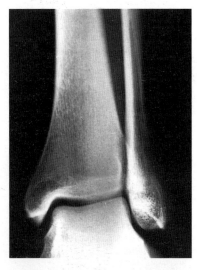

6.4.3 Ankle joint (AP); note the uniformity of the gap between the talus and the tibia and fibula and their malleoli.

means of an interosseous membrane, which serves principally for the attachment of muscles. The lower ends of the shafts of the tibia and fibula are united by a fibrous **inferior tibio-fibular** joint at which little movement can occur (see **6.4.2**). Anterior and posterior ligaments and a deep transverse tibio-fibular ligament reinforce this joint and contribute to the socket into which the wedge-shaped superior articular surface of the talus fits.

Ankle joint

The ankle joint is a synovial hinge joint, with a single axis passing transversely through the body of the talus and the two malleoli lying on either side. The lower end of the tibia articulates with the upper and medial articular surfaces on the body of the talus; the lower end of the fibula articulates with the lateral aspect of the articular surface of the talus.

Because the lower end of the tibia and fibula are so firmly held together, the presence of the two malleoli extending down on either side of the talus creates a mortice-type joint, which prevents almost all abduction and adduction.

Similarly, because the superior articular surface on the talus is slightly wider anteriorly than posteriorly, it is more firmly held between the malleoli and therefore more stable when the joint is extended (dorsiflexed), i.e. in the position of maximum thrust during locomotion.

Examine antero-posterior and lateral radiographs of the ankle joint (**6.4.3**, **6.4.4**) and note that:

- In the adult there is overlap between the tibia and fibula at the inferior tibio-fibular joint. In a normal joint it is not possible to see between them; if you can, then a fracture of the joint has occurred.
- The ankle joint space is uniform. The maximum distance between the medial surface of the talus and the lateral articular surface of the medial malleolus should be about the same as that between the lateral

surface of the talus and the articular surface of the fibula. If it is much greater, then the talus has moved laterally and the medial ligament must have ruptured.

- In the radiograph of a young patient (see **6.1.15**), the epiphyseal plate of the lower end of the fibula lies at the same level as the line of the ankle joint, i.e. at a lower level than that of the tibia.

The ankle joint can also be imaged by MRI. An example is shown in **6.5.4**.

The **capsule** of the ankle joint is attached around the articular margins of the tibia, fibula, and talus (**6.4.2**). As in other hinge joints, the capsule is reinforced by strong lateral and medial ligaments. The **lateral ligament** (**6.4.5**) has three parts, each of which may be separately damaged in a 'sprain' of the joint. The **anterior talofibular** part is attached superiorly to the lateral malleolus and runs forward and medially to the neck of the talus; the **calcaneofibular** part runs downward and backward from the tip of the malleolus to the lateral side of the calcaneus; the **posterior talofibular** part (**6.4.6**) runs horizontally from the malleolar fossa on the inner aspect of the medial malleolus to the posterior aspect of the talus. The fan-shaped **medial (deltoid) ligament** (**6.4.7**) is attached above to the medial malleolus of the tibia and below to the navicular and

> ### 'Sprains', and fracture dislocations at the ankle
>
> Walking on very uneven surfaces places considerable strains on the medial and lateral ligaments. When these are excessive, tears can occur in the ligaments ('sprains'). However, such is the strength of the medial ligament that, when excessive eversion twists the talus in its mortice to the extent that ligaments or bones give way, it is more common for the medial malleolus to be pulled off the shaft of the tibia than for the medial ligament to rupture. Such a fracture is shown in **6.4.8**.
>
> By contrast, in inversion injuries it is usually the rather thinner lateral ligament that gives way.

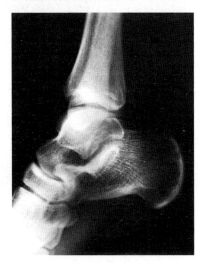

6.4.4 Ankle, subtalar, and mid-tarsal joints (lateral).

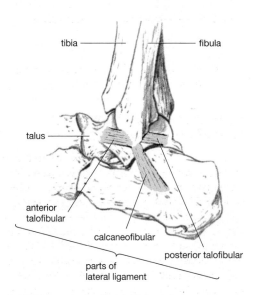

6.4.5 Ligaments of ankle joint, lateral view.

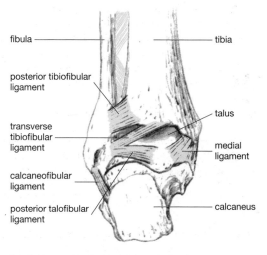

6.4.6 Ligaments of ankle joint, posterior view.

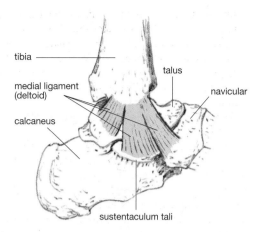

6.4.7 Ligaments of ankle joint, medial view.

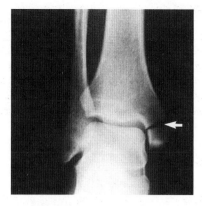

6.4.8 Fracture (arrow) of medial malleolus (compare with **6.4.3**); the radiolucent space between the bones is not uniform.

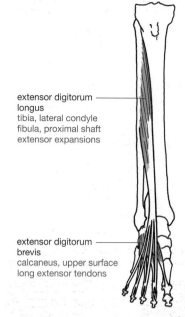

6.4.10 Extensor digitorum longus and extensor digitorum brevis.

the sustentaculum tali of the calcaneus. It is very strong compared to the lateral ligament.

Movements at the ankle joint: muscles and innervation

Extension (dorsiflexion)

Any muscle attached to the tibia or fibula which passes in front of the ankle joint to an insertion in the foot must extend the joint. Prime movers in this action are all located in the anterior compartment of the leg and supplied by the deep branch of the common peroneal nerve. They are:
* tibialis anterior (**6.4.9**);
* extensor hallucis longus (**6.4.9**);
* extensor digitorum longus (**6.4.10**).

Qu. 4A *What other actions do these muscles have, particularly tibialis anterior?*

Flexion (plantar flexion)

Muscles of the calf which arise from the posterior aspect of the tibia and fibula which pass posterior to the axis of the ankle joint will plantar-flex the foot. However, the posterior extension of the calcaneus to form the heel means that the deep muscles of the calf must pass medially around the calcaneus to reach the foot. The prime movers, which are all supplied by the tibial nerve, are:
* the superficial calf muscles—gastrocnemius and soleus (**6.4.11**);
* the deep calf muscles—flexor digitorum longus (**6.4.12**), flexor hallucis longus (**6.4.13**), and tibialis posterior (**6.4.14**).

Qu. 4B *What are the other actions of the superficial calf muscles?*

Qu. 4C *What effect would rupture of the calcaneal tendon have on the function of the foot if the foot were (a) free of the ground; (b) weight-bearing?*

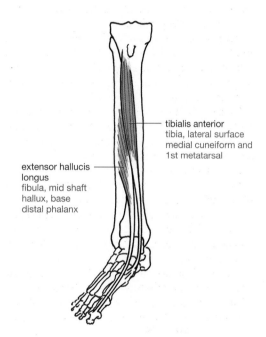

6.4.9 Extensor hallucis longus and tibialis anterior.

Qu. 4D *Why is it important to repair a ruptured calcaneal tendon as soon as possible after injury?*

Control of the tendons around the ankle

As at the wrist, the long tendons are controlled by retinacula (**6.4.15**, **6.4.16**). The extensor tendons are held in place by an **extensor retinaculum** on the front of the ankle. This is formed by two thickenings of the deep fascia: an upper band (superior extensor retinaculum) which is attached to the lower end of the tibia and fibula, and a lower Y-shaped band, the stem of which is attached to the lateral aspect of the calcaneus, while the two arms are attached to the medial malleolus and plantar fascia. Synovial sheaths surround the tendons beneath the retinacula.

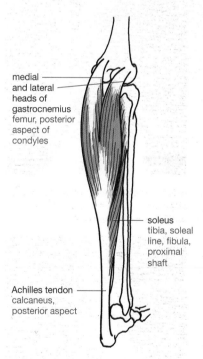

6.4.11 Gastrocnemius and soleus.

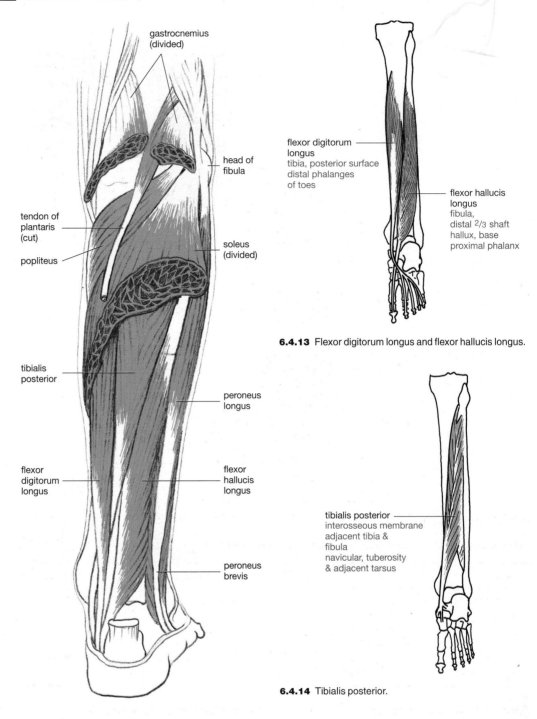

gastrocnemius
(divided)

head of
fibula

tendon of
plantaris
(cut)

popliteus

soleus
(divided)

tibialis
posterior

peroneus
longus

flexor
digitorum
longus

flexor
hallucis
longus

peroneus
brevis

6.4.12 Deep muscles of the calf (plantaris may or may not be present).

flexor digitorum
longus
tibia, posterior surface
distal phalanges
of toes

flexor hallucis
longus
fibula,
distal 2/3 shaft
hallux, base
proximal phalanx

6.4.13 Flexor digitorum longus and flexor hallucis longus.

tibialis posterior
interosseous membrane
adjacent tibia &
fibula
navicular, tuberosity
& adjacent tarsus

6.4.14 Tibialis posterior.

The flexor tendons derived from the deep calf muscles pass behind and then inferior to the medial malleolus. The **flexor retinaculum** that holds them in place is attached to the medial malleolus above and the calcaneus below, and also to the sustentaculum tali.

On the lateral side of the ankle the tendons of the peroneal muscles which evert the foot (p. 171), are held down by peroneal retinacula. The peroneal muscles have little if any action on the ankle joint, except that, like muscles acting around any joint, their contraction provides active stability to the joint.

Qu. 4E *If a patient complained of pain in the left ankle after 'twisting' it by falling off a kerb, what structures might have been damaged?*

Blood and nerve supply to the ankle joint

The arterial supply is derived from the surrounding arteries (anterior tibial, peroneal, and posterior tibial); the nerve supply from the deep peroneal and tibial nerves.

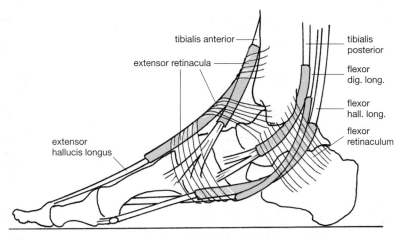

6.4.15 Tendons, synovial sheaths, and retinacula on the medial side of the ankle and foot.

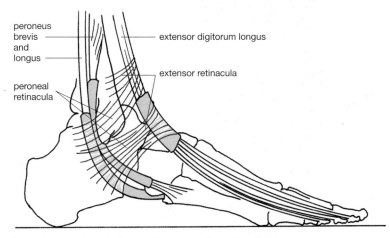

6.4.16 Tendons, synovial sheaths, and retinacula on the lateral side of the ankle and foot.

Table 6.4.1 Ankle joint: movements, principal muscles and their innervation.

Movement	Principal muscles	Peripheral nerve	Spinal root origin
Flexion (plantar flexion)	gastrocnemius soleus tibialis posterior long flexors of toes	Tibial nerve	L 4, 5
Extension (dorsiflexion)	tibialis anterior long extensors of toes	Deep peroneal nerve	L 5, S1

Imaging the ankle joint

Like other joints, the ankle can be imaged by conventional radiography (**6.4.3, 6.4.4, 6.4.8**), CT (see **6.5.14**), MRI and ultrasound. MRI **6.4.17** shows a coronal section through the right ankle. A substantial part of the lower end of the tibia is seen, but only the lateral malleolus of the fibula is in the plane of section. The mortice made by these bones with the talus is clear. The light area within the mortice between the bones is the articular cartilages. Between the talus and calcaneus is an interosseous ligament. Abductor hallucis is obvious on the medial side of the foot.

Questions and answers

Qu. 4A *What other actions do these muscles have, particularly tibialis anterior?*

Answer The anterior compartment muscles dorsiflex (extend) the foot at the ankle, while tibialis anterior also inverts the foot and helps to support the medial aspect of the transverse arch.

Qu. 4B *What are the other actions of the superficial calf muscles?*

Answer Because gastrocnemius is attached to both the right and left femoral condyles and its fibres pass

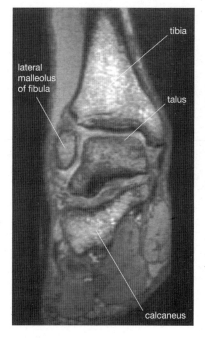

6.4.17 T$_2$-weighted coronal MRI of ankle joint.

posterior to the knee joint before inserting into the calcaneus, it must help to flex the knee joint.

Qu. 4C *What effect would rupture of the calcaneal tendon have on the function of the foot if the foot were (a) free of the ground; (b) weight-bearing?*

Answer (a) If the foot is free of the ground a ruptured calcaneal tendon will have no effect except that plantar flexion would be weaker. (b) While weight-bearing, however, the heel could not be raised from the ground, and forward propulsion in walking would be impossible in that limb.

Qu. 4D *Why is it important to repair a ruptured calcaneal tendon as soon as possible after injury?*

Answer Rapid repair of a torn calcaneal tendon is important because the muscle tends to retract and approximation of the two ends then becomes progressively more difficult.

Qu. 4E *If a patient complained of pain in the left ankle after 'twisting' it by falling off a kerb, what structures might have been damaged?*

Answer The lateral ligament (usually its anterior talofibular part) may be damaged (with or without fracture of the lateral malleolus) in hyper-inversion injuries of the foot. A hyper-eversion injury would damage the medial (deltoid) ligament, with the likelihood that the distal part of the medial malleolus (to which the ligament is attached) would be torn off.

Joints and movements of the foot   SECTION 5

Joints and movements of the foot   SECTION 5

Like the hand, the foot is constructed of numerous small bones, ligaments, long tendons from the leg, and intrinsic small muscles. Together these form a resilient and pliant arch through which the weight of the body is transmitted to the ground. Its structure provides shock absorption, stability, and propulsion of the body during locomotion. However, such are the stresses to which the feet are subject that they are frequently injured, and these injuries can cause prolonged pain and difficulty with walking.

Because we often walk on very uneven ground, the foot must be able to act with the sole in a variety of different orientations. Movements which orient the foot on uneven surfaces occur primarily at a 'subtalar' joint between the talus and other bones of the foot. Smaller gliding movements also occur at a 'transverse tarsal' joint. The final thrust-off in walking derives from a powerful flexion of the toes, in particular the great toe. Indeed, the axis of the foot has moved toward the great toe and passes, not through the middle digit as in the upper limb, but through the second toe.

Living anatomy

Examine the orientation of the feet of a colleague standing naturally. They may face directly forward or point somewhat outward or inward.

Qu. 5A *If a foot is rotated laterally or medially, which joint is implicated?*

Arches of the foot

Examine the **shape** of the feet. The medial aspect of a foot should form a distinct longitudinal **arch** between the heel and the metatarsal heads (**6.5.1**). Examination of other feet will reveal differences in the height of this arch. On the lateral side of the foot the skin is probably touching the ground, but this conceals a shallow lateral arch in the bones. Now examine the sole of the foot and note the transverse curvature which forms half of an arch. Look at the heel from behind, noting that it is somewhat everted. Ask your colleague to stand 'on tip-toe'; the heel should move from slight eversion to slight inversion.

Qu. 5B *Does the longitudinal arch become more or less accentuated when one stands on tip-toe?*

Note any angulation of the great toe with respect to the foot and first metatarsal.

Examine the skin of the foot, noting the natural thickenings over the heel and pads of the toes and any abnormally thickened areas ('corns') resulting from pressure (e.g. of ill-fitting shoes). Examine the toes for any inflammation at the sides of the nails caused by 'ingrowing toenails', another consequence of wearing shoes. Examine the skin webs between the toes; they can vary considerably in extent.

Movements of the foot

Examine the movements of the foot which do not involve the ankle joint. Explore the amount of inversion (sole moving medially) and eversion (sole moving laterally; **6.5.3**) that is possible.

Qu. 5C *At which joint does the movement occur, and which tarsal bones move and which do not during these movements?*

Hallux valgus and bunions

In people who wear tight shoes, and especially in women over sixty, lateral angulation of the great toe (hallux valgus) is common (**6.5.2**). Once the great toe starts to angle laterally, the pull of flexor hallucis longus (p. 172) tends to increase the deformity. If the head of the first metatarsal becomes prominent a protective bursa develops between it and the skin which can become inflamed (a 'bunion'). This may, in time, require surgery to reshape the metatarsal.

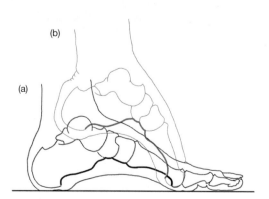

6.5.1 (a) Medial longitudinal arch of the foot when standing. (b) Change in medial arch and dorsiflexion of metatarso-phalangeal joint when standing on tip-toe and at the start of locomotion.

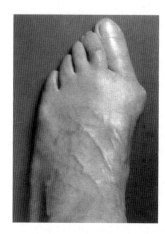

6.5.2 Enlarged and deformed metatarso-phalangeal joint ('bunion').

Explore the range of movements at the metatarso-phalangeal and interphalangeal joints (see **6.4.1**). Although the movements are similar in type to those of the hand, they are, in general, much more restricted in extent.

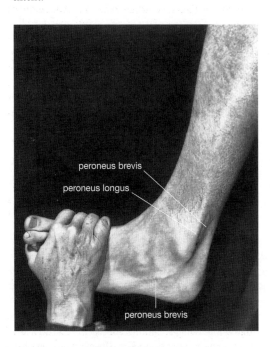

6.5.3 Eversion of the foot against resistance.

Stand up and take a step forward. Note how, as the heel of the weight-bearing foot rises from the ground, the toes, in particular the big toe, are passively dorsi-flexed at the metatarso-phalangeal joints. This stretches flexor hallucis longus, which then contracts to provide the final thrust-off in the striding gait (see Figure 8.5 on p. 217). The dorsiflexion (extension) of the toes also stretches ligaments in the sole of the foot, tensing and accentuating the arch.

Protective features of the sole of the foot

The skin of the sole is repeatedly subjected to shearing and impact stresses, especially over the heels and the pads of the sole and toes. Protecting the underlying structures are:

- skin which is thickened, especially over pressure points;
- a thick layer of subcutaneous fat, which is loculated by fine, but collectively strong, bands of connective tissue (**6.5.4**) which run from the skin to the deep fascia;

Qu. 5D *How would this arrangement be protective?*

- the **plantar aponeurosis** (**6.5.5**), a dense fibrous sheet attached posteriorly to the calcaneus and dividing anteriorly into five slips which attach to the sides of the proximal phalanges of the toes.

The subtalar joint

The **subtalar joint** (**6.5.6**) is the synovial articulation situated beneath the talus. It has two parts, the

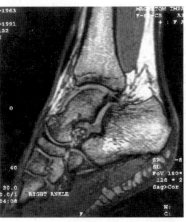

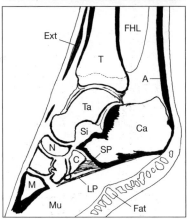

6.5.4 MRI of ankle, subtalar, and mid-tarsal joints (sagittal section). T, Tibia; Ta, talus; Ca, calcaneus; N, navicular; C, cuboid; M, metatarsal; Ext, extensor tendon; FHL, flexor hallucis longus; A, Achilles tendon; Si, tarsal sinus containing interosseous ligament; SP, short plantar ligament; LP, long plantar ligament; Mu, muscles of sole; Fat, loculated subcutaneous fat in sole.

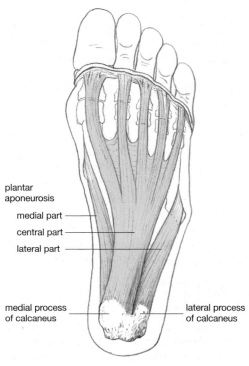

6.5.5 Plantar aponeurosis.

articular surfaces of which are reciprocally curved to permit inversion and eversion of the foot. Examine the lateral radiograph (see **6.4.4**) and sagittal MRI (**6.5.4**) showing the ankle and subtalar joints.

The posterior articulation (to which the term 'subtalar joint' is often restricted) is between the concave facet on the undersurface of the talus and the convex facet on the upper surface of the calcaneus (talocalcaneal joint). Its capsule is strengthened by medial and lateral ligaments and by an **interosseous ligament** which occupies the **tarsal canal** between the bones.

The anterior articulation (talo-calcaneo-navicular joint) is effectively a synovial ball and socket joint between the head of the talus and a socket formed by the concave posterior surface of the navicular, the anterior facet on the upper surface of the calcaneus, and the upper surface of the 'spring' ligament.

The '**spring**' (plantar calcaneo-navicular) **ligament** (**6.5.7**) is a broad, thick band which connects the anterior margin of the sustentaculum tali of the calcaneus to the navicular. It therefore 'ties' the apex of the medial arch of the foot, preventing the talus from being forced down between the calcaneus and the navicular by the weight of the body. Its upper surface is covered with articular cartilage. The calcaneus and navicular are also connected dorsally by a bifurcate ligament. This also connects the calcaneus to the cuboid, and forms the main bond between the two rows of tarsal bones.

Movements at the subtalar joint: muscles and innervation

Eversion

The peroneal muscles which arise from the fibula and have tendons which pass behind the lateral malleolus to insert in the foot evert the joint (**6.5.3**). They are:
- **peroneus longus** and **peroneus brevis** (**6.5.8**). Behind the lateral malleolus their tendons are held in place by the peroneal retinaculum (see **6.4.16**). Both are supplied by the superficial peroneal branch of the common peroneal nerve.

Inversion

Muscles which arise from the anterior surface of the tibia and fibula and pass distally across the ankle to insert into the medial side of the foot not only extend (dorsiflex) the foot, but also invert it. Prime movers in inversion are:
- **tibialis anterior** (see **6.4.9**, **6.4.15**);
- **extensor hallucis longus** (see **6.4.9**).

Like all the extensors, they are supplied by the deep peroneal branch of the common peroneal nerve.

Other joints of the tarsus, metatarsus, and phalanges

The **calcaneo-cuboid joint**, which lies at the apex of the 'lateral arch' of the foot, is strengthened dorsally by the bifurcated ligament and, on its plantar aspect by the short and long plantar ligaments.

The **short plantar ligament** (**6.5.7**) fills the depression between the anterior tubercle of the calcaneus and the ridge on the plantar aspect of the cuboid. The **long plantar ligament** extends from a broad attachment on the undersurface of the calcaneus to the ridge on the cuboid, and then forward, over the tendon of peroneus longus, to the bases of the second to fifth metatarsals.

The calcaneo-cuboid and calcaneo-navicular articulations together form a '**mid-tarsal joint**' which crosses the foot transversely and moves a little during inversion and eversion. Minor twisting injuries to the foot can cause dislocation of the mid-tarsal and tarsometatarsal joints, which is difficult to diagnose and which can cause prolonged discomfort.

The remaining intertarsal joints—tarso-metatarsal, metatarso-phalangeal, and interphalangeal joints—are very similar to their counterparts in the hand. The joints of the big toe, like its bones, are particularly strong, and the head of the first metatarsal is grooved on its plantar surface for two sesamoid bones which protect the tendon of flexor hallucis longus as it passes beneath the joint to insert into the distal phalanx.

Movements of the toes: muscles and innervation

The toes are capable of movements similar in type to those of the fingers but, because of the adaptation of the foot to locomotion and weight-bearing rather than to precise manipulations, there are some important differences.

Flexion (plantar flexion)

Muscles arising from the posterior aspect of the tibia and fibula, with tendons which pass behind the medial malleolus and run through the sole to insert into the phalanges, will flex both the ankle and the toes. The prime movers (**6.5.10**, and see **6.4.12**, **6.4.15**), both of which are supplied by the tibial branch of the sciatic

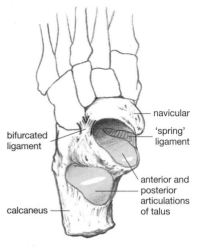

6.5.6 Subtalar joint.

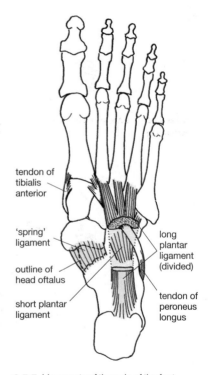

6.5.7 Ligaments of the sole of the foot.

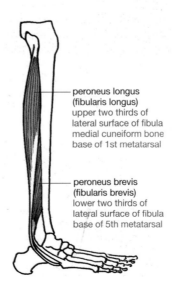

peroneus longus (fibularis longus) upper two thirds of lateral surface of fibula medial cuneiform bone base of 1st metatarsal

peroneus brevis (fibularis brevis) lower two thirds of lateral surface of fibula base of 5th metatarsal

6.5.8 Peroneus longus, peroneus brevis.

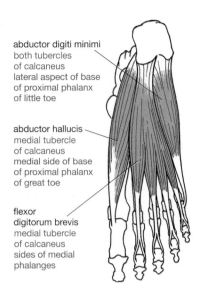

abductor digiti minimi
both tubercles
of calcaneus
lateral aspect of base
of proximal phalanx
of little toe

abductor hallucis
medial tubercle
of calcaneus
medial side of base
of proximal phalanx
of great toe

flexor
digitorum brevis
medial tubercle
of calcaneus
sides of medial
phalanges

6.5.9 Sole of foot, muscle layer 1.

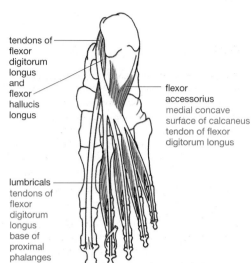

tendons of
flexor
digitorum
longus
and
flexor
hallucis
longus

flexor
accessorius
medial concave
surface of calcaneus
tendon of flexor
digitorum longus

lumbricals
tendons of
flexor
digitorum
longus
base of
proximal
phalanges

6.5.10 Sole of foot, muscle layer 2.

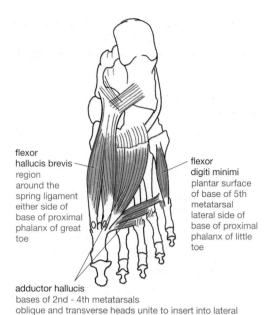

flexor
hallucis brevis
region
around the
spring ligament
either side of
base of proximal
phalanx of great
toe

flexor
digiti minimi
plantar surface
of base of 5th
metatarsal
lateral side of
base of proximal
phalanx of little
toe

adductor hallucis
bases of 2nd - 4th metatarsals
oblique and transverse heads unite to insert into lateral
side of base of proximal phalanx of great toe

6.5.11 Sole of foot, muscle layer 3.

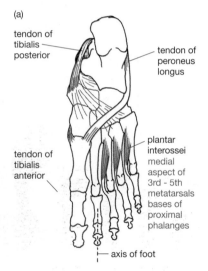

(a)

tendon of
tibialis
posterior

tendon of
peroneus
longus

tendon of
tibialis
anterior

plantar
interossei
medial
aspect of
3rd - 5th
metatarsals
bases of
proximal
phalanges

axis of foot

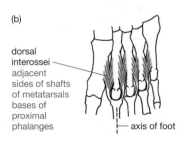

(b)

dorsal
interossei
adjacent
sides of shafts
of metatarsals
bases of
proximal
phalanges

axis of foot

6.5.12 Sole of foot muscle layer 4:
(a) plantar interossei; (b) dorsal interossei.

nerve, are:

- **flexor hallucis longus**, which flexes the big toe via an attachment to its distal phalanx;
- **flexor digitorum longus**, which divides into four tendons which, via insertions into their distal phalanges, flex the other toes. Lumbrical muscles are associated with these tendons.

However, because the development of the heel has caused the pull of these tendons to be oblique, an additional muscle—flexor accessorius (**6.5.10**)—which arises from the sides of the undersurface of the calcaneus, inserts into the tendons to straighten their pull with respect to the axis of the foot.

Short muscles arising from the plantar surfaces of the bones of the foot and inserting into the phalanges also flex the toes. They are **flexor digitorum brevis** (**6.5.9**), the tendons of which divide around those of flexor digitorum longus before inserting into the middle phalanges, and the short flexors of the big and little toes, **flexor hallucis brevis** and **flexor digiti minimi brevis** (**6.5.11**).

In addition, the lumbrical and interosseous muscles (**6.5.10**, **6.5.12**) flex the metatarso-phalangeal joints.

All these are innervated by the (medial and lateral) plantar nerves derived from the tibial nerve.

Extension (dorsiflexion)

Muscles attached to the anterior aspect of the tibia and fibula or dorsum of the foot which insert into the phalanges must extend the toes. The muscles are:

- **extensor hallucis longus** (see **6.4.9**);
- **extensor digitorum longus** (see **6.4.10**);
- **extensor digitorum brevis** (see **6.3.16**, **6.4.10**).

They are all supplied by the deep peroneal branch of the common peroneal nerve.

Abduction and adduction (6.5.9–6.5.12)

These movements are possible in all toes but, compared to those of the hand, are very limited. The big toe has its own abductor and adductor (**abductor** and **adductor hallucis**) and the little toe has its own abductor. Four dorsal and three plantar **interossei** arise from the metatarsals. As in the hand, the dorsal abduct and the plantar adduct the toes. However, in the foot the axis around which they are organized passes longitudinally through the second toe. The flexor action of the interossei and lumbricals on the metatarso-phalangeal joint enables the toes to 'grip' the ground, but this action is not very important when shoes are worn. Like the other muscles in the sole of the foot, they are supplied by plantar branches of the tibial nerve.

'Layers' of the foot

The small muscles and long tendons in the sole of the foot are, for convenience, often described as forming four layers. These layers have no functional significance and there is no need to memorize them or the origins and insertions of the small muscles.

- Layer 1 (**6.5.9**) comprises abductor hallucis, flexor digitorum brevis, and abductor digiti minimi.
- Layer 2 (**6.5.10**) comprises the tendons of flexor digitorum longus and flexor hallucis longus, flexor accessorius, and the lumbrical muscles associated with flexor digitorum longus.
- Layer 3 (**6.5.11**) comprises flexor hallucis brevis, adductor hallucis, and flexor digiti minimi brevis.
- Layer 4 (**6.5.12**) comprises the dorsal and plantar interossei and the tendon of peroneus longus which passes behind the lateral malleolus, then crosses the

sole in the groove on the cuboid bone (covered by the long plantar ligament) to insert into the medial cuneiform bone and the base of the first metatarsal.

Functions of the small muscles of the foot

The actions of individual small muscles of the sole have been difficult to investigate electromyographically. With a subject standing quietly, the body weight being transmitted through the heels and heads of the metatarsals to the ground, no electrical activity can be recorded other than that associated with postural adjustments.

However, these muscles become very active when locomotion is initiated, the heel is lifted, the concavity of the sole is increased, and the foot becomes somewhat inverted. As the weight of the body and muscular thrust is transferred forward to the heads of the metatarsals and the toes (which become extended at the metatarso-phalangeal joints), the foot then acts as a lever which helps to propel the body forward. The small muscles of the sole, which have their line of pull along the long arch of the foot, maintain the arch of the foot and stabilize the transverse tarsal joint.

The arch of the foot

The arch of the foot, which is shaped like a half-dome, is usually described as consisting of three component arches: medial and lateral longitudinal arches and a transverse arch (though this is only half an arch, as is apparent when the feet are placed together). The apex of all the arches has the talus as its 'keystone'. Uniting the individual tarsal bones which make up the arches are plane synovial joints reinforced by intrinsic ligaments and muscle action.

The arch receives passive support from:
- the long and short plantar ligaments (**6.5.4, 6.5.7**)
- the very strong spring ligament (**6.5.6, 6.5.7**)
and active support from:
- the small muscles of the sole
- muscles of the leg and their tendons, especially: tibialis anterior (which pulls up the medial aspect of the arch via its insertion to the navicular); flexor hallucis longus and flexor digitorum longus (which 'tie' the extremities of the arch together).

The functions of the arch are:
- to distribute the weight of the body from the talus backward to the tubercles of the calcaneus in the heel, and forward to the sesamoid bones of the first metatarsal and the head of the lateral four metatarsals;
- to provide pliability, which enables the foot to adapt its shape while walking, running, and jumping on even or uneven surfaces;
- to act as a slightly elastic 'shock absorber' that adds 'spring' to the step.

A newborn baby's foot (**6.5.13**) does not have an obvious arch. When the child begins to walk, toward the end of the first year, the relatively large amount of fat in the sole of the foot regresses, and the arch begins to appear.

Flat foot

This term implies that the medial arch has collapsed so that the medial border of the foot almost touches the ground. This can cause chronic discomfort. In children, the normal arch may never appear. Apart from rare deformities of the talus, the cause is unknown, but muscle weakness or joint laxity (for example due to defective collagen synthesis) may be present.

Qu. 5E *What simple methods might be used initially to treat a child with flat feet?*

Flat foot may also be acquired: if the muscles are weakened by poliomyelitis; if tendons are ruptured; if the joints are damaged (e.g. by rheumatoid arthritis). One interesting form of flat foot is very occasionally seen in young people whose peroneal muscles go into spasm ('spasmodic flat foot'), causing a rigid eversion of the foot.

Qu. 5F *What is the link between eversion and flattening of the arch of the foot?*

The opposite condition, where the arch is abnormally high, is usually due to weakness of the intrinsic muscles of the foot. The toes may be 'clawed' (cf. clawing of fingers in damage to the ulnar nerve, (see **6.5.14**)).

Imaging the foot

MRI and CT can both be useful in determining the extent of bony injuries in the foot. CT **6.5.14** shows a horizontal section through the foot of a patient who had been involved in a car accident.

Qu. 5G *Which bone has been fractured?*

6.5.13 Development of footprints from 6 months to adult.

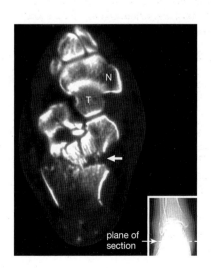

plane of section

6.5.14 CT of injured foot. See Qu. 5G. Inset shows the level of the section. T, Talus; N, navicular.

Table 6.5.1 Joints of foot: movements, principal muscles, and their innervation.

Movement	Principal muscles	Peripheral nerve	Spinal root origin
Subtalar joint			
Inversion	Tibialis anterior	Deep peroneal nerve	L 5
Eversion	Peroneus longus and brevis	Superficial peroneal nerve	L 5, S1
Joints of toes			
Flexion (plantar flexion)	Flexor hallucis longus and brevis	Tibial nerve	L 5, S1, 2
	Flexor digitorum longus and brevis	Tibial nerve (lateral plantar branch)	L 5, S1, 2
	Flexor digiti minimi		S1, 2, 3
	Flexor accessorius		S1, 2, 3
Extension (dorsiflexion)	Extensor hallucis longus	Deep peroneal nerve	L 5
	Extensor digitorum longus and brevis		
Abduction	Abductor hallucis	Tibial nerve (medial plantar branch)	S1, 2
	Dorsal interossei	Tibial nerve (lateral and medial plantar branches)	
Adduction	Adductor hallucis	Tibial nerve (lateral plantar branch)	S 2, 3
	Plantar interossei		

Questions and answers

Qu. 5A *If a foot is rotated laterally or medially, which joint is implicated?*

Answer The hip joint, because it is the only joint of the lower limb that can medially and laterally rotate more than 5°.

Qu. 5B *Does the longitudinal arch increase or decrease as one stands on tip-toe?*

Answer The longitudinal arch of the foot increases in height when standing on tip-toe because (a) the ligaments of the sole of the foot become tense, and (b) the dorsiflexion of the toes tenses the tendon of flexor hallucis longus.

Qu. 5C *At which joint does the movement occur, and which tarsal bones move and which do not during these movements?*

Answer Inversion and eversion of the foot take place at the subtalar and transverse tarsal joints. The main movement is that of the rest of the skeleton of the foot swinging obliquely on the fixed talus.

Qu. 5D *How would this arrangement be protective?*

Answer The locuted arrangement of the fibro-fatty fascia of the sole, like bubble-wrap, helps to distribute the forces exerted on the sole. Also, should infection occur in the sole, it helps to limit its spread.

Qu. 5E *What simple methods might be used initially to treat a child with flat feet?*

Answer Flat feet in children are most often due to 'small muscle' weakness. This can be helped by muscle strengthening exercises such as picking up pencils with the toes. The arch can also be supported by an insert in the shoe.

Qu. 5F *What is the link between eversion and flattening of the arch of the foot?*

Answer Eversion of the foot brings the medial side of the foot into contact with the ground, thus eliminating the medial arch. In addition, eversion will reduce dorsiflexion of the big toe and prevent reflex contraction of flexor hallucis longus, which enhances the arch.

Qu. 5G *Which bone has been fractured? Why does the talus not appear on the image?*

Answer The calcaneus has been badly damaged (crush fracture). There is a lack of continuity of the cortical bone posteriorly, and the gap between the posterior fragment and the rest of the bone is large. The posterior aspect of the cuboid is also fractured. In front of the calcaneus, the section cuts through the head of the talus, then the navicular bone.

Blood supply and lymphatic drainage of the lower limb

Blood supply and lymphatic drainage of the lower limb

The arterial supply to the lower limb, like that to the upper limb, is derived primarily from a single artery, the femoral artery, although branches of the internal iliac artery supply the buttock. The lower limbs are, however, affected by peripheral arterial disease much more than those of the upper limb, in part because of their distance from the heart.

The majority of the veins drain into the femoral vein. Because of our upright posture, venous drainage from the lower limbs has to occur against a substantial hydrostatic pressure. Therefore, the venous valves and muscle pump acting on the deep veins, and a system of communicating veins between the superficial and deep systems, are particularly important. Problems with venous drainage (e.g. varicose veins) are also much more common in the lower than in the upper limbs.

A large group of lymph nodes in the inguinal region drain not only the lower limb but also the superficial tissues of the lower part of the trunk and of the perineum.

Living anatomy

Arterial pulses

It is important to know how and where to feel arterial pulses in the lower limb (**6.6.1**) because their quality or absence can signify arterial disease. With a colleague lying on a couch, feel first for the pulsation of the **femoral artery** in the groin. Press gently with one or two fingertips just below the 'mid-inguinal point' (midway between the pubic symphysis and the anterior superior iliac spine). To feel the **popliteal artery** flex the knee to a right angle (to relax the overlying tissues) and press your fingertips firmly into the centre of the popliteal fossa.

The **posterior tibial artery** should easily be felt behind the medial malleolus, where it passes deep to the flexor retinaculum. The **dorsalis pedis** artery can usually be felt at the mid point between the medial and lateral malleoli; it continues distally on the dorsum of the foot lateral to the tendon of extensor hallucis longus until it reaches the proximal end of the first intermetatarsal space, where it may also be palpable. If you cannot feel a dorsalis pedis pulse at the ankle, feel a little more laterally. Sometimes the dorsum of the foot is supplied by a peroneal artery, which emerges low down between tibia and fibula.

The lower limb also receives blood from the gluteal arteries in the buttock, but these are deep and their pulsations cannot be felt.

Major veins

With your colleague standing, identify the **venous arch** on the dorsum of the foot. Trace it laterally into a short **saphenous vein** which passes behind the lateral malleolus, and a larger **long (great) saphenous vein** which runs in front of the medial malleolus and up the medial aspect of the calf and thigh. You may be able to see the small normal dilatations of the veins associated with the valves. Now ask your colleague to lie down and note how the veins empty as the hydrostatic column of blood is reduced.

Qu. 6A *What problems has the adoption of the upright stance created for venous drainage of the lower limb?*

The ankle is only a suitable site for intravenous infusion when hand and arm veins are difficult to find. The long saphenous vein can usually be located if a small transverse incision is made 2 cm above and 2 cm anterior to the medial malleolus.

Lymph nodes

Most of the lymphatic system cannot be seen or felt, but you may be able to feel a few **superficial inguinal lymph nodes** in the groin just distal to the mid section of the inguinal ligament.

Arterial supply to the lower limb

This is derived very largely from the external iliac artery, although branches of the internal iliac artery contribute to the supply of the gluteal region.

Femoral artery

The external iliac artery passes under the inguinal ligament (at the 'mid-inguinal point') to enter the thigh,

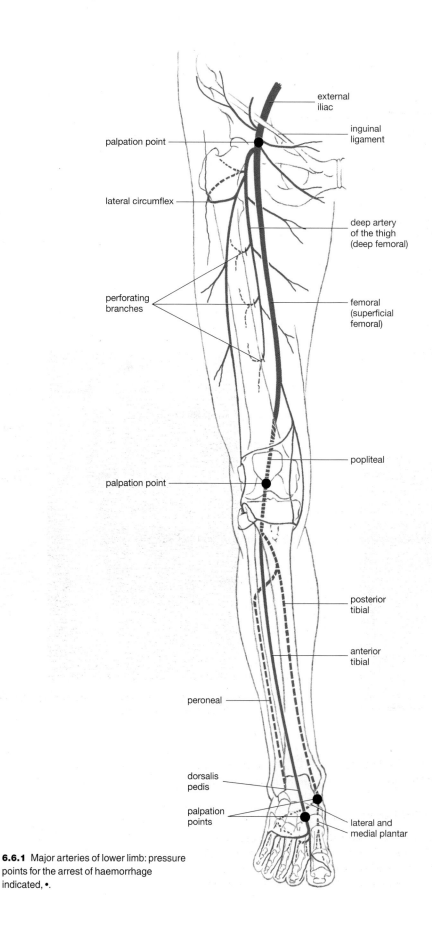

6.6.1 Major arteries of lower limb: pressure points for the arrest of haemorrhage indicated, •.

where it is renamed the **femoral artery** (**6.6.2, 6.6.3**). Here it lies first in the **femoral triangle** which is defined by the inguinal ligament above, the medial border of sartorius, and the medial border of adductor longus. The floor of the triangle is formed by muscles: adductor longus medially, pectineus, and ilio-psoas laterally.

Qu. 6B *How could you demonstrate this muscular triangle on yourself?*

The femoral artery is accompanied on its medial side by the femoral vein. Both these lie within a fibrous **femoral sheath** (**6.6.2**)—a funnel-shaped prolongation of the fascia lining the abdominal cavity. Lateral to the artery, but outside the femoral sheath, is the femoral nerve. Within the sheath on the medial side of the femoral vein is a small compartment, the **femoral canal**, occupied only by a deep inguinal lymph node and its associated vessels passing into the abdomen.

Qu. 6C *What is the advantage of having such a potential space adjacent to the main vein of the lower limb?*

Qu. 6D *What problem could arise as a result of the presence of this space which is continuous with the abdominal cavity?*

Arterial catheterization

Because of its size and accessibility, the femoral artery is commonly used for the introduction of arterial catheters. These can be guided radiologically up the external and common iliac arteries to any part of the aorta. Radiopaque material can then be introduced into any of the branches of the aorta to generate an arteriogram. The coronary arteries, which arise from the aorta immediately above the aortic valve, can be accessed in this way, and a catheter can even be passed up the carotid arteries and into the head. In this way blocked arteries can be dilated and wire coils inserted to treat aneurysms.

Deep artery of thigh

In the femoral triangle, the femoral artery gives a large branch, the **deep artery of the thigh** (**deep femoral; profunda femoris artery**) (**6.6.1, 6.6.4**), which arises from the back of the femoral artery and then runs distally, passing deeply between adductor longus and adductor magnus. The deep femoral artery forms the principal supply to the thigh. It gives off **medial** and **lateral circumflex femoral arteries,** which not only encircle the femur but also give ascending and descending branches which supply thigh muscles and the hip joint (via the trochanteric anastomosis), and **perforating arteries** which supply the adductors and pierce their insertion to supply the hamstrings.

On leaving the femoral triangle, the femoral artery, accompanied by the vein, passes beneath sartorius

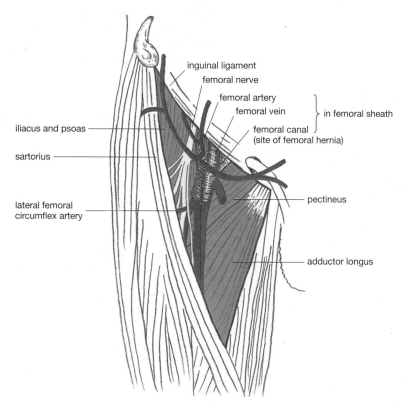

6.6.2 Femoral triangle.

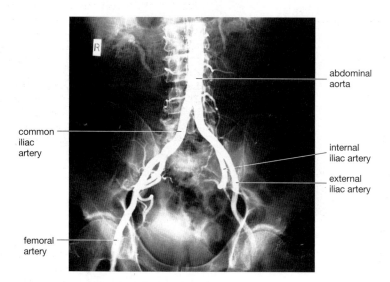

6.6.3 Arteriogram of iliac and femoral arteries.

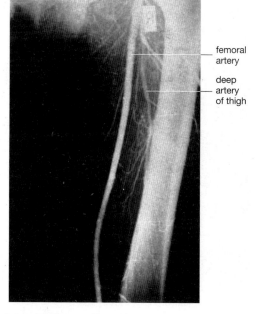

6.6.4 Arteriogram of femoral artery and the deep artery of the thigh (deep femoral artery).

(which crosses the anterior compartment of the thigh obliquely) and, continuing under this muscle, runs vertically down the medial aspect of the thigh, lying on adductor longus and then adductor magnus. It subsequently passes through the gap between the adductor part of adductor magnus (attached to the linea aspera) and the hamstring part of the muscle (which is attached to the adductor tubercle above the medial femoral condyle) to reach the popliteal fossa (**6.6.5**) at the back of the knee. Here the artery is renamed the popliteal artery.

Popliteal artery

The **popliteal artery** (**6.6.5, 6.6.6**) lies close to the bone, and supplies branches to the knee joint (genicular arteries) and others which form an anastomotic plexus around the lower end of the femur and upper end of the

semitendinosus

semimembranosus

tibial nerve

popliteal artery

lateral and
medial heads of
gastrocnemius

tendon of
biceps femoris

common peroneal
(fibular) nerve

head of fibula

level of knee
menisci

sural nerve

short saphenous
vein

6.6.5 Popliteal fossa; popliteal vein removed above entrance of short saphenous vein. In the boxed area, the muscles have been removed to show the relationship of the common peroneal nerve to the neck of the fibula.

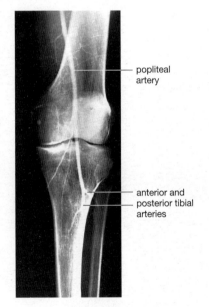

popliteal
artery

anterior and
posterior tibial
arteries

6.6.6 Arteriogram of popliteal artery and its branches.

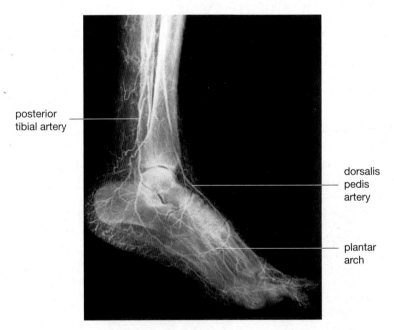

posterior
tibial artery

dorsalis
pedis
artery

plantar
arch

6.6.7 Arteriogram showing main vessels supplying the foot.

tibia. As it leaves the popliteal fossa, the popliteal artery divides into anterior and posterior tibial arteries.

Anterior tibial artery

The **anterior tibial artery** passes forward between the tibia and fibula above the interosseous membrane and descends on its anterior surface to supply the muscles of the anterior compartment of the leg, and medial and lateral malleolar branches to the ankle.

As the anterior tibial artery crosses the front of the ankle joint it is renamed the **dorsalis pedis artery** (**6.6.7**). This passes down over the dorsum of the foot to reach the interval between the first and second metatarsal bones, through which it passes to reach the sole of the foot and anastomose with the plantar

arterial arch. On the dorsum of the foot it gives off a transverse metatarsal branch which runs laterally to supply small paired arteries to the toes.

Posterior tibial artery

The **posterior tibial artery** supplies the superficial and deep muscles of the calf, and passes, with the long flexor tendons, around the back of the medial malleolus. It gives off a **peroneal artery**, which runs distally deep to flexor hallucis longus (it can pass through the interosseous membrane to the dorsum of the foot and take over the distribution of the dorsalis pedis artery). At the ankle, the posterior tibial artery passes deep to the flexor retinaculum, where it divides into medial and lateral plantar arteries which enter the sole (**6.6.7**).

The **medial plantar artery** is small and runs along the medial side of the foot. The **lateral plantar artery** is larger; it runs obliquely across the sole of the foot between the first and second layers of muscles toward the base of the fifth metatarsal. Here it passes deeply between the third and fourth layers of muscles and runs medially across the interossei, forming a **plantar arterial arch**, which gives off metatarsal branches and ends by anastomosing with the end of the dorsalis pedis artery, which passes into the sole through the first intermetatarsal space.

Qu. 6E *How comparable is this arrangement to that in the palm of the hand?*

Qu. 6F *If a patient who complained of intermittent pain in the legs (intermittent claudication) during and after exercise also had a toe which was becoming gangrenous, what would you deduce?*

Superior and inferior gluteal arteries

The **superior** and **inferior gluteal arteries** arise from the internal iliac artery within the pelvis. They reach the gluteal region by passing through the greater sciatic foramen on either side of piriformis (**6.6.8** and see **6.2.8**). They supply the muscles and skin of the buttock and also send small branches which descend into the posterior compartment of the thigh, where they anastomose with branches of the femoral (external iliac system).

Anastomoses between lower limb arteries

A number of important anastomoses link the arteries of the lower limb to form a chain of anastomoses in the thigh (**6.6.8**). The **trochanteric anastomosis** in the trochanteric fossa provides the vessels which pass along the neck of the femur to supply the head of the femur. The anastomosis is formed by branches of the gluteal arteries with ascending branches of the medial and lateral femoral circumflex arteries. A little more distally, at the upper border of adductor magnus, is a **cruciate anastomosis**, formed by a descending branch from the inferior gluteal artery, transverse branches of the circumflex arteries and the highest perforating branch of the deep femoral artery (deep artery of the thigh). Further down the thigh, the perforating arteries anastomose among themselves and with the genicular vessels. At the knee and ankle, branches of the principal arteries form an anastomotic network around the joints. Finally, in the foot, the dorsalis pedis branch of the anterior tibial artery anastomoses with the plantar arch derived from the posterior tibial artery. You should consider ways in which the limb can derive arterial supply if the femoral artery is blocked at different sites.

Innervation of lower limb arteries

The vessels of the lower limb are innervated by sympathetic fibres. Preganglionic fibres originate from cell bodies situated in the lower thoracic and highest lumbar

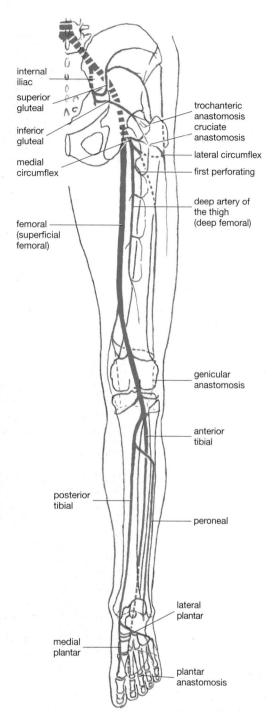

internal iliac
superior gluteal
inferior gluteal
medial circumflex
femoral (superficial femoral)
posterior tibial
medial plantar

trochanteric anastomosis
cruciate anastomosis
lateral circumflex
first perforating
deep artery of the thigh (deep femoral)
genicular anastomosis
anterior tibial
peroneal
lateral plantar
plantar anastomosis

6.6.8 Anastomoses between arteries of lower limb; posterior view.

segments of the spinal cord. Postganglionic fibres arise from the lumbar sympathetic chain and form a plexus around the external iliac artery. Others join the femoral, obturator, and sciatic nerves to reach the vessels. If the arterial flow to the lower limb becomes inadequate, the lumbar sympathetic nerves may be surgically divided in an attempt to reduce the vasoconstrictor tone.

Imaging lower limb arteries

Study arteriograms **6.6.3**, **6.6.4**, **6.6.6** and **6.6.7** and identify the major branches. Compare the normal

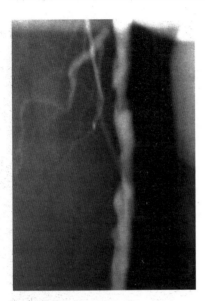

6.6.9 Arteriogram showing distortion of femoral artery due to atheroma.

6.6.10 Arteriogram of gunshot wound to knee; blocked popliteal artery (arrow).

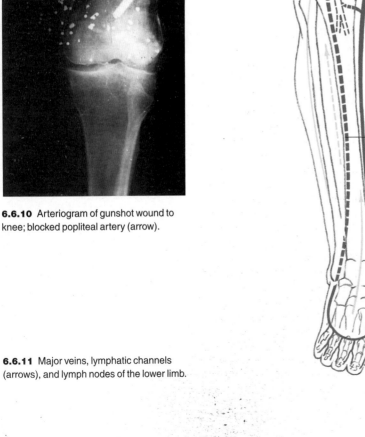

femoral vein (deep)

superficial Inguinal lymph nodes

saphenous opening in fascia lata

long (great) saphenous vein

popliteal nodes

popliteal vein

short (small) saphenous vein

6.6.11 Major veins, lymphatic channels (arrows), and lymph nodes of the lower limb.

femoral arteriogram with the vessel shown in **6.6.9**. The difference is due to the presence of atheroma, a cholesterol-containing deposit in the tunica intima of the vessel wall. This narrows the lumen of the vessel, sometimes blocking it completely, causing gangrene of the parts supplied.

Study arteriogram **6.6.10**. What has happened? The leg suffered a gunshot injury, shattering the bone and destroying the popliteal artery. The fractured bones were stabilized as well as was possible, but gangrene of the foot would have occurred if the blood supply had not been restored surgically.

Venous drainage of the lower limb

As in the upper limb there is a system of **superficial veins** which drain the skin and superficial fascia, and a system of **deep veins** which accompany the major arteries (**6.6.11**), commencing as small, paired venae comitantes. These two systems, which are separated by the deep fascia which envelops the muscle compartments, are connected by a number of very important **communicating veins**.

The superficial system commences as a **dorsal venous arch**, similar to that on the dorsum of the hand, which drains the toes, the veins of which pass dorsally from the sole. The lateral aspect of the arch is drained by the **short (small) saphenous vein** which runs behind the lateral malleolus and up the back of the calf to pierce the deep fascia of the popliteal fossa and drain into the popliteal vein (**6.6.12**).

The medial side of the dorsal venous arch is drained by the larger **great (long) saphenous vein**, which

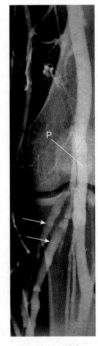

6.6.12 Normal venogram; short saphenous vessels (arrow) entering the popliteal vein (P).

passes in front of the medial malleolus, where it can usually be seen and felt. It then ascends unsupported in the subcutaneous tissue along the medial aspect of the leg and thigh. At the top of the thigh, about 5 cm below the pubic tubercle, it pierces a 'saphenous opening' in the fascia lata and empties into the **femoral vein** in the femoral triangle. It is here that the great saphenous vein can be tied off if it becomes varicose. Several smaller veins draining the iliac and pudendal regions also join the femoral vein at this point.

The deep veins commence as venae comitantes around smaller arteries and eventually join to form the **anterior tibial** and **posterior tibial veins**, which unite to form the **popliteal vein**. In the popliteal fossa, this vein lies superficial to the popliteal artery and receives the short saphenous vein. The popliteal vein and artery then pass together through the hiatus in adductor magnus to enter the adductor compartment of the thigh, where the vein is renamed the **femoral vein**. This follows the artery proximally to the femoral triangle, receiving large tributaries such as the deep vein of the thigh and the great saphenous vein. It then passes deep to the inguinal ligament to enter the pelvis as the **external iliac vein**.

A system of **communicating veins** joins the superficial veins, especially the great saphenous vein, to the deep veins running with the major arteries. The valves in communicating veins normally permit blood to flow from the superficial to the deep veins, but not vice versa. The largest communicating veins pierce the deep fascia just above and just below the knee, on its medial aspect.

The adoption of an upright posture means that venous return from the lower limbs occurs against a large potential hydrostatic pressure. In both the superficial and the deep system the hydrostatic pressure in the veins is minimized by the presence of numerous valves.

Varicose veins

If, for any reason, the valves in the veins become incompetent, the hydrostatic columns of blood become greater and the superficial veins become progressively more dilated, and become **varicose veins (6.6.13)**. If the communicating veins become dilated and their valves incompetent, the action of the muscle pump only exacerbates the problem, because blood is now pumped *into* the superficial veins rather than away from them.

The site of dilated communicating veins can often be detected by probing with the tip of a little finger, because the hole they create in the fascia lata is felt as a depression in the fascia which is tender when pressed.

When the superficial veins become varicose, the drainage of the skin by superficial veins becomes compromised and the haemodynamics of the capillary bed are disturbed. This leads to changes in the skin which can progress to severe ulceration.

The contraction of muscles within the fascial envelope that surrounds them, together with the presence of numerous valves in the vessels, provides a '**muscle pump**' which actively empties the deep veins, forcing the blood proximally. Soleus, a postural muscle in the calf, is particularly important in this respect. As the muscles relax, the valves in the connecting veins allow blood in the superficial veins to drain into the deep veins, from which it is pumped by subsequent muscle contraction. Thus, the muscle pump empties the deep veins directly and the superficial veins indirectly.

Compartment syndromes

Dense deep fascia surrounding the muscles of the lower limb enhances the venous muscle pump but can also cause problems. Any bleeding into or swelling of tissues in a muscle compartment can compress the deep veins causing oedema which sets up a vicious circle that can even compromise arterial perfusion. In the leg, the anterior (extensor) and deep posterior (flexor) compartments are small and restricted by the tibia, fibula, interosseous membrane, and roofs of deep fascia; the superficial calf flexor compartment (soleus, gastrocnemius) is larger. Closed fractures of the tibia and/or fibula cause bleeding into the deep compartments. Swelling of the extensors in the anterior compartment can be caused by unaccustomed heavy exercise (eg in army recruits wearing heavy boots). Rest does not alleviate the pain (as it does with intermittent arterial insufficiency). To prevent muscle death the deep fascia may need to be divided along the length of the compartment.

Qu. 6G *Could the same problem develop in the thigh?*

6.6.13 Varicose veins on a calf (posterior view).

Lymphatic drainage of the lower limb

The lymphatic drainage of the lower limb (**6.6.11**, **6.6.14**) follows the general pattern found in the upper limb: superficial lymphatics running with superficial veins drain the skin and subcutaneous tissues, while deep lymphatics running with the neurovascular bundles drain structures deep to the deep fascia. However, compared to the upper limb, there is very little communication between superficial and deep lymphatics.

Superficial lymph nodes are found in the superficial fascia just beneath the inguinal ligament and at the junction of the great saphenous and femoral veins. These nodes drain the skin and superficial fascia of the lower limb and of the trunk below the waistline. They also drain the lower parts of the anal canal and vagina and the external genitalia, because their epithelia develop from ectoderm. A group of **deep inguinal nodes** around the femoral artery drains the deep tissues.

Lymph vessels leaving the superficial inguinal nodes pierce the fascia lata around the saphenous opening to drain into the deep inguinal nodes. The lymphatics leaving the deep nodes pass upward through the femoral canal medial to the femoral vein to join the chain of

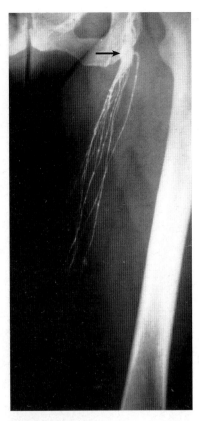

6.6.14 Lymphangiogram of vessels draining into superficial inguinal lymph nodes (arrow).

nodes that lies along the external and common iliac arteries and the aorta. By this route, they reach the cisterna chyli, a distended sac which lies between the aorta and the bodies of the L1 and L2 vertebrae (Vol. 2, Ch. 6, Sect. 3). This cistern gives rise to the thoracic duct which passes upward on the posterior wall of the thorax and eventually joins with lymphatics from the head and left upper limb (p. 105) to drain into the confluence of the left subclavian and internal jugular veins. In this way the lymph is returned to the bloodstream.

Imaging the lower limb vessels

Vessels cannot be seen on conventional radiographs, but can be filled with radiopaque contrast media (**6.6.3, 6.6.4, 6.6.6, 6.6.7, 6.6.9, 6.6.10, 6.6.12, 6.6.14**) or visualized by CT or MRI (see **6.3.20**).

Questions and answers

Qu. 6A *What problems has the adoption of the upright stance created for venous drainage of the lower limb?*

Answer With the attainment of the upright stance, venous return to the heart from the superficial veins of the lower limb has to travel a greater vertical distance against gravity. The valves and the communicating veins, which allow blood to drain from the superficial to the deep veins (which are emptied by the muscle pump), aid venous return.

Qu. 6B *How could you demonstrate this muscular triangle on yourself?*

Answer By resisting lateral rotation of the hip with the knee of the same side flexed (i.e. resistance to sitting cross-legged on the floor) sartorius will contract visibly.

Qu. 6C *What is the advantage of having such a potential space adjacent to the main vein of the lower limb?*

Answer It allows for expansion of the large femoral vein, which occurs when standing up from a recumbent position, or when the limb is very active.

Qu. 6D *What problem could arise as a result of the presence of this space which is continuous with the abdominal cavity?*

Answer The space creates a weak point in the wall of the abdomen. When intra-abdominal pressure is increased, for example when lifting a heavy weight, abdominal contents (e.g. extraperitoneal fat, small bowel) can herniate through the weakness, creating a femoral hernia. Because women have a wider pelvis than men, the femoral canal is a little larger and femoral hernias are relatively more common in women than men (although hernias of all types are more common in men than women).

Qu. 6E *How comparable is this arrangement to that in the palm of the hand?*

Answer The deep plantar and deep palmar arches are comparable but, in the foot, there is no equivalent of the superficial palmar arch, presumably because of the pressure exerted by the body weight during standing.

Qu. 6F *If a patient who complained of intermittent pain in the legs (intermittent claudication) during and after exercise also had a toe which was becoming gangrenous, what would you deduce?*

Answer Insufficient blood supply. The extent of any pulsations in the main arteries to the limb (e.g. the tibial artery behind the medial malleolus) should be determined and the cause of the problem investigated.

Qu. 6G *Could the same problem develop in the thigh?*

Answer Yes, the fascia lata surrounds the thigh and fractures of the femur can cause extensive bleeding.

CHAPTER 6

Innervation of the lower limb

Innervation of the lower limb   SECTION 7

All the functions of the lower limb, such as the upright stance and locomotion, depend on both voluntary movement and stretch and postural reflexes controlled by the nervous system. The somatic innervation of the lower limb, like that of the upper limb, is derived from a nerve plexus (the lumbosacral plexus) formed from the anterior primary rami of lumbar and sacral spinal nerves. The plexus redistributes the somatic motor and sensory fibres into peripheral nerves which carry the individual fibres to their destinations. As in the upper limb, anterior divisions of the anterior primary rami supply flexor muscles, and posterior divisions supply extensors.

Autonomic innervation to the blood vessels and sweat glands of the lower limb is provided by postganglionic sympathetic fibres derived from neurons of the lumbar and sacral sympathetic ganglia. The sympathetic fibres either join the spinal nerves and are distributed with their branches, or form a plexus which passes distally along the arteries.

Arrangement of segmental nerve supply to the lower limb

The arrangement of the segmental nerve supply to the muscles and skin has essentially the same pattern as in the upper limb. Movements at most joints are controlled by four adjacent segments of the spinal cord; the upper two segments innervating movement, the lower two innervating the opposing movement. As in the upper limb, more distal muscles are supplied by progressively lower segments of the spinal cord (Table 6.7.1). Muscles which are embryologically flexors are supplied by anterior divisions of the anterior primary rami, extensors by their posterior divisions. However, the medial rotation of the lower limb has carried the extensor compartment to the front of the thigh and leg. Thus, quadriceps femoris, supplied by the femoral nerve (derived from the posterior divisions of L2—4) is the lower limb equivalent of triceps, supplied by the radial nerve (derived from posterior divisions of the branchial plexus). Triceps is situated in the posterior compartment of the arm, whereas quadriceps is situated in the anterior compartment of the thigh.[1]

A dermatome map of the lower limb (**6.7.1**) shows that, as in the upper limb, nerve roots derived from progressively more caudal segments of the spinal cord supply the skin of the pre-axial border, the distal extremity, and the postaxial border of the limb. However, rotation of the lower limb means that the pre-axial border runs from the anterior aspect of the thigh to the great toe. There is, of course, considerable overlap between adjacent dermatomes, but less across axial lines, but the axial lines are less well defined than in the upper limb. (S4 and S5 dermatomes supply the perineum.)

---

[1] In addition to differences caused by developmental rotation, another apparent difference is that the sciatic nerve combines fibres from anterior and posterior divisions of the anterior primary rami and therefore supplies both flexors and extensors. However, these groups of fibres are separate and the sciatic nerve may emerge from the pelvis already divided into tibial (flexor) and common peroneal (extensor) components or divide early in its course down the thigh.

Table 6.7.1 Main spinal nerve root supplying the movements of the lower limb.

	Movement	Main nerve roots
Hip	Flexion, adduction	L 2, 3, 4
Knee	Extension, abduction	L 4, 5, S1
	Extension	L 3, 4
Ankle	Flexion	L 5, S1
	Flexion (plantar flexion)	L 4, 5
Subtalar joint	Extension (dorsiflexion)	L 5, S1
	Inversion	L 5
Toes (long muscles)	Eversion	L 5, S1
	Flexion (plantar flexion)	L 5, S1, 2
Toes (small muscles of foot)	Extension (dorsiflexion)	L S1, 2, 3
		S1, 2, 3

Because of the rotation of the lower limb, extension of the knee is supplied by higher segments.

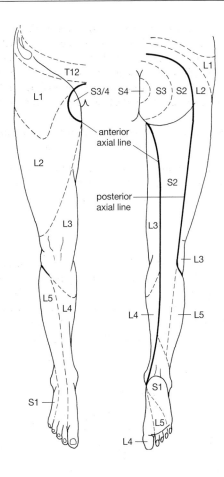

6.7.1 Dermatomes of lower limb; note the axial lines.

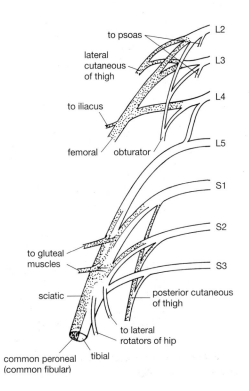

6.7.2 Lumbosacral plexus.

Living anatomy

Following Table 6.7.1, make the movements of your lower limb and note the spinal segments which 'supply' each movement.

With a skin pencil, mark out the dermatome lines. The dermatome pattern in the lower limb is considerably distorted compared with that of the upper limb, largely because the lower limb has become medially rotated during development. As in the upper limb, the middle spinal nerve root of the plexus supplies the most distal skin (i.e. the sole of the foot and middle three digits is supplied by L5).

Qu. 7A *Which spinal nerve supplies the area of skin on which you sit?*

Reflexes in the lower limb

Ask a colleague to sit down and cross one leg over the other. Using a reflex-testing hammer, tap the patellar tendon of the crossed leg lightly between the patella and the tuberosity of the tibia. The resulting stretch reflex or 'knee jerk' is produced by the contraction of quadriceps. Compare the reflex on the two sides.

Qu. 7B *What are the basic neural mechanisms underlying this reflex response?*

Hold the foot at a right angle to the leg and tap the Achilles tendon to produce a reflex plantar flexion 'ankle jerk'. If the stretch reflexes are overactive, as happens, for example, after a 'stroke' then ankle 'clonus' may be present. To elicit this, the foot is sharply dorsiflexed and held in this extended position. 'Ankle clonus', if present, consists of repeated rhythmic contractions of the plantar flexor muscles and differs sharply from the single reflex contraction produced by the stretch reflex of a normal ankle.

Another reflex that gives information about the state of the central nervous system is the 'plantar reflex'. If a blunt object, such as the end of a key, is pressed firmly along the lateral aspect of the sole of the foot, and across the ball of the foot, the normal reflex in an adult is for the great toe to flex. However, in very young infants (whose motor systems are not yet fully developed), and in adults with damage to motor centres in the brain, the great toe extends.

Lumbosacral plexus and its branches

The **lumbosacral plexus** (**6.7.2**) has two components: a lumbar plexus formed from lumbar spinal nerves, situated on the posterior abdominal wall deep within psoas major; and a sacral plexus formed from sacral spinal nerves, situated on the posterior wall of the pelvis. Psoas, which is developmentally a body wall muscle, derives its innervation from the spinal nerve roots.

The *lumbar* part of the plexus gives rise to two major branches: the **femoral nerve,** which supplies the muscles of the anterior (extensor) compartment of the thigh and the skin over it; and the **obturator nerve,** which supplies the muscles of the adductor (medial) compartment of the thigh and the skin over it. Both nerves supply sensory branches to the hip and knee joints.

Femoral nerve

The femoral nerve (L2, L3, L4; posterior divisions) (**6.7.2–6.7.4**) emerges from the lateral side of psoas within the abdomen and runs distally in the groove between psoas and iliacus (supplying iliacus). It passes under the inguinal ligament lateral to the femoral artery but outside the femoral sheath and, on emerging into the thigh, divides into its terminal branches.

The femoral nerve supplies:

- muscular branches to all the muscles of the extensor compartment of the thigh (quadriceps, sartorius);
- cutaneous sensory branches to the skin over the anterior and medial aspects of the thigh (medial and intermediate cutaneous nerves of thigh) and a long sensory branch, the **saphenous nerve,** which leaves the femoral triangle and runs through the adductor canal. On leaving the canal at the knee, it joins the long saphenous vein and, running distally alongside it, supplies a strip of skin down the medial side of the knee and leg as far as the first metatarso-phalangeal joint;

- articular sensory branches to the hip and knee that reach the joints via the muscles that act on them.

Qu. 7C *If a middle-aged man complained of a limp and a pain in his left knee, what initial steps might you wish to take in order to reach a diagnosis?*

Obturator nerve

The obturator nerve (L2, L3, L4; anterior divisions) (**6.7.2, 6.7.5, 6.7.6**) emerges from the medial aspect of psoas at the pelvic brim and runs distally across the lateral wall of the pelvis toward the obturator foramen. It passes through a canal in the upper part of the foramen, supplies obturator externus, and reaches

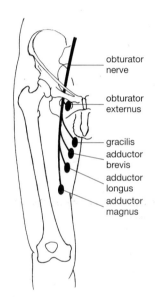

6.7.5 Obturator nerve; supply to muscles.

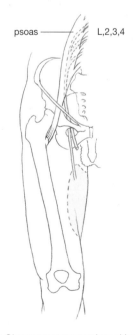

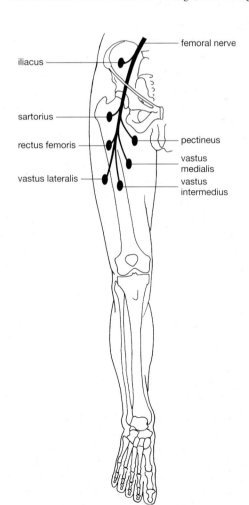

6.7.3 Femoral nerve; supply to muscles.

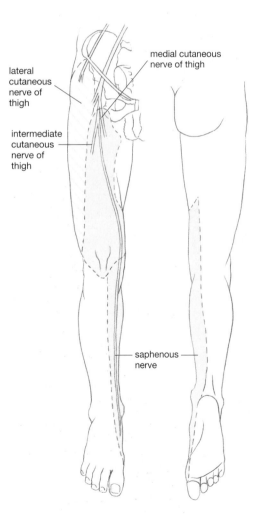

6.7.4 Femoral nerve; supply to skin. Also lateral cutaneous nerve of thigh.

6.7.6 Obturator nerve; supply to skin.

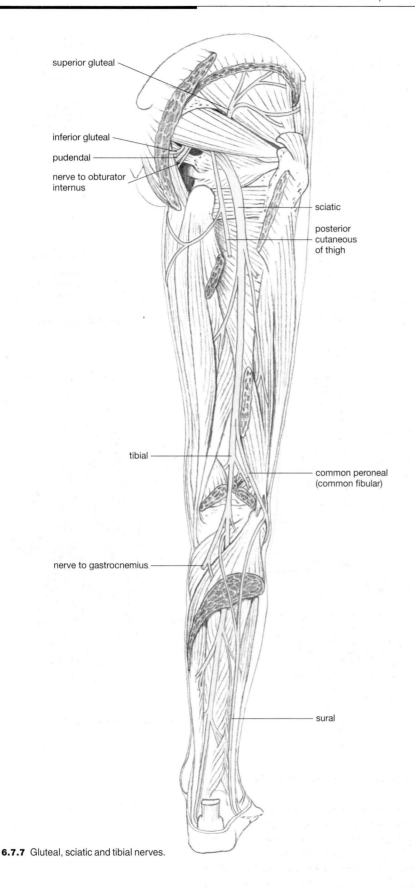

6.7.7 Gluteal, sciatic and tibial nerves.

Labels: superior gluteal; inferior gluteal; pudendal; nerve to obturator internus; sciatic; posterior cutaneous of thigh; tibial; common peroneal (common fibular); nerve to gastrocnemius; sural

the adductor compartment on the medial aspect of the thigh. Here it supplies:

- muscular branches to all the adductor muscles;
- sensory branches to the skin of the medial aspect of the thigh;
- articular branches to the hip and knee joints.

Qu. 7D *Why might a woman feel monthly discomfort on the medial aspect of the thigh?*

The plexus gives three other small branches. The **ilio-inguinal nerve** (L1) (see Vol. 2) runs laterally from the lumbar plexus into the neurovascular plane of the anterior abdominal wall, runs around the abdominal wall and leaves through the superficial inguinal ring to supply the skin of the scrotum. It also supplies some skin on the medial aspect of the thigh adjacent to the groin. Sensory fibres from this area form the afferent limb of a reflex (cremasteric reflex) which elevates the ipsilateral testis.

The **genito-femoral nerve** (L1, L2) (see Vol. 2) emerges through the middle of psoas and runs downward on its anterior surface. Its genital branch (L2) enters the inguinal canal and passes in it to supply the cremaster muscle (which raises the testis). Its femoral branch (L1) supplies a hand's breadth area of skin just distal to the inguinal ligament.

The **lateral cutaneous nerve of thigh** (L2, L3) passes under the lateral end of the inguinal ligament and supplies the skin over the lateral aspect of the thigh. It can become trapped under the inguinal ligament by thickened fibrous tissue, causing pain down the lateral side of the thigh.

The *sacral* part of the lumbosacral plexus also gives rise to two major nerves—the tibial and common peroneal nerves. These supply, respectively, the muscles of the flexor and of the extensor compartment of the leg and foot, the overlying skin, and the joints, including the knee. However, the two nerves usually emerge from the plexus as a single very large trunk, the **sciatic nerve**. The plexus also supplies all the muscles of the gluteal region, the perineum and one main cutaneous branch to the back of the thigh.

Sciatic nerve

The **sciatic nerve** (L4–S3 anterior and posterior divisions) (**6.7.2, 6.7.7, 6.7.8** and see **6.2.8**) is formed from the union of the 'lumbosacral trunk' with the S1–S3 spinal nerves. (The lumbosacral trunk is a large nerve formed from a branch of L4 with the L5 spinal nerve; it descends from the posterior abdominal wall medial to psoas, over the sacroiliac joint to join the sacral nerves; **6.7.2**). The sciatic nerve leaves the pelvis by passing through the greater sciatic foramen inferior to piriformis and enters the gluteal region. Here, it is covered by gluteus maximus, and it curves downward and laterally over the short lateral rotator muscles of the hip (see **6.2.8**) to enter the posterior compartment of the thigh.

In the buttock and thigh the sciatic nerve lies deeply and cannot be felt. However, sometimes injections are given into the mass of the gluteal muscles, and it is important to avoid the sciatic nerve. The nerve runs a curved course from a point midway between the posterior superior iliac spine and the ischial tuberosity, to a point midway between the tuberosity and the greater trochanter of the femur (**6.7.9**). Therefore intramuscular injections into the buttock should be restricted to its upper outer quadrant.

Damage to sciatic nerve from posterior dislocation of the hip

Sometimes, in car accidents, the head of the femur is forced back through the posterior margin of the acetabulum and into the gluteal region. Here, only the short lateral rotator muscles separate it from the sciatic nerve, which may therefore be damaged by fragments of bone. Thankfully this is less common now that seat belts restrain most drivers and passengers.

The sciatic nerve passes down through the posterior compartment of the thigh, lying close to the posterior border of the femur, and crossed by biceps femoris.

In the thigh, it supplies
• the hamstring muscles (including the 'hamstring' part of adductor magnus);
• branches to the hip and knee joints.

At about the mid point of the thigh it usually divides into its component tibial and common peroneal nerves (though the two bundles may separate much higher up).

The **tibial nerve** (**6.7.8, 6.7.10**) supplies:
• the (plantar) flexor muscles of the leg and all the muscles of the sole of the foot;
• the skin of the lower half of the back of the leg, the heel and sole of the foot;
• joints of the knee, ankle and foot.

In the popliteal fossa the tibial nerve gives branches to the knee joint and a contribution to the sural nerve. It passes into the leg between the two heads of gastrocnemius and supplies popliteus, then passes under the upper border of soleus to lie between the superficial and deep muscles of the calf. At the ankle it passes behind the medial malleolus under the flexor retinaculum (with the tendons of tibialis posterior, flexor digitorum longus and flexor hallucis longus, and the tibial nerve) where its pulsations can be palpated. Here, it divides into **medial** and **lateral plantar nerves** (**6.7.11**) which are the equivalent, respectively, of the median and ulnar nerves in the palm of the hand.

The medial plantar nerve runs forward on the medial side of the sole. It supplies flexor digitorum brevis, the small muscles of the great toe apart from adductor hallucis, and sensory branches to the medial aspect of the sole and the medial three and a half toes. The lateral plantar nerve (with its companion artery) crosses the sole of the foot obliquely, deep to flexor digitorum brevis, to supply the remaining muscles and

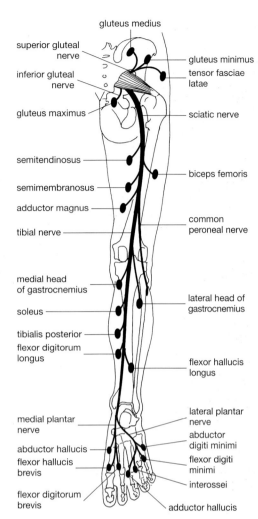

6.7.8 Sciatic and tibial nerves: supply to muscles.

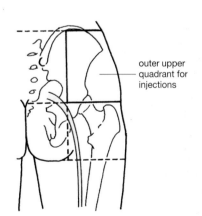

6.7.9 Sciatic nerve and site for injections into the buttock.

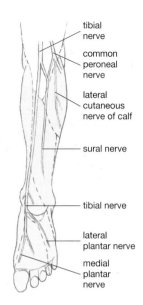

6.7.10 Sciatic and tibial nerves: supply to skin.

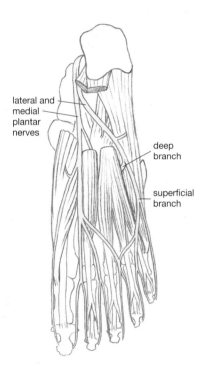

6.7.11 Medial and lateral plantar nerves.

skin. It is instructive to compare this pattern of supply with that of the median and ulnar nerves in the palm.

The **common peroneal nerve** (common fibular nerve; **6.7.2, 6.7.12–6.7.14**) supplies:
• the extensor muscles of the leg and foot (tibialis anterior, extensor hallucis and extensor digitorum longus and brevis);

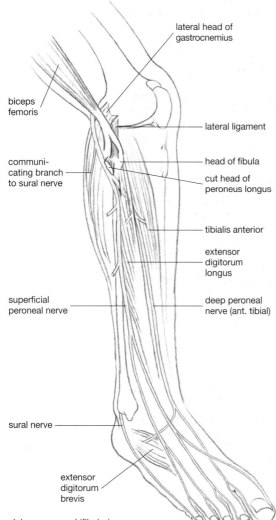

6.7.12 Superficial and deep peroneal (fibular) nerves.

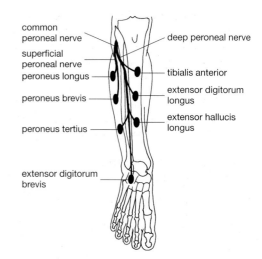

6.7.13 Common peroneal nerve: supply to muscles.

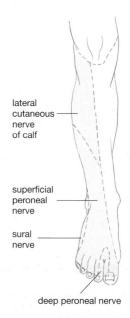

6.7.14 Common peroneal nerve: supply to skin.

- the peroneal muscles (peroneus longus and brevis);
- skin on the anterior aspect of the leg and dorsum of the foot;
- the joints of the knee, ankle, and foot.

The common peroneal (fibular) nerve passes through the lateral part of the popliteal fossa closely applied to biceps femoris, then curves forward around the lateral aspect of the neck of the fibula. Here, it is very superficial and easily palpated, facilitating diagnosis of diseases such as leprosy which infiltrate and enlarge the nerves. It gives branches to the knee joint and the skin of the calf (lateral cutaneous nerve of calf and a contribution to the sural nerve) and then passes deep to the upper part of peroneus longus and divides into superficial and deep peroneal nerves.

The **superficial peroneal nerve** supplies peroneus longus and brevis in the peroneal (lateral) compartment of the leg, then, about two-thirds of the way down the leg, emerges through the deep fascia covering the compartment and runs distally over the front of the leg and ankle. At the ankle it divides into branches which supply the skin over the lateral aspect of the leg, the

front of the ankle and the dorsum of the foot (but not the cleft between the first and second toes).

The **deep peroneal nerve** enters the extensor (anterior) compartment of the leg and supplies its muscles. It descends on the interosseous membrane, accompanied by the anterior tibial vessels which join it from the calf by passing over the top of the interosseous membrane. The neurovascular bundle then crosses the ankle joint midway between the malleoli (between the tendons of extensor hallucis longus and extensor digitorum longus), where it is vulnerable to sharp objects dropped on to the foot. In the foot it supplies extensor digitorum brevis, joints of the ankle and foot, and the skin of the cleft between the great and second toes.

The **sural nerve** is formed from branches of the tibial and common peroneal nerves. It runs down the back of the calf, alongside the short saphenous vein, and supplies the skin of the back of the calf, the heel, and the lateral side of the foot. This is the nerve most commonly used by surgeons for grafting a gap between the ends of an injured nerve.

Superior and inferior gluteal nerves

The **superior** and **inferior gluteal nerves** (see **6.2.8**) both leave the pelvis through the greater sciatic foramen with their respective vessels. The superior gluteal nerve emerges above piriformis and supplies gluteus medius, gluteus minimus, and tensor fasciae latae.

Qu. 7F *What action do these three muscles share?*

The inferior gluteal nerve and artery emerge under piriformis and pass directly into the overlying gluteus maximus.

Qu. 7G *If the inferior gluteal nerve was damaged, what would be the consequences?*

Other branches of sacral plexus

Other branches of sacral plexus supply the short lateral rotators obturator internus and quadratus femoris.

The **posterior cutaneous nerve of thigh** (S1, S2, S3) emerges under the lower border of gluteus maximus and runs down the posterior aspect of the thigh, sending branches through the fascia lata to the skin.

The **pudendal nerve** (S2, S3, S4; see **6.2.8** and see Vol. 2) leaves the pelvis through the greater sciatic foramen below piriformis with its accompanying artery, then immediately winds round the ischial spine and sacrospinous ligament, and passes through the lesser sciatic foramen to enter the perineum. Here the nerve supplies motor fibres to the voluntary sphincters of the anal and urinary tracts, and sensory fibres to the posterior part of the perineum.

Referred pain in the leg

The hip joint is supplied by branches from the femoral, obturator, and gluteal nerves, the root values of which extend from L2 to S1. Likewise the knee joint is supplied by the femoral, obturator, tibial, and common peroneal nerves, the roots of which extend from L2 to S3. ·

Thus, there is considerable overlap of the sensory supply to the two joints. This influences the presentation of disease: patients with disease restricted to the hip joint commonly complain of pain down the front of the thigh and knee. For instance, early slipping of the capital epiphysis of the femur often causes discomfort in the knee (see **6.1.14**). Also, disease within the pelvis which affects the sciatic nerve can cause pain referred down the back of the thigh.

Autonomic innervation to the lower limb

The lower limb receives sympathetic fibres from the lumbar and sacral parts of the sympathetic chain. These run with vessels and nerves to supply the vessels and sweat glands of the limb. The sympathetic fibres are vasoconstrictor and, therefore, lumbar sympathectomy may be performed in an attempt to improve blood supply to a limb in which the arteries are severely narrowed by atherosclerosis.

Lesions to lumbar and sacral nerve roots

Damage to individual or multiple lumbar and sacral spinal nerve roots can occur as a result of pressure from a prolapsed intervertebral disc or discs. These press on the nerve as it leaves the intervertebral foramen (see **7.25**). The results can be predicted from a knowledge of the dermatomes (**6.7.1**) and the segmental supply to muscles (Table 6.7.1), and it is often important to differentiate, by symptoms and clinical signs, which roots are involved.

The most commonly affected roots are those of L4, L5, and S1. Disturbance of sensory roots can cause either pain or blunting of sensation in the area of their distribution; disturbance of motor roots causes weakness and ultimately wasting of the muscles innervated. However, nearly all muscles are supplied from more than one root. It is therefore usually much easier to diagnose lesions of a single root from the sensory than from the motor disturbance. The reflexes on the leg require both sensory input and motor output, so that damage to either will affect the reflexes. When the **L4** root is damaged:
- **sensory** change affects the front and medial side of the shin as far as the metatarso-phalangeal joint of the great toe (i.e. the distribution of the saphenous nerve);
- **motor** changes may be less obvious, but there may be some wasting of quadriceps, and some weakness of inversion, because quadriceps, tibialis anterior, and tibialis posterior all receive a substantial contribution from L4;
- the **knee jerk** may be diminished on the affected side because of the effect on quadriceps; the ankle jerk is not affected.

Qu. 7H *What would be the signs of damage to the L5 nerve root? Would the knee and ankle jerks be affected?*

When the **S1** root is damaged:
- **sensory changes** will occur down the back and lateral aspect of the calf, spreading on to the dorsal and plantar surfaces of the lateral margin of the foot;
- **weakness** of gluteus maximus in hip extension and of plantar flexion of the ankle is likely;
- the **ankle jerk** may be lost but the knee jerk is not affected.

Questions and answers

Qu. 7A *Which spinal nerve supplies the area of skin on which you sit?*

Answer S3, S4; note that this reflects the caudal origin of this area. The lower limbs develop cranial to this region, as lateral extensions of the trunk, and subsequently rotate to their definitive position.

Qu. 7B *What are the basic neural mechanisms underlying this reflex response?*

Answer L2, L3, L4, sensory nerve roots are stimulated. Sensory (afferent) fibres synapse with motor (efferent) neurons at spinal cord levels L2, L3, L4, thus forming a monosynaptic reflex arc. The knee jerk is elicited in order to test the integrity of the sensory and motor fibres which comprise the arc, and especially their excitability, which depends on influences from higher nervous centres. The reflex response on one side must always be compared with that on the opposite side.

Qu. 7C *If a middle-aged man complained of a limp and a pain in his left knee, what initial steps might you wish to take in order to reach a diagnosis?*

Answer Physical and radiological examination of both the knee joint and the hip joint (from which pain can be referred to the knee).

Qu. 7D *Why might a woman feel monthly discomfort on the medial aspect of the thigh?*

Answer The medial side of the thigh is supplied by the obturator nerve. In the pelvis this nerve lies immediately adjacent to the ovary. A little bleeding from the ovary occurs when a follicle ruptures, and this can irritate the obturator nerve, giving pain referred to the thigh.

Qu. 7E *What would be the most obvious functional effect of such an injury, and what other functions should be tested to assess the completeness of the injury?*

Answer The most obvious effect would be an inability to dorsiflex the ankle ('foot drop'). An inability to evert and loss of sensation over the dorsum of the foot might also be detectable.

Qu. 7F *What action do these three muscles share?*

Answer These three muscles are responsible for tilting the pelvis during walking. The abduction of the pelvis on the femur enables the non-weight-bearing leg to swing forward without the heel catching on the ground.

Qu. 7G *If the inferior gluteal nerve was damaged, what would be the consequences?*

Answer The inferior gluteal nerve supplies gluteus maximus, which is a powerful extensor of the hip joint. If it were paralysed, it would be difficult for the person to get up out of a chair, or to walk up stairs.

Qu. 7H *What would be the signs of damage to the L5 nerve root? Would the knee and ankle jerks be affected?*

Answer Damage to L5 would cause slight weakness of dorsiflexion (extension) of the ankle and of extensor hallucis longus. The standard knee, ankle, and plantar reflexes would be unaffected. Sensation may be diminished over the antero-lateral aspect of the shin, across the dorsum of the foot, and in the centre of the sole.

Spinal column

Spinal column

The spine forms the central axis of the body and, by its shape, dominates the appearance of the trunk. It consists of a series of vertebrae, ligaments, and intervertebral discs which form a flexible column. Bipedalism, which emerged in hominids about 2 million years ago as a result of a combination of selection pressures concerned with carrying objects, the use of tools and weapons, and perhaps the need for vision over an increased distance, has profoundly altered the functional demands on the spine. The flexible, multi-unit spine with its associated ligaments and muscles evolved long ago with the first vertebrates, protecting the spinal cord and supporting the thoracic cage and limb girdles. In parallel, specialized joints developed between the spine and skull which gave the head an increased range of movement for visual scanning.

The human upright stance involves a series of alternating curvatures of the spine (forward facing in the neck and lumbar regions, and backward facing in the thorax and pelvis) which balance the head on the neck and balance the trunk on the lower limbs, reducing the need for the very powerful spinal extensors found in semi-erect primates such as the gorilla. The upright stance exposes more of the vulnerable abdomen, a disadvantage that was countered by a reduction in the number of lumbar vertebrae, bringing the ribs closer to the pelvis. The upright stance also means that the weight of a large part of the body is transmitted through the lumbar spine and sacrum to the pelvis and lower limbs. These forces are magnified many times in running and jumping and place considerable strains both on the vertebrae and on the intervertebral discs which provide shock-absorbing resilience. Although the human spinal column has become adapted to the upright stance in many ways, back problems are very frequent in modern humans. Not surprisingly, most occur more frequently in the lower lumbar spine than in any other region.

The cervical and lumbar regions of the spine are much more mobile than the thoracic region. The junctions between the thorax and the more mobile regions create areas of potential weakness. Injuries to the spine occur most frequently in the cervical region (e.g. 'whiplash' injuries).

The spine is moved by a series of postural and 'prime mover' muscles in order to orient the limb girdles and the head. It also provides attachment for other muscles (e.g. girdle muscles) and for the ribs. The vertebral bodies have the additional function of housing red bone marrow throughout life.

Development of the spine

The first axial skeletal element to be formed is the **notochord** (7.1). This mesodermal structure under-lies the neural plate/tube (future spinal cord). On each side of the axis formed by the neural tube and notochord mesodermal **somites** form in rostro-caudal sequence. The ventromedial part of each somite loses its epithelial arrangement to form a **sclerotome**, which will give rise to cartilaginous and bony elements.

Sclerotome cells migrate to surround the notochord and neural tube to form a mesenchymal precursor of the vertebral column. Other somite cells form a **myotome** which gives rise to the segmental muscles of the spine.

The mesenchyme of the sclerotomes is segmentally arranged; but each sclerotome becomes divided into rostral and caudal halves by the formation of an intrasegmental fissure. Each intrasegmental fissure lies opposite the middle of the overlying myotome and marks the position at which the intervertebral disc will develop. Above and below the centre of each somite a condensation of notochord and sclerotome-derived cells forms a **perichordal disc** which is thought to con-tribute to both the intervertebral disc and the centra (bodies of the vertebrae). It is generally assumed that the centra of vertebrae form from the adjoining halves of two adjacent sclerotomes; however, individual sclerotomes could form individual vertebrae if, when the sclerotome cells migrate toward the notochord, they also migrate rostrally by about half a segment.

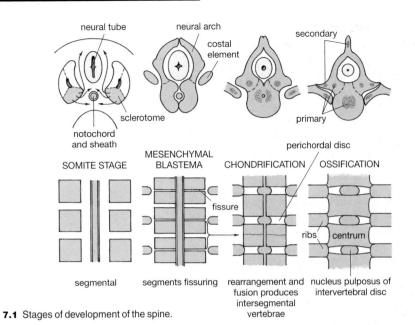

7.1 Stages of development of the spine.

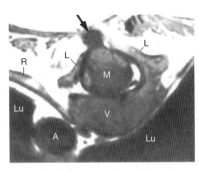

7.3 Horizontal MRI of spina bifida, showing protruding meningeal sac (arrow). V, body of thoracic vertebra; L, lamina of vertebra; M, meningeal sac containing spinal cord; R, rib; A, aorta; Lu, lungs.

Spina bifida

Failure of neural arches to fuse during development can occur in any part of the spine, but occurs most commonly in the lumbosacral region. It is often associated with maldevelopment of the neural tube and overlying skin and, when neural elements are involved there is often paralysis, loss of sensation, and loss of sphincter control.

The condition varies in severity, from an isolated midline failure of the laminae to fuse (spina bifida occulta—hidden) to a complete absence of the laminae with neural tissue that has failed to form a tube lying exposed on the surface ('open' meningomyelocoele).

7.2 is a radiograph of the lumbar spine of a young person with spina bifida. The neural arches of L2 and L3 (dotted) can be seen, but those of L4, L5, and S1 are missing. **7.3** is a horizontal MRI through such a defect, showing the gap in the neural arch through which the meningeal sac has herniated.

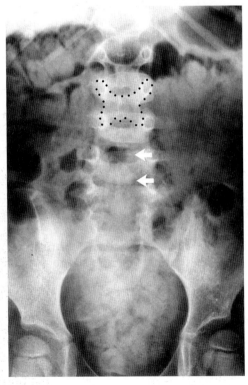

7.2 Radiograph of spina bifida, showing intact neural arch of L3 (dotted), missing neural arches of L4, L5 (arrows).

Whatever the mechanism, the development of the perichordal discs out of phase with the original somites allows the correct alignment of several important features:
• the segmental spinal nerves pass out between individual vertebrae;
• the intersegmental arteries (e.g. intercostal arteries, lumbar arteries) lie on the vertebral centra;

• the axial muscles derived from each myotome span two adjacent vertebrae, enabling movement of one vertebra on the next.

Chondrification of the centra starts at about the sixth week of intrauterine life. Each half of the neural arch chondrifies from a centre at its base, and does not unite in the midline until the fourth month *in utero*. Costal elements chondrify separately.

Ossification of typical vertebrae starts in **primary centres** in the centra and neural arches at 7–8 weeks *in utero*. The neural arches unite during the first year, but the neurocentral joint between the arch and the centrum persists for the first few years of life.

At puberty **secondary centres** appear in the spinous process and transverse process, and circumferential, annular epiphyseal discs form at the cranial and caudal ends of the vertebral bodies.

The anterior arch of the atlas forms from tissue (hypochordal bow) which unites the costal elements anterior to the centra. The centrum of the first cervical somite forms the odontoid peg of the axis. The pattern in the sacrum is essentially similar to that in typical vertebrae, except that the vertebrae fuse with each other and with the costal elements which form the alae.

Congenital anomalies

Congenital anomalies of the spine are relatively common. The spine is a functional unit made up of many vertebrae, each of which is formed from a number of elements which must segment, chondrify, and ossify correctly. A defect in a single vertebra, such as a hemivertebra (see **7.15**), can make the spine **unstable**, so that when the stresses of post-natal life are imposed, progressive deformation will result. Other anomalies such as fusion of two or more adjacent vertebral bodies may produce a minor loss of movement which can easily be compensated, but they are essentially **stable** and do not lead to progressive deformity. Many spinal anomalies, in particular spina bifida, are associated with nervous system defects and the spinal deformity can damage the spinal cord and nerves. Congenital anomalies of thoracic vertebrae also have profound effects on the thoracic cavity and respiration.

Living anatomy

Overall form of the spinal column

Compare the back of a colleague (**7.4**), with that of an articulated skeleton (**7.5**) and with radiographs of appropriate regions of the spine (see **7.6–7.12**). The spinal column normally lies strictly in the median sagittal plane (provided that the legs are of equal length).

Stand to one side and note the three spinal curvatures (see also **3.20**):

- a **cervical lordosis** (dorsal concavity);
- a **thoracic kyphosis** (ventral concavity);
- a **lumbar lordosis**.

Compare the spinal curvature of different people, particularly the degree of thoracic kyphosis. One rapid way to assess this is to ask the subject to stand with the back pressed firmly against a wall, holding the head in the natural erect posture. The extent of thoracic kyphosis can be assessed by the horizontal distance

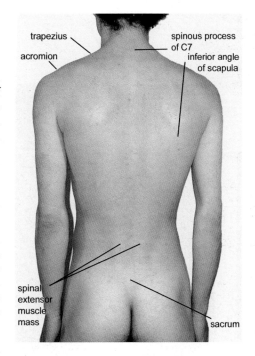

7.4 Normal back (male).

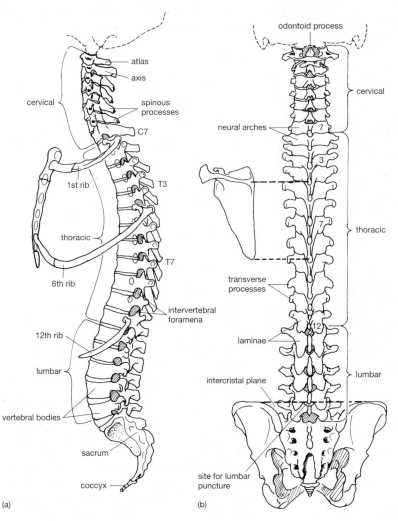

(a)   (b)

7.5 Vertebral column: (a) lateral view; (b) posterior view.

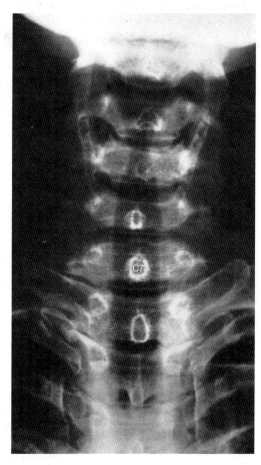

7.6 Cervical spine (AP).

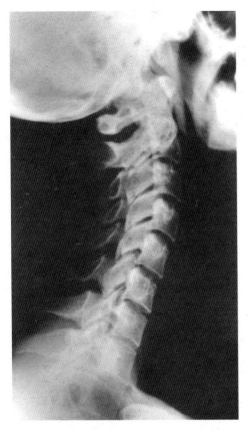

7.7 Cervical spine (lateral).

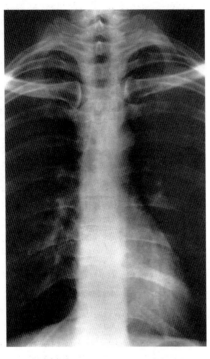

7.8 Thoracic spine (AP).

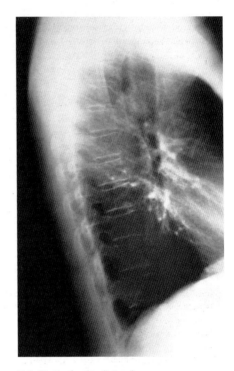

7.9 Thoracic spine (lateral).

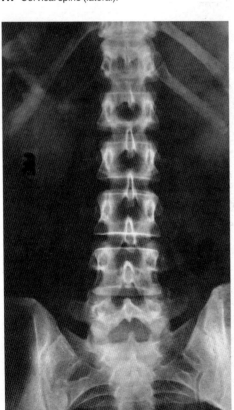

7.10 Lumbar spine (AP).

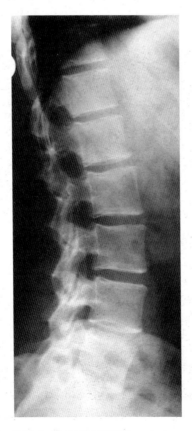

7.11 Lumbar spine (lateral).

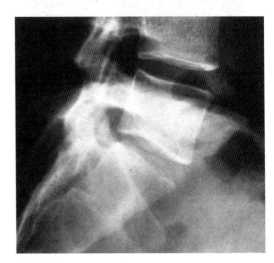

7.12 Fifth lumbar vertebra and upper part of sacrum.

from the wall to the tragus of the ear (the cartilaginous lump just in front of the external auditory meatus).

Qu. A *What are the advantages of having a curved rather than a straight vertebral column?*

Abnormal spinal curvature

Any deviation to the right or left of the midline vertical constitutes a deformity known as a **scoliosis** (**7.13–7.15**). Minor degrees of 'postural' scoliosis are unimportant and may disappear on flexion of the spine. 'Structural' scoliosis is a permanent deformity. Scoliosis may result from maldevelopment such as a hemivertebra (**7.15**; failure of one side of a vertebra to develop, or presence of an additional half-vertebra on one side), or from contracture of one side of the chest wall due to underlying lung disease. Most scolioses, however, are of unknown origin. They occur particularly in adolescent girls and involve rotational displacement of all the adjacent vertebrae, the bodies of the vertebrae pointing to the concavity of the curvature.

The normal thoracic **kyphosis** may be increased (**7.13b**), particularly if the bones become weak through lack of calcium, as may occur in the elderly (structural kyphosis). Localized injury or collapse of a single vertebral body can produce an angular kyphosis, the visible bony apex of which is called the kyphus.

Severe scoliosis may be associated with an increased kyphosis which severely diminishes the volume of the thoracic cavity and causes lung and heart problems.

Identification of vertebrae in the living back

Run a finger down the midline of a colleague's back, starting at the base of the skull. The spinous processes of upper cervical vertebrae lie deeply within the neck muscles, covered by the ligamentum nuchae and therefore cannot be felt. The first easily felt spinous process (the '**vertebra prominens**') is C7 (or T1). Spinous processes of thoracic vertebrae and lumbar vertebrae can then be identified.

The scapula is very mobile but, with the arms at rest by the side, the spine of T3 is usually at the level of the base of the spine of the scapula, and the spine of T7 opposite the inferior angle of the scapula.

Draw a line joining the uppermost parts of the iliac crests (intercristal plane). It crosses the midline between the spinous processes of L4 and L5.

Qu. B *Locate the spinous process of L1. The spinal cord ends at this level in the adult although it extends to L5 in the newborn child. Why is this?*

Skin dimples overlie the posterior superior iliac spines of the pelvis.

Assessment of spinal movements

Assess the **movement** of a colleague's spine. The extent of **flexion** can be roughly assessed if you ask a subject to stand, with knees straight, and then bend forward to try to touch the ground. The distance between ground and fingertip provides a measure of the flexion achieved, but the assessment is complicated by the

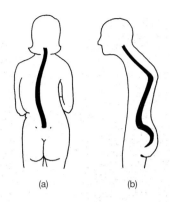

(a)   (b)

7.13 (a) Scoliosis; (b) kyphosis.

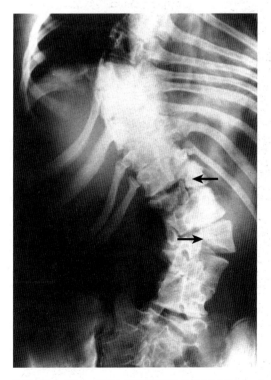

7.14 Radiograph (AP) showing scoliosis.

7.15 Congenitally maldeveloped spine showing two hemivertebrae (arrows) causing marked scoliosis.

degree of hip flexion and tension of the hamstring muscles. Measure the distance between the spine of S1 and the vertebra prominens in a colleague standing upright and then fully flexed (i.e. touching toes).

Qu. C *What is the difference and why does it occur?*

The extent of **lateral flexion** of the spine is assessed from the level attained by the tips of the fingers reaching down the side of the thigh toward the knee, without rotation of the trunk or flexion of the knees.

Extension and **rotation** of the spine are less easy to measure and are usually assessed by eye.

Qu. D *Which regions of the spine contribute most to (a) flexion and extension; (b) rotation; and (c) lateral flexion?*

Feel the prominence of muscular columns (spinal extensors) on either side of the lumbar vertebral spines.

Qu. E *When standing on one leg the muscular column becomes particularly prominent on one side. On which side, and what is the explanation?*

Bones of the spine

Examine isolated vertebrae and radiographs (**7.5, 7.16–7.23**) from different regions of the spine. There are usually 7 cervical, 12 thoracic, 5 lumbar, and 5 sacral vertebrae, but the number of vertebrae in a region may vary, usually by only one element. Most commonly this occurs in the lumbo-sacral region, due to the complete or incomplete sacralization of a lumbar vertebra.

Common features of vertebrae

On each vertebra and on the corresponding radiograph, identify:
- the **centrum** (body) of the vertebra;
- the **vertebral arch**. Each arch comprises, on each side, a **pedicle** attached to the vertebral body and a broad **lamina**. Together with the vertebral body, the arch encloses the **vertebral foramen**;
- a **spinous process** which projects from the arch dorsally in the midline;
- two **transverse processes**;
- paired **superior** and **inferior articular facets**, which project from the pedicles so that the vertebral arch articulates with the vertebra above and below.

Note the shape and orientation of the superior and inferior articular facets in the different regions. These form synovial joints, at each of which a small amount of gliding movement occurs.

Qu. F *How does the shape of the articular surfaces relate to the movement possible in a particular region of the spine?*

Multiple small vascular foramina can be found on the bone. The largest are seen on the dorsal surface of the centrum, where basivertebral veins drain the red marrow to the internal vertebral venous plexus (p. 208).

Costal elements develop in all regions but normally form separate ribs only in the thoracic region. In the cervical region they form the part of the transverse process anterior to the foramen transversarium; in the lumbar region they are incorporated into the transverse process; in the sacral region they fuse with transverse process elements to form the alae of the sacrum.

Cervical vertebrae

- **C1, atlas (7.16)**: the atlas does not have a centrum; during the course of evolution this became the odontoid process of the axis. Its short **anterior arch** has an anterior tubercle to which the anterior longitudinal spinal ligament is attached at its apex, and an articular facet for the dens. The larger **posterior arch** is grooved on its upper surface by the vertebral artery and its spinous process is represented by a posterior tubercle. The **lateral masses** are each pierced by a foramen transversarium for the vertebral artery; the **transverse processes** are prominent and can be felt just beneath the mastoid processes. Within the vertebral canal they give attachment to the transverse ligament of the atlas. Large con-cave superior facets articulate with the occipital condyles; flatter inferior facets with the body of the axis.

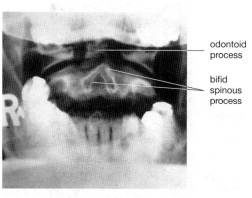

7.18 Radiograph of axis viewed through open mouth.

odontoid process

bifid spinous process

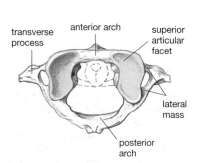

transverse process

anterior arch

superior articular facet

lateral mass

posterior arch

7.16 Atlas (C1) from above.

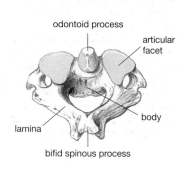

odontoid process

articular facet

lamina

body

bifid spinous process

7.17 Axis (C2) from above.

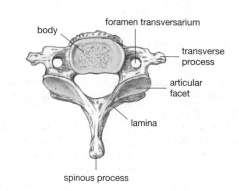

body

foramen transversarium

transverse process

articular facet

lamina

spinous process

7.19 Cervical vertebra C7, from above.

- **C2, axis** (**7.17, 7.18**): The axis is easily distinguished by the **odontoid process** (dens; **7.28c, 7.29b**) which has facets for articulation with the anterior arch of the atlas on its anterior surface and for the transverse ligament of the atlas on its posterior surface, and for the attachment of the alar ligaments above. The **body** has prominent oval articular facets on which rotation of the atlas occurs. The **laminae** are very thick and the **spinous process** large and bifid, as in most cervical vertebrae.
- **Cervical vertebrae C3–6** (**7.19**) are the 'typical' cervical vertebrae. Each has a relatively small **body**, a **transverse process** pierced by a foramen transversarium (which transmits the vertebral artery and vein) with an anterior tubercle (costal element) and posterior tubercle. Note the lips on the upper surfaces of the bodies and the shape and orientation of the articular facets. The **spinous processes** are bifid for the attachment of the ligamentum nuchae.
- **C7 vertebra** (**7.19**) is the 'vertebra prominens'— the first that can easily be felt as the examining hand descends the neck. Its spinous process is horizontal and not bifid, and the vertebral artery does not traverse its (often narrow) foramen transversarium.

Thoracic vertebrae

Thoracic vertebrae (**7.20**) have 'heart-shaped' bodies of increasing size, which typically bear upper and lower hemifacets for the heads of the ribs. The vertebral foramen is relatively small; the laminae are thick, broad, and overlapping; the spinous processes are long and slant downwards and backwards; the transverse processes are substantial and most bear facets for articulation with the tubercles of the numerically corresponding ribs.

Some thoracic vertebrae have distinguishing features:
- T1 has a complete upper facet for the first rib on the body and a thick, horizontal spine.
- T9 often does not articulate with the heads of the tenth ribs.
- T10 articulates with only the tenth ribs.
- T11 articulates with only the eleventh ribs and has no facets on its transverse processes.
- T12 articulates with only the twelfth rib and lacks facets on the transverse processes.

Interlocking articular facets of the lumbar type start at the lower border of T11 or T12.

Lumbar vertebrae

Lumbar vertebrae (**7.21, 7.22**) have large, deep bodies; short, stout pedicles; quadrangular spinous processes and long, thin transverse processes (developmentally costal elements); the articular processes are of the interlocking type.

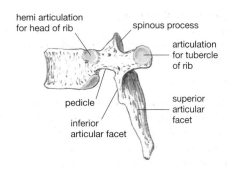

7.20 Typical thoracic vertebra (T5) from side.

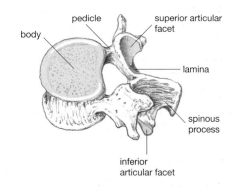

7.21 Typical lumbar vertebra (L4) from above and side.

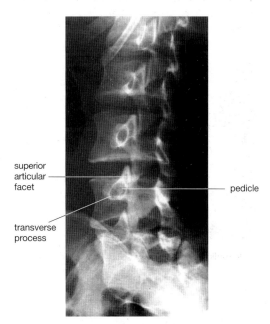

7.22 Lumbar spine (oblique) to show 'Scottie dog' appearance.

L5 has short, thick, conical transverse processes that give attachment to the iliolumbar ligaments connecting it to the pelvis.

An oblique radiograph of the lumbar spine (**7.22**) presents a 'Scottie dog' appearance in which the dog's nose is the transverse process, its ear the superior articular facet, and its eye the pedicle. The dog's collar is the interarticular part of the lamina (see spondylolisthesis, below).

Cervical and lumbar ribs

Abnormally separate ribs may develop in either region but are most common at C7 and L1.

Qu. G *A greater proportion of people with a cervical accessory rib complain of symptoms than those with an extra lumbar rib; why?*

Spondylolisthesis

Spondylolisthesis (forward slipping of the spine) is a condition in which L5 starts to slide forward on S1 (or L4 on L5). It is usually caused by a defect like a stress fracture in the interarticular part of the lamina between the superior and inferior facets of L5. The body of L5, carrying the spinal column above it, can then move forward, leaving the posterior facets, neural arch, and spinous process behind. Less commonly it starts in childhood, due to maldevelopment of the articular facets, or in old age if the facets degenerate due to arthritis.

Whatever the cause, as displacement of the spine continues, compression of the nerves in the sacral canal (particularly S1) can occur.

Sacrum

The **sacrum** (**7.23**) is large, triangular, and normally consists of five fused vertebrae. It articulates with L5 at the sacrovertebral angle and projects anteriorly as the sacral promontory. The whole sacrum forms a gently curving roof and posterior wall of the pelvis.

The pelvic surface of the sacrum is marked by four anterior sacral foramina from which emerge the anterior primary rami of the sacral spinal nerves. Lateral to the foramina, costal elements have fused with the transverse processes to form the lateral part or ala (wing) of the sacrum, which bears the L-shaped articular facet for the ilium.

On the dorsal surface of the sacrum is a median sacral crest representing the spinous processes and fore dorsal foramina (for the posterior primary rami).

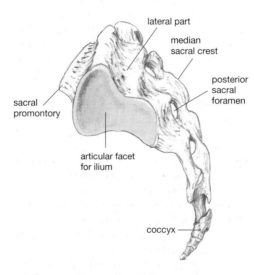

7.23 Sacrum and coccyx from side.

Coccyx

Below the sacrum the **coccyx** consists of 3–5 rudimentary vertebrae.

The erect posture places particular stresses on the articulation between L5 and the sacrum. The upper surface of the body of S1 slopes downward and forward when the trunk is erect (**7.23**), leading to a tendency for L5 to move forward on S1. This is normally prevented by the articular facets of the sacrum which lie anterior to those of L5, by the ligaments of those joints, and by the integrity of the intervertebral disc between the L5 and S1 vertebrae.

Joints of the spine

Facet joints

The articular processes of adjacent vertebrae are united by **plane synovial 'facet' joints** which allow gliding movements. The orientation and curvature of the joint surfaces vary in the different regions of the spine to allow for different movements. The articular facets allow flexion and extension in the cervical and lumbar regions and rotation between thoracic vertebrae; they are described with the individual vertebrae. (For the atlanto-occipital, atlanto-axial and cervical intervertebral joints see Vol. 3, Ch. 6, Sect. 2)

Intervertebral discs

These fibrocartilaginous joints (**7.24, 7.25**) unite the adjacent surface of the vertebral bodies from the axis to the sacrum. The bones are covered with hyaline cartilage and united by a fibrous outer ring, the

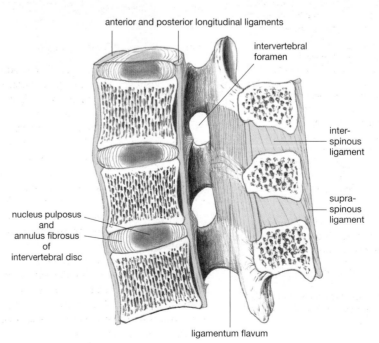

7.24 Midline sagittal section through lumbar spine to show discs and ligaments.

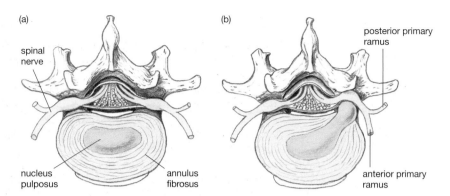

7.25 (a) Lumbar intervertebral disc viewed from below. (b) Prolapse of nucleus pulposus ('slipped disc').

annulus fibrosus, consisting of collagen and a little elastic tissue. The circumferential fibres are reinforced by layers of fibres which pass obliquely in different directions between the bones, giving great torsional strength. Within the annulus fibrosus is a less fibrous, more hydrated region, **nucleus pulposus**.

Together the annulus and nucleus form an incompressible but deformable cushion between individual vertebrae, which allows a small amount of movement and acts as a shock-absorber. Fluid can be forced out of the nucleus by the compressive force of the body weight, and discs are thinner in the evening than in the morning. Moreover the nuclei become smaller with ageing, hence the loss of height in older people.

'Slipped disc'

Weakening of the fibres of the annulus combined with excessive stress (e.g. trying to lift a heavy object with the lumbar spine flexed) can cause herniation (prolapse) of the nucleus pulposus through the weakened annulus (7.25–7.27) (NB the entire disc does not 'slip'!). Because, with age, the nucleus takes up a more posterior position, the herniation is likely to occur in a posterior or postero-lateral direction, on either side of the posterior longitudinal ligament.

The problem is most common in the lower lumbar region of the spine (L4/L5 and L5/S1) where body weight causes the greatest compression and, perhaps more importantly, where severe hyperlordosis can cause abnormal stresses on the posterior part of the disc, leading to degeneration and prolapse.

7.26 shows a prolapsed disc revealed as a filling defect in a myelogram (contrast medium injected into the lumbar CSF). **7.27** is a sagittal MRI of the lumbosacral region in which the L5/S1 disc is protruding and compressing the anterior aspect of the CSF-filled meningeal sac and the nerve roots within it.

Qu. H *What are the possible effects of a 'slipped disc' in the lower lumbar region? How might the effects differ if the mid cervical region was affected?*

Less commonly a cervical disc (often that above or below C6) can prolapse as a result of local strain or injury. These can press on C6/7 spinal nerves, and also, if they herniate posteriorly, on the anterior part of the spinal cord.

In the child the annulus is thin and the nucleus central. With ageing the annulus becomes thicker at the front and the nucleus comes to lie more posteriorly in the disc.

In addition to the intervertebral discs and synovial joints, the laminae, spines, and transverse processes of all the vertebrae are connected by **short** and **long** ligaments (**7.24, 7.28**) distinct from the synovial joint capsules; these attachments can be thought of as extrinsic ligaments or fibrous joints.

The *short* ligaments are the:
- **interspinous ligaments** between adjacent spinous processes;
- **intertransverse ligaments** between adjacent transverse processes;
- **ligamenta flava** between the laminae of the neural arches; these are yellow, elastic ligaments.

The *long* ligaments are:
- the **anterior longitudinal ligament** on the anterior aspect of the vertebral bodies;
- the **posterior longitudinal ligament** on the posterior aspect of the bodies;
- the **supraspinous ligament** over the tips of the spinous processes. This becomes the **nuchal ligament** between C7 and the skull.

Joints allowing skull movements

In the region immediately beneath the skull, both the vertebrae and the ligaments are specialized for the movements that occur between the occiput and the atlas, and between the axis and the atlas.

By moving your own head and studying isolated bones, examine the movements of this region. Nodding flexion/extension occurs at the atlanto-occipital joint with very minor lateral flexion possible. The atlanto-axial joint is specialized to allow rotation; other movements are prevented by the transverse ligament of the atlas, which holds the odontoid peg within the anterior arch of the atlas. The ligaments of this region (**7.28**) are:
- the **anterior atlanto-occipital membrane**—continuous with the anterior longitudinal ligament;
- the **tectorial membrane**—continuous with the posterior longitudinal ligament;
- the **posterior atlanto-occipital membrane**—the homologue of ligamenta flava;

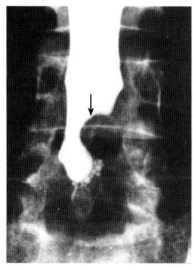

7.26 Myelogram showing protruding lumbar intervertebral disc (arrow).

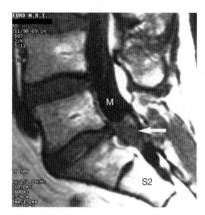

7.27 MRI of lumbar spine (sagittal section) showing protrusion (arrow) of L5/S1 disc. Note the ending of the CSF-filled meningeal sac (M) opposite the lower border of S2.

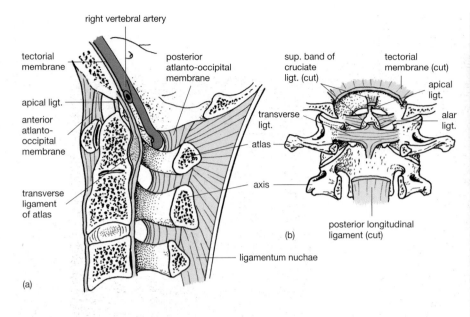

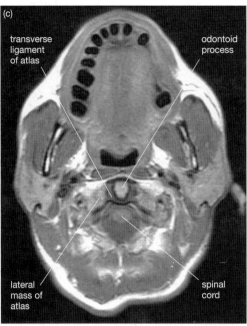

7.28 Ligaments of occipito-atlanto-axial region. (a) Sagittal section through cervical spine; (b) dorsal view with neural arches of atlas and axis and the posterior part of occiput removed; (c) axial MRI to show the atlanto-axial joint in horizontal section.

- the **cruciate ligament**—this comprises the **transverse ligament of the atlas** (7.28c) with upward and downward extensions;
- **alar ligaments,** which extend from the top and sides of the odontoid process laterally to the margin of the foramen magnum;
- the **apical ligament**—this thin band, formed from the notochord, may have a small bone, a pro-atlas, within it.

Qu. I *What is the function of the transverse ligament of the atlas?*

Qu. J *What movements do the alar ligaments restrain?*

Sacroiliac joint

The sacrum articulates with the innominate bones of either side to form the bony pelvis which supports and protects the pelvic viscera and, in the standing position, transmits the weight of the trunk to the lower limbs.

The **sacroiliac joint** which unites the bones is, perhaps surprisingly, a synovial joint. However, normally no movement occurs there because the articular cartilage on the facets on the sacrum and ilium are irregular and interlock, and some fibrocartilage extends between the articular surfaces. The bones are held firmly together by ventral and dorsal sacroiliac ligaments and by the very strong interosseous sacroiliac ligament that fills the irregular space above and behind the joint cavity. These are reinforced by the iliolumbar ligament (from the transverse process of L5 to the iliac crest) and by the sacrotuberous and sacrospinous ligaments (p. 140).

The weight of the body tends to push the sacrum forward into the pelvis, but this cannot happen unless the ligaments have become very lax. This occurs naturally as a preparation for childbirth and so dislocation of the sacroiliac joint is sometimes seen in women in under-developed countries who return to hard, stooping work in the fields soon after giving birth.

Movements and muscles of the spine

Movement between adjacent vertebrae is limited but, combined over the column as a whole the effect is considerable. Movements occur at the intervertebral disc as a result of elastic deformation.

Flexion

Flexion (**7.29**) occurs in the cervical and lumbar regions. It is produced by muscles lying anterior to the spine, whether attached to it or at a distance, all of which are supplied by anterior primary rami of spinal nerves. Muscles acting directly on the spine are:
- in the neck, longus colli and longus capitis, which extends from T4 to the base of the skull with attachments to all cervical vertebrae;
- in the lumbar region, psoas major acts as a powerful flexor.

Muscles flexing at a distance from the spine are sternomastoid in the neck and rectus abdominis in the trunk.

Lateral flexion

Lateral flexion also occurs primarily in the cervical spine, where it is produced by muscles lying lateral to the spine. In the neck these are:
- The **scalene** muscles (scalenus anterior, medius and posterior). These run from cervical transverse

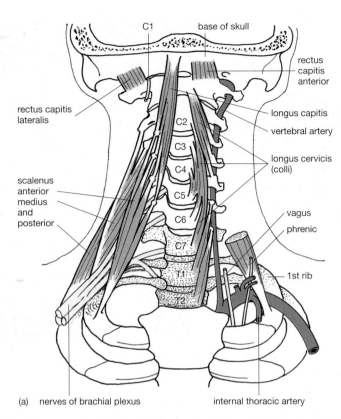

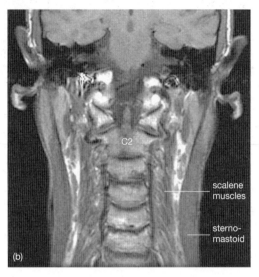

7.29 (a) Spinal long flexor and scalene (lateral flexor) muscles. (b) Coronal MRI showing the joints between the occiput, atlas and axis. The scalene muscles can be seen originating from the transverse processes of the vertebrae.

processes to the first and second ribs (**7.29b**), and act as 'guy lines' supporting the head on the trunk (see Vol. 3).
• In the lumbar region, **quadratus lumborum** (Vol. 2, Ch. 6, Sect. 3) runs from posterior third of the iliac crest upward and medially to the lumbar transverse processes and the twelfth rib.

Extension

Extension of the spine (**7.30**) occurs primarily in the cervical and lumbar regions and is produced by muscles lying posterior to the spine. This is a large group which consists of short, medium, and long muscles.

The shortest, deepest muscles are those attached between individual transverse processes and between individual spinous processes. They are mainly **postural** in function, producing only a little extension and rotation. Medium-length muscles lie superficial to these and run from transverse processes to spinous processes of vertebrae adjacent or of more distant regions.

The longest and most superficial muscles form the **erector spinae**. This group is firmly anchored to the dorsum of the sacrum and is the prime mover in extension of the spine. Muscle bundles are attached to spinous processes, transverse processes, and ribs. Some of its components extend up to the occiput and thus produce extension of the head.

In the region immediately beneath the skull, a specialized group of **suboccipital muscles** (**7.31**) controls

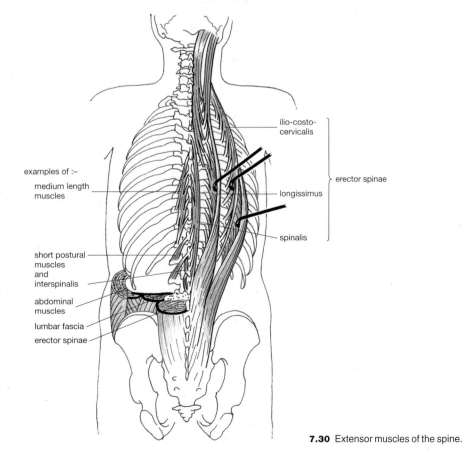

7.30 Extensor muscles of the spine.

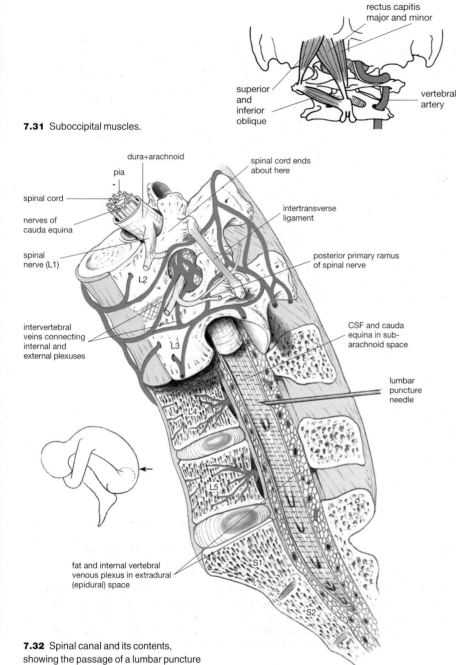

7.31 Suboccipital muscles.

rectus capitis
major and minor

superior
and
inferior
oblique

vertebral
artery

dura+arachnoid

pia

spinal cord ends
about here

spinal cord

nerves of
cauda equina

spinal
nerve (L1)

intertransverse
ligament

posterior primary ramus
of spinal nerve

L2

L3

intervertebral
veins connecting
internal and
external plexuses

CSF and cauda
equina in sub-
arachnoid space

lumbar
puncture
needle

L4

L5

fat and internal vertebral
venous plexus in extradural
(epidural) space

S1

S2

7.32 Spinal canal and its contents,
showing the passage of a lumbar puncture
needle.

extension and rotation at the atlanto-occipital and atlanto-axial joints, respectively (see Vol. 3).

All the muscles of the extensor group are supplied by the **posterior primary rami** of the spinal nerves, which also supply the skin of the back.

Rotation

Rotation occurs primarily in the upper thoracic spine. The muscles involved are:

- short, deep, rotator muscles lying posterior to the spine, which pass obliquely upward and medially

from transverse processes to adjacent spinous processes;
- the external and internal oblique muscles of the anterior abdominal wall (see Vol. 2, Ch. 6, Sect. 2).

Contents of the spinal canal

Within the **spinal canal** lie the spinal cord and spinal nerve roots, surrounded by protective membranes, the **meninges** (**7.32**). The outer tough fibrous layer is called the **dura mater** and this extends from the head throughout the length of the spine to S2 where it narrows to a thin cord. In the **extradural space** between the bone and dura lies an **internal vertebral venous plexus** and a little fat. This plexus drains the red bone marrow in the vertebral bodies via basivertebral veins, which emerge from the dorsal surfaces of the centra and communicate with the **external vertebral venous plexus** outside the spinal column via the intervertebral foramina. Blood flow in this system offers a venous pathway to the heart which can bypass the abdominal cavity, particularly when intra-abdominal pressure is raised. It is also an important route for the spread of (pelvic) malignancy, because it has no valves and is connected to veins of the pelvis, the flow of blood eddying to and fro through the external and internal plexuses with, for example, changes of posture.

The dura mater is lined by a cobwebby membrane, the **arachnoid mater**, within and by which the spinal cord is suspended in **cerebrospinal fluid** (CSF). The CSF-filled subarachnoid space ends at S2 level.

Sampling the CSF for analysis

The diagnosis of nervous system disease often requires the analysis of a sample of CSF. This can be obtained by inserting a needle into the subarachnoid space in the lower lumbar region ('lumbar puncture'). The pressure of the CSF should always assessed by examining the optic disc of the eye (see Vol. 3) before a lumbar puncture is performed. Withdrawing CSF from a patient who has raised intracranial CSF pressure can have fatal consequences (the raised intracranial pressure forces the brainstem through the foramen magnum in the base of the skull, compressing its vital centres) and should, therefore, never be done.

To perform a lumbar puncture, the skin over L4 and L5 is anaesthetized and the patient either lies on one side, or sits, curled up as much as possible (**7.32 insert**). A lumbar puncture needle is introduced in the midline, pointing forward and slightly toward the head, between the spines of L4 and L5 vertebrae (the intercristal plane) (**7.32**). The needle pierces the interspinous ligament and the ligamentum flavum, and so enters the vertebral canal. Advancing further, the needle will pierce the dura and arachnoid membranes and enter the CSF-containing subarachnoid space which, below the level of L1, contains the mass of lower lumbar and sacral nerve roots known as the **cauda equina**. Before any fluid is withdrawn for analysis the CSF pressure can be measured with a manometer.

Take an articulated lumbar spine and pass a needle as you would in a lumbar puncture, mentally noting the structures which are traversed.

Qu. K *Why is a patient undergoing lumbar puncture asked to curl up as much as possible?*

Uses of lumbar puncture

Access to the spinal dural sac permits an anaesthetist to inject local anaesthetic into the CSF around the roots of the cauda equina, to allow surgery to be performed on the pelvis (e.g. during childbirth) or legs. Such **spinal anaesthesia** is especially useful where general anaesthesia is contraindicated, although if raised intracranial pressure is suspected, lumbar puncture should not be performed. Extradural application of anaesthetic around emerging spinal nerves (**epidural anaesthesia**) is also used.

In the past, radiologists have used lumbar puncture to inject radiopaque dye into the CSF so that radiological examination (myelogram, **7.26**) can reveal the shape of the dural sac, and the outline of the dural 'sleeves' at the origin of the roots as they pass through the dura. The patient is tilted to allow the viscous dye to reach the appropriate level. However, myelograms are now very rarely performed because MRI, which is non-invasive and carries less risk of side-effects, is preferred. A distortion of the normal outline of the dural sac can reveal any narrowing (stenosis) of the spinal canal caused, for instance, by protrusion of an intervertebral disc, osteoarthritis, or spondylolisthesis.

Intervertebral foramina

Because the spinal canal is surrounded by bone, any expanding structure in the canal can quickly compress the spinal cord or the motor and sensory nerve roots in the intervertebral foramina. This can occur at any level of the spine.

The boundaries of an intervertebral foramen are formed by edges of the centrum and pedicle, the intervertebral disc, and the facets of the posterior intervertebral joints. Expansion of any of these, caused, for example, by a disc prolapse, arthritic joint changes with bony overgrowth, or disc protrusion, will encroach on the intervertebral foramen and damage the nerve roots.

Compression of a nerve root in a lumbar intervertebral foramen can be tested by a 'straight leg raise' test. The patient lies supine on a couch and one leg is raised, making sure that the knee is fully extended. There is a limit to which this can be done without causing discomfort. As the straight leg is raised the spinal nerve roots which contribute to the sciatic nerve are stretched and move several millimetres through their respective intervertebral foramina thereby pulling the dural sac downward and to one side.

If the nerve root is already being compressed, this test will increase the pain. Dorsiflexion of the foot during a straight leg raise will have the same effect for similar reasons. The extent to which a 'straight leg raise' can be achieved in comfort can be used to assess progress of a disc lesion (**7.33**).

Qu. O *Can you devise a similar test to detect compression of the roots of the femoral nerve?*

7.33 Straight leg raise test.

Spinal injuries affecting the spinal cord and spinal nerves

The spinal cord and spinal nerve roots are usually well protected by the vertebral bodies and by the joints and ligaments which connect them. However, in severe injuries (e.g. a car accident, collapse of a rugby scrum, a roof fall in a mine) the spine may break, especially at the junctions of relatively mobile and immobile segments (the lower cervical and thoraco-lumbar regions). One vertebra and the spinal column above it can shear away completely from the adjacent vertebra and spinal column below. It is important for the doctor attending such a patient to appreciate the damage that can be caused by movement after, as well as at the time of the accident, and is the reason why surgical 'collars' are frequently applied.

Qu. L *If the injury was between C6 and C7, such that the spinal cord was transected, what would be the results? Would the patient be able to breathe? What voluntary arm movements would still be possible?*

If the injury were of a similar nature but between T12 and L1, there could be damage to either or both the spinal cord (its terminal sacral part) and the nerve roots that are passing down to their respective intervertebral foramina. It is important to distinguish between nerve root and spinal cord damage since, in the former, there is the possibility of some recovery as fibres can regrow down Schwann cell sheaths. With cord injuries the damage will be permanent.

Qu. M *How will the results of an injury between T12 and L1 differ from those of an injury between C6 and C7?*

Qu. N *In a head-on collision car injury, what injuries other than damage to the spinal column at the T12–L1 boundary are likely?*

If the level of spinal injury is below the L1 vertebra then only nerve roots will be damaged.

Low back pain

Back pain is a very common complaint and is responsible for much time off work.

Sudden pain in the lower part of the back can extend into the buttock and upper thigh. The sufferer is typically aged between 20 and 60 and the onset of pain usually follows minor muscular trauma (twisting or lifting). This suggests that the disorder is not generally attributable to tissue degeneration, and lumbar nerve roots are unaffected.

Chronic low back pain is a disorder of middle age usually associated with tissue degeneration. This can cause inflammation or arthritis of the synovial joints with the formation of bony outgrowths (osteophytes) between articular facets between vertebrae, or disc degeneration with herniation of lumbar discs. Either of these can press on nerve roots in the lumbar intervertebral canals.

Imaging the spine and spinal canal

The spine can be imaged by conventional AP and lateral radiography (**7.2, 7.6–7.12, 7.18**). AP views are used to detect scoliosis (**7.14, 7.15**); lateral views of the thoracic spine are usually more clear as there is less superimposed tissue. Oblique radiographs are used particularly for the lumbar spine ('Scottie dog appearance; **7.22**). The use of contrast media to visualize the CSF space (myelogram; **7.26**) has now been superceded by much less invasive CT and MRI investigations (**7.3, 7.27, 7.29b**, see **3.20**). MRI **7.28c** shows the joint between the atlas and the odontoid process. Unlike in radiographs, the transverse ligament of the atlas can be seen clearly.

Questions and answers

Qu. A *What are the advantages of having a curved rather than a straight vertebral column?*

Answer The three curves of the vertebral column (cervical and lumbar lordosis, thoracic kyphosis) allow for an increased amount of shock-absorption. Also, active straightening of the thoracic curvature during deep inspiration increases the chest volume.

Qu. B *Locate the spinous process of L1. The spinal cord ends at this level in the adult, although it extends to L5 in the newborn child. Why is this?*

Answer Growth during development causes a greater elongation of the vertebral column than the spinal cord. Early in development the segments of the spinal cord and of the spinal column are in register.

Qu. C *What is the difference and why does it occur?*

Answer Flexion of the spine will 'stretch' the synovial joints between the vertebrae. Therefore, the distance between the spine of C7 (vertebra prominens) and S1 is greater when the spine is flexed than in the upright, weight-bearing position.

Qu. D *Which regions of the spine contribute most to (a) flexion and extension; (b) rotation; and (c) lateral flexion?*

Answer (a) flexion and extension take place in the cervical and lumbar regions of the spine; (b) rotation occurs at the atlanto-axial joint and in the thoracic spine; (c) lateral flexion occurs in the cervical and lumbar spine.

Qu. E *When standing on one leg the muscular column become particularly prominent on one side. On which side, and what is the explanation?*

Answer The side on which the leg is lifted. Erector spinae contracts to laterally flex the spine away from the supporting leg and thus restore the centre of gravity which has been disturbed.

Qu. F *How does the shape of the articular surfaces relate to the movement possible in a particular region of the spine?*

Answer
- At the atlanto-occipital joint, nodding movements are possible with slight lateral flexion but no rotation; at the atlanto-axial joint, the atlas rotates around the dens of the axis.
- The articular facets between typical cervical vertebrae lie on a sloping, transverse plane which permits flexion/extension and a small amount of lateral flexion.
- The articular facets between thoracic vertebrae lie on the circumference of a large circle, the centre of which is in the trunk, thus permitting rotation, but rather little flexion or extension, which is limited by the ribs.
- The facets between lumbar vertebrae also lie on the circumference of a circle but, because the centre of that circle is dorsal to the trunk, the facets form strong interlocking articulations which permit some flexion and extension but no rotation of the trunk.

Qu. G *A greater proportion of people with a cervical accessory rib complain of symptoms than those with an extra lumbar rib; why?*

Answer Accessory cervical ribs give rise to more problems. The first thoracic nerve (T1), which forms the lowest root of the brachial plexus, has to emerge from the chest and pass over the first rib to reach the plexus. If an accessory rib is present, it also passes over this and is stretched, especially when the arm is carrying a heavy weight.

Qu. H *What are the possible effects of a 'slipped disc' in the lower lumbar region? How might the effects differ if the mid cervical region was affected?*

Answer This lesion, which is relatively common, could give rise to pain down the lower and lateral aspect of the leg, passing into the foot (S5 dermatome). It would also lead to weakness of eversion of the foot. Retention of urine may also occur due to damage to the pelvic parasympathetic nerves which control bladder emptying. Disc lesions in the cervical region may compress not only the nerve roots but also the anterior aspect of the spinal cord, and cause muscle weakness due to damage to the motor nerve cell bodies and descending tracts that control them.

Qu. I *What is the function of the transverse ligament of the atlas?*

Answer The transverse ligament of the atlas prevents the odontoid peg from moving backwards and therefore damaging the medulla and upper cervical spinal cord.

Qu. J *What movements do the alar ligaments restrain?*

Answer The alar ligaments restrain both rotation and flexion/extension between the occiput and the axis.

Qu. K *Why is a patient undergoing lumbar puncture asked to curl up as much as possible?*

Answer Flexion of the spine stretches all the extensible tissues (ligamenta flava, interspinous ligament) dorsal to the spinal cord. This increases the distance between the spines of the lumbar vertebrae through which the lumbar puncture needle must be passed.

Qu. L *If the injury was between C6 and C7, such that the spinal cord was transected, what would be the results? Would the patient be able to breathe? What voluntary arm movements would still be possible?*

Answer Paralysis and loss of sensation in structures innervated by spinal nerves below the level of the lesion. Autonomic responses would lack higher control, therefore co-ordination of pelvic visceral reflexes would be lost. (Remember that C6 spinal nerve emerges beneath C6 vertebra and would therefore be likely to be involved.) The patient would have the use of the diaphragm (C3, 4, 5) and could therefore breathe, but intercostal muscles would be paralysed. Assuming C5 remained intact, some movement of the shoulder joint would be possible, though adduction and medial rotation would be most affected. Flexion of the elbow would be weaker, but wrist and hand movement would be lost.

Qu. M *How will the results of an injury between T12 and L1 differ from those of an injury between C6 and C7?*

Answer Arm movements, intercostal muscle activity in breathing, and abdominal muscle activity would all be intact, as would sympathetic reflexes.

Qu. N *In a head-on collision car injury, what injuries other than damage to the spinal column at the T12–L1 boundary are likely?*

Answer The junction between C7 and T1 vertebrae, where the cervical and thoracic curvatures meet, is potentially weak (similar to the T12–L1 junction). A head-on car collision can cause a 'whiplash' injury leading to a fracture–dislocation at this level.

Qu. O *Can you devise a similar test to detect compression of the roots of the femoral nerve?*

Answer The femoral nerve is formed from lumbar roots L2, L3, L4. To stretch its nerve roots, the subject is asked to lie prone and the hip is then extended.

Human upright stance, sitting, and locomotion

CHAPTER 8

Human upright stance, sitting, and locomotion

The evolution of the human upright stance has involved the balancing of the trunk on the lower limbs, and balancing the head on the trunk. The lower limbs came to support the entire weight of the body and to provide for most forms of locomotion. Thus, the upper limbs were freed for the manipulation of a wide range of objects and tools, and for gesticulation, which provided an early means of communication.

Standing rest position

In the upright 'standing rest' position, the arms hang loosely on either side and the weight of the body is evenly distributed between the two legs (although most people shift their body weight alternately from one leg to the other). The weight of the body above the pelvis is transmitted through the bones and intervertebral discs of the flexible vertebral column to the sacrum. The sacrum is therefore thrust downward and forward between the two sides of the pelvis. The downward force is countered by the interdigitating surfaces of the sacroiliac joints and the strong sacroiliac ligaments; the forward rotatory force is countered by the sacrotuberous and sacrospinous ligaments (**8.1a**). Weight transmitted from the sacrum to the pelvis is then transmitted via the femur and tibia to the talus at the apex of the arch of each foot, and from the talus obliquely forward to the heads of the metatarsals and backward to the posterior tubercles of the calcaneus.

The body's **centre of gravity** (a point from which the weight of the body may be considered to act) in the standing rest position lies immediately in front of the second sacral segment. However, it is not static because the body constantly sways backward and forward at the ankles, though to a small extent. From the centre of gravity, the body weight is transmitted downward through both legs, passing just behind the head of the femur and through the patella (i.e. just in front of the centre of the knee articulation) to intersect the arch of the foot in front of the ankle joint.

The weight of the head acts downward in front of the atlanto-occipital joints. The flexion force on this joint is well demonstrated by a drooping head when one 'nods off' during a lecture! The rapid contraction of skull extensors as they reflexly return the head to the horizontal can be equally embarrassing! Skull extensors therefore act as continuously active postural muscles to keep the head upright.

The centre of gravity of the trunk in an upright standing rest position is just in front of the eleventh thoracic vertebra, and the spine therefore tends to flex. This is countered by activity in the small deep postural components of the spinal extensor muscle groups. Even a small forward inclination is sufficient to require increased activity in these muscles.

At the hip, the line of transmission of body weight passes just behind (or even through) the axis of the hip joint; this creates a small backward-falling (extensor) force on the joint. This requires little muscular counterbalance (by psoas and iliacus) and is resisted largely by the strong iliofemoral ligament. Electromyographic (EMG) studies of muscle activity in the lower limb indicate that gluteus medius is also active, its anterior fibres contracting to prevent extension and its posterior fibres contracting to prevent flexion as the trunk sways slightly about a transverse axis through the hip joints. The deep, short muscles around the hip (e.g. obturator externus) may also play a role in hip stability, but EMG evidence for this is difficult to obtain.

At the knee, where the body weight is transmitted close to the axis of the joint, less active muscular counterbalance is required than at the hip or the ankle. In the 'standing rest' position, the knee is not locked in full extension, but is near its most stable (close-packed) position. You can demonstrate that quadriceps is inactive in the standing rest position because the patella can easily be displaced laterally. The hamstrings are also inactive and thus no very obvious muscle contraction stabilizes the knee. However, the tone in gluteus maximus, acting through the iliotibial tract attachment to the tibia, is said to contribute to knee stability. The small forward-falling force at the knee joint is largely taken by the posterior and collateral ligaments, and by the large contact area between the condyles and menisci. If, however, the knee is either fully extended or slightly flexed then both quadriceps and the hamstrings become active.

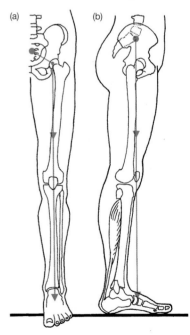

8.1 Lines of gravity: (a) antero-posterior view; (b) lateral view (most of the fibula has been removed).

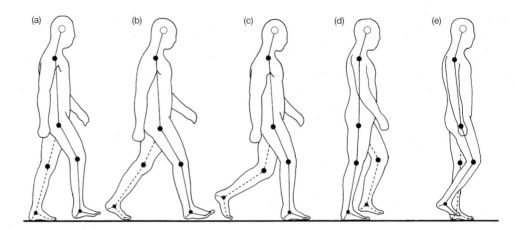

(a) (b) (c) (d) (e)

8.2 Walking cycle.

At the ankle, as a result of both the femur and tibia being angled forward at 5° from the vertical, the line of body weight transmission passes well in front (2–5 cm) of the joint. Thus a forward rotatory force exists at the ankle which is countered, in the standing rest position, by contraction of soleus. Soleus is therefore an important postural muscle which needs to be relaxed when walking is initiated.

Sitting

There are a variety of different sitting positions, which depend in part on the extent of external support provided (bench, chair with back, etc.). If the trunk is upright, or sloping backward, then the centre of gravity is above the ischial tuberosities which provide the principal bony contact with the surface. However, if the trunk is bent forward, the centre of gravity lies well anterior to the tuberosities, somewhere above the middle of the thighs, and there is then a considerable flexor moment on the hips and spine. The extent to which the pelvis is flexed or extended on the thighs also varies. Because of the considerable problems humans have with their lumbar intervertebral discs, and the fact that many spend much of their life sitting, there has been special interest in the relationship between disc loading and the sitting posture. Although the deep back muscles are more active in the upright positions, the load on the dorsal aspect of the L4–5 intervertebral disc (where rupture usually occurs; p. 205) is greater in forward-hunched sitting positions. This is a complex subject and the load on the back also depends on the position of the arms and whether or not they are supported. There is probably no one ideal sitting position, but a number from which to choose. Also small shifts of position alter the loads and tensions and relieve the strain.

Locomotion

Striding gait

Humans achieve locomotion in many different ways, depending on the circumstances (e.g. crawling,

hopping, sliding), but the two most common bipedal forms of locomotion are both variants of the **striding gait**—walking and running. Other animals may walk on two legs intermittently, but the striding gait is unique to humans. The basis of the striding gait is that, while one leg supports and propels the body forward (**support phase**), the other swings forward free of the ground (**swing phase**) to a new position where it, in turn, supports and propels the body as the cycle is repeated (**8.2**).

Walking is an exceptionally energy-efficient form of locomotion, in part because the centre of gravity of the body is disturbed very little (**8.3**), and in part because of the storage of elastic recoil energy in the muscles and tendons. The more rapid but less energy-efficient running also evolved to carry our ancestors away from danger or towards prey. The speed of locomotion can, of course, be varied in both walking and running.

If you walk slowly, or watch someone walking, you will see that the support phase of one leg does not end immediately the opposite foot strikes the ground (**heel strike**). Rather, for a brief period, both feet are simultaneously in contact with the ground (**double-support phase**) (**8.2b**). As walking quickens, so the double-support phase shortens until running is achieved, in which, for a period, neither foot is on the ground (**float phase**).

Stand with your feet together at rest, and then slowly start to walk forward. Walking is initiated by relaxation of soleus which causes the ankle joints to dorsiflex passively because the line of transmission of body weight runs in front of the ankle (**8.2a**). The weight is transferred from the heel to the toes, especially the great toe, along the lateral side of the foot. The limb which will enter the swing phase is then actively flexed at the hip to propel the limb forward and flexed at the knee and dorsiflexed at the ankle to take the foot clear of the ground. As the body continues to swing forward on the supporting leg, the knee of the swinging leg is increasingly extended and hip flexion is braked as heel strike approaches. At the same time the hip and knee of the supporting limb become fully extended (**8.2a, d**) so that the limb becomes, momentarily, a rigid prop as the ankle

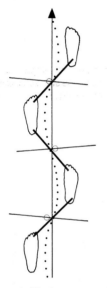

8.3 Movement of the transverse axis of the pelvic girdle (thick line) and shoulder girdle (thin line) and centre of gravity (dotted line) in relation to foot positions when walking in the direction of the arrow.

and then first metatarso-phalangeal joints are forcibly (plantar) flexed to provide the propulsive thrust (**8.2b**).

As each leg is swung forward, the *pelvis* also rotates about a vertical axis to increase the length of the stride (**8.3**). Therefore, in order that the feet shall keep pointing forward during walking, each lower limb is laterally rotated on the pelvis during the swing phase, and medially rotated during the stance phase. When a leg is swung forward free of the ground it can no longer support the body weight, which is taken by the support-phase leg. To prevent the pelvis from dropping on the unsupported side, the pelvis is abducted on the femur of the supporting leg. This also helps to enable the swinging leg to move forward clear of the ground (**8.4**; see **6.2.11**).

It is not only the lower limbs and pelvis which move during walking. The trunk (carrying the body's centre of gravity with it) moves to the side of the supporting leg by lateral flexion of the spine. Also, the shoulder girdle swings clockwise around the vertical axis so that, as the pelvis rotates in one direction the shoulders swing in the opposite way to balance the trunk (**8.3**). The arms are also swung to act as balancers and to increase the impetus of movement, especially in running and jumping.

The activity of the various groups of lower limb muscles during walking is shown in **8.5**. From this you should identify the principal muscles causing the following active movements of the striding gait.

Movements of the *hip joint* during walking are largely those of flexion and extension. However, in the double support phase, when the trailing leg is about to make its thrust, the hip is extending while that of the front leg about to take on a single support role, is flexed (**8.2b**). There is associated torsion at the lower end of the spine so that the pelvis rotates towards the supporting leg. Since the axes of the feet are considered to be parallel with each other in the direction of motion, the forward hip rotates laterally while the thrusting leg rotates medially (**8.3**). The abduction of the pelvis on the femur of the supporting leg is difficult to perceive, but if you palpate gluteus medius just beneath the iliac crest, you will feel it contract during each supporting phase. If gluteus medius and minimus are paralysed, the pelvis does drop on the unsupported side and a very abnormal gait ensues (p. 142) in which excessive lateral flexion of the spine compensates in order to keep the head upright.

During the support phase the *knee joint* becomes progressively more extended (**8.2, 8.4**). After the propulsive thrust, the knee of the swinging leg is increasingly flexed until the middle of the swing phase, to help the swinging foot clear the ground. It then extends again so that it forms a firm prop when the heel touches the ground at heel-strike.

At the *ankle joint* plantar flexion forms part of the propulsive thrust; it ends early in the swing phase when the ankle becomes dorsiflexed (extended) to

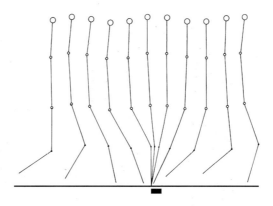

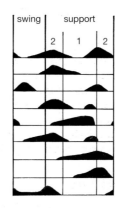

8.4 Vertical movements of the hip, shoulder and head during a walking cycle. (Support phase marked by a block.)

swing | support

erector spinae
gluteus medius & minimus
iliacus and psoas major
vasti (quadriceps)
tensor fasciae latae
hamstrings (biceps)
soleus
flexor hallucis longus
extensor hallucis longus

8.5 Activity of various muscles and muscle groups during the swing and single (1) and double (2) support phases of walking.

help the foot to clear the ground (**8.2**). Some plantar flexion starts just before or at heel-strike, to bring the forefoot into contact with the ground, but the ankle passively dorsiflexes through the single support phase as the body swings forward over the fixed foot (**8.2a, b**). During the double support phase active plantar flexion again occurs to generate thrust.

At the *metatarso-phalangeal joints* there is passive dorsiflexion as the ankle is plantar-flexed, and then active plantar flexion, particularly of the great toe, as the thrust-off mechanism is completed.

At the *subtalar* and *transverse tarsal* joints, movement is minimal during the support phase. However, when the backward thrust commences, the heads of the metatarsals are fixed on the ground and the posterior part of the foot can move on the transverse tarsal joint as the heel is raised from the ground.

Because of the greater breadth of the female pelvis in relation to the length of the stride, women rotate their hips about a vertical axis more than do men when they walk, and in some cultures this is accentuated as a sexual attractant. In fact, each person has his or her own characteristic gait which can, moreover, strongly reflect their mood. The differences between individual gaits can be very difficult to analyse in anatomical terms but, such is the importance to us of being able to recognize individuals, we can often recognize a person in the distance by their gait long before we can distinguish their face.

Experimental examination of tissues

Experimental examination of tissues

The purpose of this appendix is to suggest some simple experiments that you can perform to examine the function of tissues in the living body.

The action of muscles

The actions of muscles can be investigated by many different methods:
- performing different movements and feeling which muscles contract;
- pulling on dissected tendons, and making inferences from morphology;
- electrical stimulation;
- recording by electromyography, cinematography, flashing light photography, and kinesiology.

Each method has its advantages and limitations. The results taken together provide more understanding than the results of any one of them taken alone.

Always remember that a muscle never acts in isolation, but always as one of a number of groups of muscles involved in a movement. Also, remember that many muscles act over more than one joint. If such muscles are involved in producing movement at a single joint, their actions at the other joints over which they act must be prevented by the action of synergists and fixators.

Physical examination

When studying any movement, feel your own body or that of a colleague to determine which muscles are contracting when the movement is performed against resistance.

Dissection and pulling on tendons

In dissected cadavers you can observe the effects of pulling on tendons, and combine this with inferences from morphology of the probable effect of shortening the distance between the origin and insertion of a muscle in relation to the possible movements of the joint(s) across which it pulls. However, since no muscle normally acts alone, this method shows nothing of the combinations of muscles which are naturally engaged in producing even the simplest reflex or voluntary movement.

Electrical stimulation

Motor nerves to muscles can be stimulated electrically. The nerves to superficial muscles can often be stimulated through the skin. This is conveniently done by use of an electronic stimulator which delivers 0.5 ms rectangular pulses at 35 Hz at an output voltage between 5 and 40 volts. A large, stainless-steel anode is covered with a pad soaked in saturated NaCl solution and applied firmly by a bandage to a part of the body remote from the part being stimulated. A focal cathode of cotton wool soaked in saturated NaCl solution contained in and just protruding from a perspex tube is applied to the point of stimulation (A.1).

The effective 'motor points' are at, or near to, the point of entry of motor nerves into muscles. You should begin with low voltages and, using firm pressure, explore these points. Increasing the voltage as necessary to elicit weak contractions. The effects of stimulating motor nerves to individual muscles can also be observed when these are exposed at operation.

Because no muscle normally acts alone, electrical stimulation which causes powerful contraction of a single muscle can cause dislocations. For example, powerful stimulation of deltoid can dislocate the shoulder! In natural abduction of the shoulder, the synergic actions of other muscles prevent this.

Recording muscle activity

Modern research on human movement involves recording the forces and movements at joints by force transducers, position transducers, and accelerometers ('kinesiology'), combined with simultaneous recording of the electrical activity of several of the muscles taking part (electromyography). Movements at several joints, or of the whole body, can be analysed by photographing flashing lights attached to the moving parts, or by cinematography, synchronized with electromyography.

The **electrical activity** of a muscle in any movement can be recorded. In clinical practice needle electrodes have to be used for deep muscles, but you can record

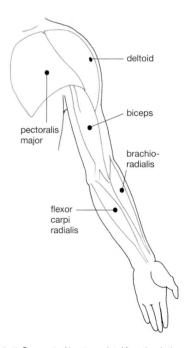

A.1 Suggested 'motor points' for stimulating muscles with surface electrodes.

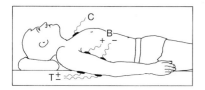

A.2 Suggested points for recording muscle electrical activity with surface electrodes. B, biceps; T, triceps; C, indifferent electrode.

from a pair of superficial muscles (biceps and triceps are convenient) through the skin. The subject should recline comfortably on a couch in a warm room and practise muscle relaxation. Muscles to be investigated should first be identified by palpation during movements performed against resistance from the examiner's hand.

The areas of skin to which electrodes are to be attached (**A.2**) should be cleaned with 70% ethanol and allowed to dry. A large disc indifferent electrode is attached over the manubrium of the sternum, and small surface electrodes to either end of the belly of the muscle(s) being investigated. These electrodes can then be connected to either an amplifier and chart recorder, or to an amplifier connected to a loudspeaker.

If recording equipment is not available, then you can investigate the action of the muscles by simply palpating their contraction during the movements. Remember that the aim of the experiments is to understand that any muscle has a role in many different movements, and not just the single (prime mover) 'action' usually quoted in textbooks. There is no need to memorize all these actions, but the general principle must be appreciated, as a muscle which is not functioning properly will be weak in *all* of its actions, and it may not be a defect in the prime mover action that a patient complains of.

A possible series of investigations of biceps and triceps (both muscles have parts which cross more than one joint) can reveal a great deal about prime mover action, synergism, essential fixation, and action against gravity (p. 15). We suggest that you investigate their electrical activity (**A.3**):

- during flexion and extension of the elbow against resistance, with the forearm both supine (**A.3a,b**) and prone (flexion **A.3c**);
- during pronation (**A.3d**) and supination (**A.3e**) against resistance;
- during the gradual squeezing of an object (a dynamometer is ideal) in the hand (**A.3f**);
- during movement of the elbow from full extension to full flexion and back to full extension, with the distal end of the limb weighted to accentuate gravity (the forearm can conveniently be inserted in a tube with a 1 kg weight at the end) (**A.3g**);

- during flexion (**A.3h**), extension (**A.3i**), adduction (**A.3j**), and abduction (**A.3k**) of the shoulder.

There are, of course, numerous other possibilities; 'press-ups' (**A.3l**) give a very dramatic recording, often causing more triceps activity than can be produced by voluntary elbow extension.

The skin

Sweat glands and dermal ridges

A replica (**A.4**) of the skin which shows any dermal ridges and the number of actively secreting sweat glands opening on to them can easily be made. Paint the area of skin with a solution of Formvar (4%) in ethylene dichloride, with Sudan black dye (1.5%) and dibutylphthalate (2%) (a plasticizer) added. When dry, the replica can be stripped off with adhesive tape, attached to a microscope slide, and examined with a low power (×4) microscope objective. The differing distributions of sweat glands in a number of different areas (e.g. finger, dorsum of hand, forehead) can be examined. To demonstrate the effect of exercise, make one replica, exercise by running up and down stairs, and repeat the replica. You can then compare the number of open sweat glands.

Skin innervation

You can test for the presence of cutaneous sense organs with different responses by exploring the skin: (1) with a fine bristle; (2) with a warm (40 °C) copper object and a cold (15–25 °C) object; and (3) *gently* with a pin. Repeat your observations on the forehead and on the hand and note spatial variation in the threshold for touch sensation, which is related, amongst other things, to the distribution of hair follicles. Cold 'spots' can be located very precisely because the receptors are very superficial, warm spots less so. You will probably find that you can locate separate spots on the palm of the hand but that, on the face, they are too densely packed to be separable.

The ability to discriminate spatially (two-point discrimination) can he tested using an instrument such as blunted divider points. Test the discriminatory power of various parts, e.g. tongue, finger tip, palm,

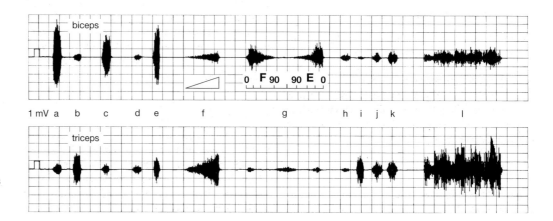

A.3 Record of muscle electrical activity from biceps and triceps during movements of the upper limb. 1 mV—calibration; see text.

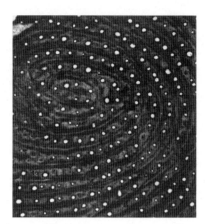

A.4 Plastic cast of finger-pad skin, showing openings of active sweat glands on to dermal ridges.

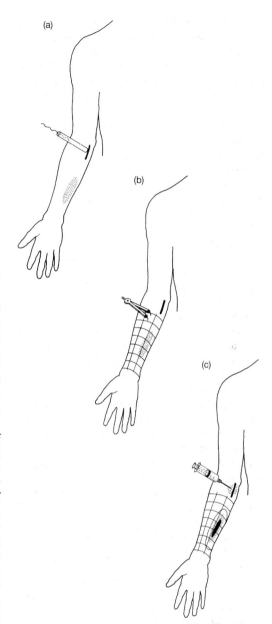

A.5 Investigation of sensory two-point discrimination on the skin. See text for details of procedure.

forearm, upper arm, back. The effects of anaesthesia on two-point discrimination can also be tested.

Locate and mark a cutaneous nerve which supplies an area of forearm skin by exploring along the known course of nerves with an electrical stimulator such as can be used to stimulate muscle contraction (**A.5a**). Mark squares 2 × 2 cm on to the forearm including, in the centre of the grid, the area supplied by the nerve (**A.5b**). Determine and record the variations in two-point threshold over the grid, preferably in both longitudinal and transverse axes, because these may differ. You can then ask a suitably qualified person (if available) to infiltrate some local anaesthetic around the marked nerve (**A3.5c**). An area of skin within the grid should become totally anaesthetized within a few minutes. Now determine and mark the boundary of the anaesthesia (if a small nerve was infiltrated, there may be no completely anaesthetized area); determine again the two-point threshold on the grid surrounding the anaesthetic area and also check that the anaesthetic area remains the same. Compare the two sets of data. You will find that the two-point threshold is diminished over a wider area of skin than that which has become anaesthetic. This is because cutaneous nerves supply overlapping territories.

The circulation

Large arteries and veins

You should investigate on yourself or a colleague all the points at which arterial pulsations can be felt. Similarly, you should examine the course of the major superficial veins by lightly restricting venous return from an area.

Ultrasonic Doppler-based probes are used clinically to map larger vessels. If one is available, choose an area such as the arm, forearm, or palm of the hand and map the course of the arteries and arterial arch.

Capillaries

You should examine capillaries at the only two readily available sites: the nail bed and the retina. Clear the skin of the nail bed by application of a small amount of light oil and observe the capillary loops with a binocular dissecting microscope. Use an ophthalmoscope to view the vessels on the surface of the retina through the pupil of the eye (see Vol. 3, Ch. 6, Sect. 7). Examination of the retinal vessels is widely used in clinical diagnosis.

Lymph nodes

If you or a colleague have an inflamed focus, such as an infected finger or throat, you may be able to feel enlarged, tender and possibly painful lymph nodes which drain these two areas and which are located, respectively, in the axilla and on the side of the neck just below the angle of the jaw.

Index